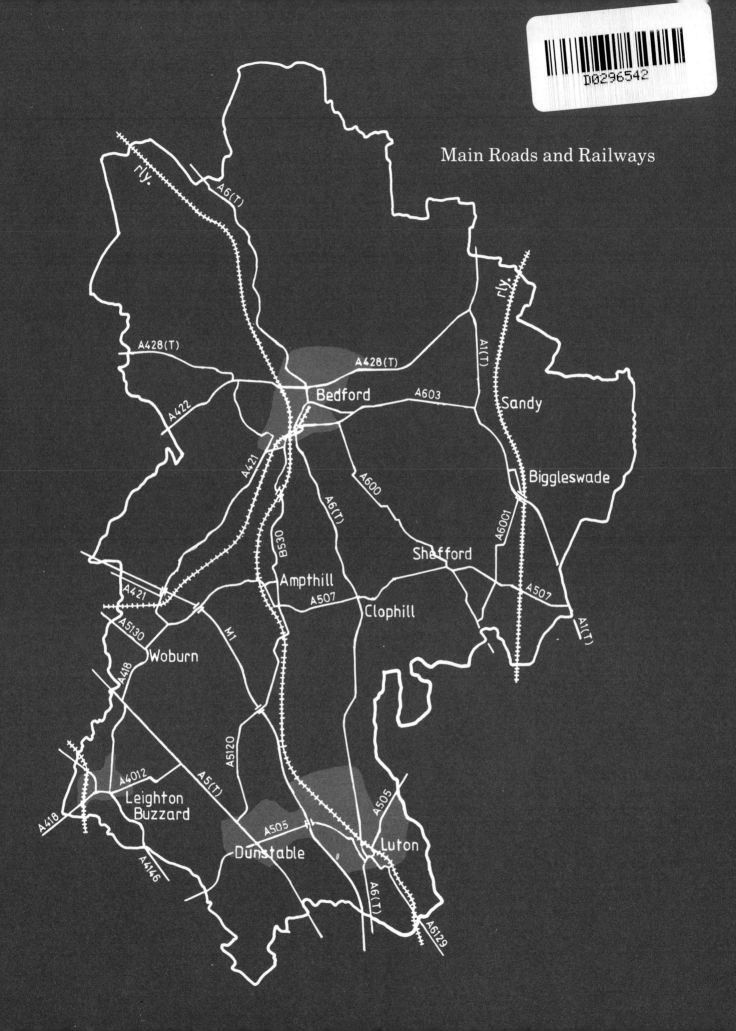

Main Roads and Railways

Bedfordshire Wildlife

Frontispiece: *'Weeds' are some of the most colourful of our flowers, these Corn Marigolds made a rare show of colour in the south of the county one year; usually herbicides suppress the once familiar flowers of the cornfields.*

© A. Ford

Bedfordshire Wildlife

Edited by

B. S. Nau, C. R. Boon and J. P. Knowles

for

The Bedfordshire Natural History Society

CASTLEMEAD PUBLICATIONS
WARE

First Published in 1987

CASTLEMEAD PUBLICATIONS
Swains Mill, 4A Crane Mead,
Ware, Herts., SG12 9PY

Publishing division of
WARD'S PUBLISHING SERVICES

© The Bedfordshire Natural History Society

Photographic Editor

Richard Revels

British Library Cataloguing in Publication Data

Bedfordshire wild life.
 1. Natural history—England—
Bedfordshire
 I. Nau, B.S.   II. Boon, C.R.   III. Knowles,
J.P.   IV. Bedfordshire Natural History
Society
 574.9425'6   QH138.B4

ISBN 0-948555-05-X

Set in 10/11 Baskerville Type and
Printed and bound in Great Britain
by The Bath Press, Avon

Acknowledgements

A book like this is only feasible as a result of countless hours of fieldwork and study by many dedicated naturalists and lovers of wildlife. The present book makes use of the results of such fieldwork by others and the editors freely express their indebtedness to all these people. However, the greatest contribution is from the body of knowledge which has been accumulated on the county's wildlife by members of the Bedfordshire Natural History Society. Chief among these are the Society's official recorders, each a knowledgeable specialist in a particular group of animal or plant life. Particular thanks are due to the present incumbents of these posts:

B. J. Nightingale (*Birds*), A. R. Outen (*Bryophytes*), J. P. Knowles (*Bumble-bees*), A. J. Martin (*Butterflies*), Dr N. Dawson (*Dragonflies*), T. Peterkin (*Fish*), Dr J. G. Dony (*Flowering Plants*), Dr D. A. Reid (*Fungi*), D. G. Rands (*Grasshoppers and Crickets*), Dr B. S. Nau (*Heteroptera*), Dr N. F. Janes (*Hoverflies*), Dr B. Verdcourt (*Lacewings*), Mrs F. B. M. Davies (*Lichens*), D. Anderson (*Mammals*), M. C. Williams (*Meteorology*), Mrs E. B. Rands (*Molluscs and Leeches*), V. W. Arnold (*macro Moths*), D. Manning (*micro Moths*), Mrs H. M. Muir-Howie (*Amphibians and Reptiles*), T. J. Thomas (*Spiders*), Dr A. J. Rundle (*Woodlice, Centipedes, and Millipedes*).

Recognition is also due to the predecessors of the above who have, over the Society's forty years of existence, built such a firm foundation to our present knowledge.

Much of the work of the recorders and other members of the BNHS has been published in the annual journal of the Society, *The Bedfordshire Naturalist*, and reference should be made to this for further information on the wildlife of the county. This journal now covers a period of forty years.

The particular thanks of the Editors are due to D. G. Rands for the thorough and painstaking way in which he has prepared the many maps and diagrams, and to R. B. Stephenson for compilation of the index.

The Editors would also like to acknowledge the help provided in various ways by Miss R. Brind, P. Clark, D. Corke, Miss A. Simco, The Reverend T. W. Gladwin, E. Meadows, Dr J. T. R. Sharrock and Mrs M. Sheridan.

The authorship of individual chapters is indicated in the Contents but in many cases additional information and other valuable contributions were specifically provided by recorders and it is appropriate here to acknowledge, on behalf of the named authors, these anonymous contributions. Many recorders have also been of great help in checking facts and other details; we thank them for this and hope that any remaining errors are few.

The illustrations which are such an essential and attractive part of this book – including drawings, diagrams and photographs – are individually acknowledged but we wish to take this opportunity to congratulate the artists and photographers for the excellence of their work and offer our thanks for their cooperation; and in particular we wish to thank the artists, Alan Harris, Peter Walton, Tony Barker, David Guntrip, Derek Rands, Bernard West and Alan Martin. We are particularly grateful to those photographers who have taken photographs at our special request.

In selecting photographs of plants and animals we have, where possible, chosen photographs taken in the wild in the county. In a few cases this was not possible and it has been necessary to use either studio shots of Bedfordshire specimens or other photographs.

The copyright of all photographs remains that of individual photographers unless indicated otherwise and we formally acknowledge their permission to publish these in this book.

The geological maps are published with permission of the copyright owners, Bedfordshire County Council. We are grateful to the County Planning Department for making them available. We are also indebted to the County Planning Officer for allowing us to examine and select from their photographic collection, and particularly to Richard Watts for his ready response to our various requests. Beds. C. C. photographs are reproduced with permission of the copyright owners, Bedfordshire County Council.

The copyright of all drawings, paintings and diagrams is the property of the Bedfordshire Natural History Society except where acknowledgement is made to other sources.

Photographic prints for reproduction were prepared by Richard Revels, to whom we offer special thanks.

Contents

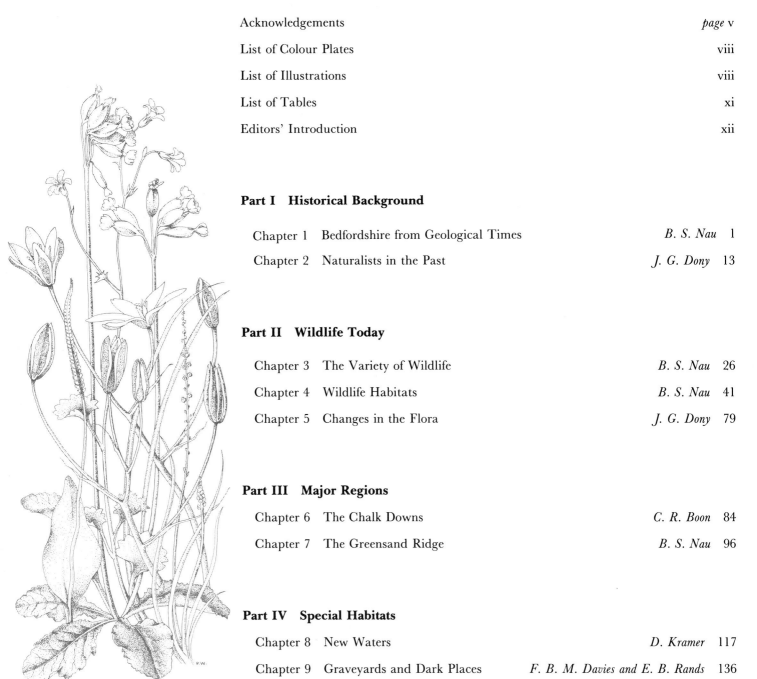

vi

Appendices

Species checklists for:

List of Colour Plates

List of Illustrations

List of Tables

Editors' Introduction

The wildlife of a county like Bedfordshire can stimulate at several different levels. The casual visitor to the countryside gains pleasure from the beauty and variety of the plant and animal life which spring most readily to eye. A lover of the countryside with a deeper interest sees much more and will go home with a correspondingly deeper satisfaction. The truly dedicated naturalist with specialist interests will see different things again and perhaps be rewarded in a more lasting way by the feeling of having understood a little more of the complex natural jigsaw.

In this book we have tried, by occasionally looking at some aspect of the subject in more depth, to present something which is a little more than a superficial account of the fauna and flora of the county, and the habitats on which they depend. It is hoped that the reader with a casual interest may be stimulated by a deeper understanding, while the reader already deeply interested in our wildlife will be spurred on to look at some new aspect in greater depth. In no way should this book be regarded as 'comprehensive'; there is still so much to be discovered and what is already known would fill more space than is available here. Having said this, we have tried to achieve a degree of cover of all the main habitat types in the county and, in dealing with each, to highlight those groups of plants and animals which are particularly characteristic of these habitats. Inevitably some groups have received more attention than others.

Where possible we have avoided scientific names but in some less familiar groups there are no accepted English names and we have not then shrunk from using scientific names. We have done this because it was the only way to present information which we felt would be of more than just specialist interest. Where English names are used the source is identified in the Appendices and can be referred to if it is desired to relate these to scientific names. This seems the best compromise between readability and scientific acceptability.

The BNHS Book Working Party:
Julian Knowles (*Secretary*)
Chris Boon
Bernard Nau

31st October 1986

Chapter 1

Bedfordshire from Geological Times

The Bedfordshire landscape is attractively varied: one need never travel far for a change of scenery – the steep chalk slopes of Dunstable Downs, the shady pinewoods of Woburn, the limestone walls of Turvey.

One soon notices an underlying pattern to the landscape. Imagine a journey northwards through the county, from the Hertfordshire border in the south, to the Northamptonshire border in the north, along the old A6 road for instance. For the first few miles the road crosses an undulating plateau, most obvious beyond the suburbs of Luton. This suddenly ends at a very steep east-west escarpment, where the road passes through Barton Cutting. From this the view is north across a vale of arable farming country to a well-wooded ridge, running across the county from Leighton Buzzard and Woburn, to Sandy. Beyond this ridge is another vale, dotted with brickworks and the clay quarries from which the brick clay is dug. East of Bedford the vale merges with the valley of the River Great Ouse. To the north it is bounded by another undulating plateau, rich farming country dotted with woods. This continues north to the county boundary. The Ouse adds interest to this landscape of north Bedfordshire, having cut a winding valley through the high ground that repeatedly gives unexpected views of the river valley.

THE 'FOUNDATIONS' OF BEDFORDSHIRE

To drive north through Bedfordshire is to drive back in time (Figure 1.1). The Chalk of the south is a younger rock than the Gault Clay of the vale to its north, which is younger than the Lower Greensand of the central ridge. This in turn is younger than the Oxford Clay of the Marston Vale and the Great Oolite Limestone of the northern plateau (Figure 1.2).

Perhaps 'rock' is not a good term for these geological deposits, since most are rather soft sedimentary rocks, accumulated deposits of silts, sands, skeletal remains of plankton and chalky precipitates. These formations were laid down in prehistoric times when this part of Britain was several times submerged beneath the waters of ancient seas. Major earth movements after the Chalk was laid down tilted the Bedfordshire strata a few degrees downwards to the south-east. Later erosion more or less levelled the surface, exposing a succession of rocks of increasing age from south to north.

The pattern of the landscape reflects the east-west 'stripes' of the rock formations hidden beneath the soil (Plates 1 and 2). The soft clays were more quickly eroded, leaving the harder rocks as high ground and ridges running across the county. The characteristics of the rocks also have a great effect on the wildlife of different regions of the county, which can be understood from a knowledge of the origins of the various geological formations in the county. The Bedfordshire deposits of arid desert origin have given rise to soils which even today are poor compared with those originating from chalk and limestone rich in plant-nutrient salts.

Bedfordshire Submerged

Bedfordshire was never far offshore when submerged by prehistoric seas. This happy chance, and the complexity of the earth's movements, raising and lowering the sea level, have given us a whole series of different marine sediment deposits. These vary depending on the nature of the lands from which they were washed or blown, and the tranquillity or turbulence of the sea in which they were deposited. The finer sediments were carried further out to sea before being deposited.

The limestone was laid down in sheltered coral seas when the land was probably dry desert country, with little silt to drain into the sea. By contrast the Oxford Clay and Gault Clay were laid down where rivers heavy with silt drained into coastal waters. Chalk is a very pure form of limestone. It was laid down in calm clear seas where there was little silt to mix with the chalky skeletons (coccoliths) of microscopic algae raining down on the sea-bed from the plankton near the surface. These accumulations, together with precipitated calcium carbonate, formed the very pure deposits we recognise as Chalk. The desert sands which formed the Lower Greensand were deposited in deltas or coastal waters, at about the time when evolution was producing the first flowering plants.

Having such different origins, it is not surprising that soils formed from these various deposits have different characteristics and such different wildlife. Over the long period since their deposition, successive erosion and deposition by water and glaciation has exposed and

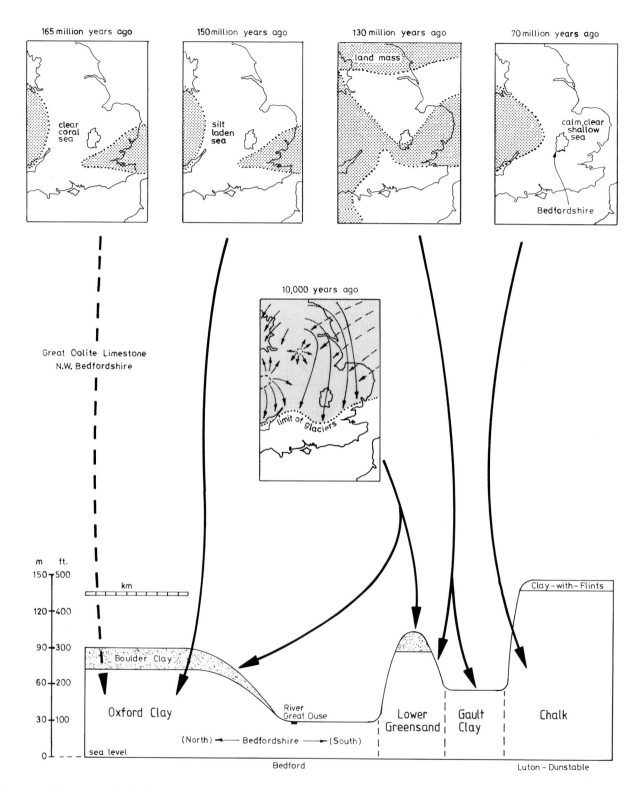

165 million years ago

clear coral sea

150 million years ago

silt laden sea

130 million years ago

land mass

70 million years ago

calm, clear shallow sea

Bedfordshire

10,000 years ago

limit of glaciers

Great Oolite Limestone
N.W. Bedfordshire

m ft.
150 — 500
km
120 — 400
90 — 300
60 — 200
30 — 100
0 — sea level

Clay-with-Flints

Boulder Clay

Oxford Clay

River Great Ouse

(North) ◄— Bedfordshire —► (South)

Lower Greensand

Gault Clay

Chalk

Bedford

Luton – Dunstable

Figure 1.1 *The origins of Bedfordshire rock formations: the maps show the extent of land, sea or ice when each deposit was laid down; the north-south cross-section of the county shows where each occurs now.*

2

covered these rock formations in complex ways. As a result, today we see in one small county a variety of landscape, fauna and flora which is much greater than in most other areas of southern Britain of similar size.

The Ice Ages

With the formation of the Chalk, the rock foundations of Bedfordshire were almost complete, seventy million years ago. Any later deposits have been almost entirely eroded away.

A series of glaciations during the Ice Age greatly modified the nature of the surface. The Ice Age ended only 10 000 years ago. At their most extensive, the ice sheet crested the Chiltern Hills and fingers extended down to what is now the outskirts of London. These glaciers were great agents of erosion, scouring the landscape and depositing the debris as clay, sand and gravel on top of the parent rocks, when finally the glaciers retreated. They also left behind deposits carried here in the ice from areas far to the north and east. This explains the presence of the strange rocks, turned up by the plough, which are unrelated to any of our native rock. These 'erratic' rocks were carried here from as far afield as north-eastern England and even from Scandinavia.

More important than the occasional erratic rock is the presence of much chalky material, contained in the massive deposits of Boulder Clay left by the ice. This has a dramatic effect on the fertility of soils formed from it, and therefore on the fauna and flora. The chalky Boulder Clay caps the Greensand Ridge across mid-Bedfordshire, almost totally covers the Oxford Clay and limestone of the north and in places overlies the Chalk of the south.

Chalk Dissolving

Another important change has taken place within the upper layers of the Chalk. Over long periods of time these have gradually dissolved and been washed away by rainwater. Overlying sand deposits, now largely eroded away, combined with the insoluble residue, this debris is now the 'Clay-with-Flints' which overlies the Chalk. In sharp contrast to the parent Chalk, the Clay-with-Flints forms neutral or acid soils, the basic salts having been leached out. This accounts for the occurrence of such lime-hating plants as Gorse and Broom growing just above the Chalk in road or rail cuttings through the Chilterns, and on common land at Whipsnade and Studham.

After the Ice

With the melting of the ice 10 000 years ago, the main

Figure 1.2 *Limestone revealed by quarrying at Bromham: limestone underlies the north-west of the county but is usually hidden under later clay deposits; stone walls in the villages reveal the presence of the rock in the vicinity. The limestone comes close to the surface along the valley of the upper Ouse as this photograph shows.* (TL 028518, April 1978) © B. S. Nau

features of our present-day waterways were defined. Most of the county is drained by the Great Ouse Basin, which drains north-eastwards into The Wash. The exception is a small area in the extreme south which the River Lea drains into the Thames Basin.

The wetlands formed at this time survived less well than the waterways. Of the lakes there is nothing left and marshes are all but extinct. This is partly the result of natural drainage but is mainly due to artificial drainage by man in the last few centuries.

The post-glacial rivers played a large part in moulding the structure of the county. Fast-flowing waters running off high ground carried away silt, sand and gravel left by the ice, and redeposited them in the river valleys. Today our valleys contain thick beds of 'river gravel' and sand, with a fertile covering of alluvial soil, which accounts for the many gravel quarries dotted over the rich farmland along the valleys of the Ouse and its tributaries.

... and Finally Peat

Between the disappearance of the glaciers and modern Man's near total control of the countryside, there was a period when marshland was extensive. These were the conditions which favoured the formation of one of our most recent deposits, peat. This is a feature of some of the most important wildlife habitats in the county.

Peat is formed from vegetable matter. When wetland vegetation dies back, it is normally recycled by a finely balanced community of small invertebrate animals, fungi and bacteria. These decompose the organic matter into materials which can be used by a new generation of plants. However, if the soil is acid or poorly oxygenated the recycling agents cannot operate and dead vegetation accumulates as fragmented black carboniferous debris, which we call peat. In south-east England suitable conditions only existed on a large scale in the fens and broadlands of East Anglia. However, in Bedfordshire there is one area where peat was formed extensively, and this is a valley within the Greensand Ridge, perhaps once a lake, between Flitwick and Clophill. Here, at Flitwick Moor, peat was extensive enough to be excavated commercially, as recently as the 1960s. Happily, this site is now managed as a nature reserve to preserve its fauna and flora, which are unique in the county.

With peat we reach almost the end of the long history of sediment deposition in the county. This began 150 million years ago in an ancient coral sea, and now continues only in a few semi-natural watercourses where silt and gravel are deposited in the slower reaches.

Each of the various deposits discussed has its influence on the wildlife of the county but in recent times Man has played an important role in modifying this geological basis, and this is a subject to which we will return later in the chapter.

A Broader View

It is fascinating to take a broader view and consider how the county's geology fits in with that of the rest of southern England.

The three strata, Chalk, Gault Clay and Lower Greensand, each partly overlying the next, south to north, form a sandwich. This sandwich curves down deep under Hertfordshire and London, having been distorted by earth movements. Then it curves up and emerges again in Kent and Surrey. Here these strata form the North Downs (Chalk), and further south the sand hills at Redhill, Leith Hill and Hindhead. In that area, therefore, our familiar Bedfordshire strata appear in reverse order, i.e., north to south.

At one time they continued even further, over what is now The Weald of Kent and Sussex, and the English Channel, to northern France. Earth movements caused them to arch up over The Weald, the arch later being eroded away leaving a pair of escarpments facing each other across the Gault and Greensand of The Weald. The escarpments are the North Downs and the South Downs.

Where the English Channel now is, subsidence resulted in the sea once again covering these marine deposits, history coming full cycle. However, further west in southern England the strata can still be seen, for example in the Isle of Wight where there are two Chalk ridges and two Greensand ridges.

This cyclic repetition of our Bedfordshire geology can be seen clearly on the Ordnance Survey Geological Map of England and Wales, and provides scope for fascinating comparisons between habitats which differ in climate and aspect though having the same geological basis.

THE CLOAK OF VEGETATION

The landscape, flora and fauna of the county today are very different from those that would have evolved without Man's intervention. Man began to have a permanent effect about 6000 years ago, roughly halfway between the end of the Ice Age and the present day. The flora and fauna at that time are therefore of special significance to us as the wildlife communities we see about us developed from this 'raw material'.

Tundra to Forest

As the ice melted the vegetation was that of arctic tundra, like northern Scandinavia or Canada today. Over the next few thousand years the warming climate allowed less hardy species of trees to move in and become established.

The Ice Age did not end suddenly; the climate alternated between warmer and cooler periods until it gradually approached what we know today. Towards the end of the Ice Age, 12 000–14 000 years ago, when the climate was still cool, the common plants of the county would probably have been tundra species such as Mountain Avens, Dwarf Birch and Dwarf Willow, with some grasses and sedges. These moved in as the first soil developed. This is indicated by studies of pollen in peat and lake silt in south-east England. Familiar birds at that time could have been Snow Bunting, Shorelark, Long-tailed Skua and Snowy Owl, any of which would be a very exciting find today!

About 12 000 years ago the climate ameliorated, remaining milder for about a thousand years. This allowed trees to develop more extensively, mainly Aspen, two species of birch, and Rowan, all of which we have in the county today. The tundra flora was eventually joined by less tolerant shrubs such as Bog-myrtle, Juniper, Crowberry and Sea-buckthorn. The mild spell was followed by five-hundred years of cooler weather which can truly be said to have been the end of the Ice Age.

Around this time the soil was much broken up by frost, enabling plants of open ground to flourish in summer. Remarkably, these are now the weeds of cultivated ground, docks, mugworts, willowherbs, plantains and buckwheats. Plants which followed these are now some of the more attractive flowers of unspoilt grassland, Hare-bell, Common Meadow-rue, Common Rock-rose, Field Scabious and Common Valerian. There were also some plants which are no longer to be found, such as Jacob's-ladder and club-mosses. To see such a flora in Britain today you would need to find lime-rich uplands beyond the reach of sheep, such as ledges and screes in the Ben Lawers range in Scotland, or parts of Upper Teesdale.

Warmer Times

Between 10 300 and 9 550 years ago the climate became much milder. Birch trees spread to form extensive forest, the resulting shade causing a sharp decline in the variety of flowering plants and shrubs. Then Scots Pine began to take over, shading out the short-lived birches. At this time too there is evidence of Man's presence as a hunter and fisher. Archaeological deposits show that among his prey were Red Deer, no longer found wild in the county. It seems, too, that Man cleared ground around his habitation, as there is evidence from pollen deposits that plants of disturbed ground, such as nettle and chickweed, were present.

Island Britain

From 9000 years ago the climate became still milder and drier, in what is called the Boreal Period. Hazel spread dramatically and Wych Elm and Pedunculate Oak began to take over from Pine, though this would probably have kept its hold on the sandy soils of our Greensand Ridge. Hazel has been one of the dominant under-shrubs of our woodland ever since.

Towards the end of the Boreal Period three more trees reached England and became an important part of the flora for a time, Alder and two species of lime (Small-leaved and Large-leaved Lime). Alder is still common in the county, Small-leaved Lime has survived in a few woods on the Greensand Ridge (notably in Chicksands Wood) but the Large-leaved Lime no longer occurs naturally.

The Boreal Period ended about 7500 years ago, soon after the English Channel had made Britain an island. With Britain separated from mainland Europe the land route for colonisation by plants and animals was closed. Most of our fauna and flora were therefore in the country by this time. This date is also significant in marking a change to the wetter, oceanic climate of the Atlantic Period, which lasted 2500 years. The wet conditions and growth of marsh and swamp, favoured the Alder tree. The vegetation was mostly forest, with a closed leaf canopy casting a heavy shade to the detriment of flowers of the ground layer. The mild temperatures at this time favoured southern species: oak, elm and lime on less waterlogged soils. On sandy soils the high rainfall leached away nutrients, creating conditions suitable for acid-loving species like Heather. Birch and pine flourished on these poorer soils and *Sphagnum* bogs developed in acid lowland lakes.

MAN'S IMPACT

With the onset of a drier, continental type climate around 6000 years ago, at the end of the Atlantic Period, Neolithic Man was developing the technology to modify his environment. He favoured lighter soils, such as that on the Chiltern Hills and river valley gravels (Figure 1.3). Using flint tools and fire he made temporary clearings in

Figure 1.3 *Ancient 'lynchets' on the upper slopes of Deacon Hill near Pegsdon mark early farming activities on a downland site which is now a Site of Special Scientific Interest for its flora and fauna.* (1983) © Beds. C. C.

the forest for pasture or for growing primitive cereals. This activity began to change the species composition of the forest. Ash and birch were favoured, being pioneering species of the regenerating woodland which would have developed in abandoned clearings. Woodland-glade flowers would also have been favoured, Bluebell, Wood Anemone and Dog's Mercury. So, over the next 3000 years, the downland habitats which are now such a valuable feature of the county's wildlife habitats began to evolve.

This was the end of the predominance of climate as the primary factor controlling the vegetation and the beginning of Man's increasing domination of the countryside.

About this time there was a dramatic decrease in the elm tree pollen record in peat and silt all over north-west Europe. It has been suggested that this was the result of Neolithic Man's activities as he had developed the practice, still in use in parts of Europe, of cutting tree foliage for cattle fodder. Elm is particularly suitable for this pur-

pose, as is lime, which also declined. Repeated cutting prevents the trees from flowering and it is this that accounts for the sudden decline in pollen.

Not long after this, Neolithic Man cleared the forest on the sandy soils of Suffolk, opening the way for Heather to flourish and creating the Breckland heaths which are still there today. Perhaps here in Bedfordshire, the sandy soils of the Greensand Ridge may have suffered a similar fate about the same time. Much of this area presumably remained as heath until conifer planting came into vogue in the 19th and early 20th centuries. Throughout this time Heather, Broom and Gorse would have been a conspicuous feature of this part of the county.

By the time the period of dry continental climate came to an end, Bronze Age Man had extensively cleared the chalk uplands. It is likely that our downland and sandy soils were already being managed as pasture in much the same way as they have been used in recent centuries. On the less easily worked soils of the Gault and Oxford Clay, Man's impact was more gradual. Later, most of the

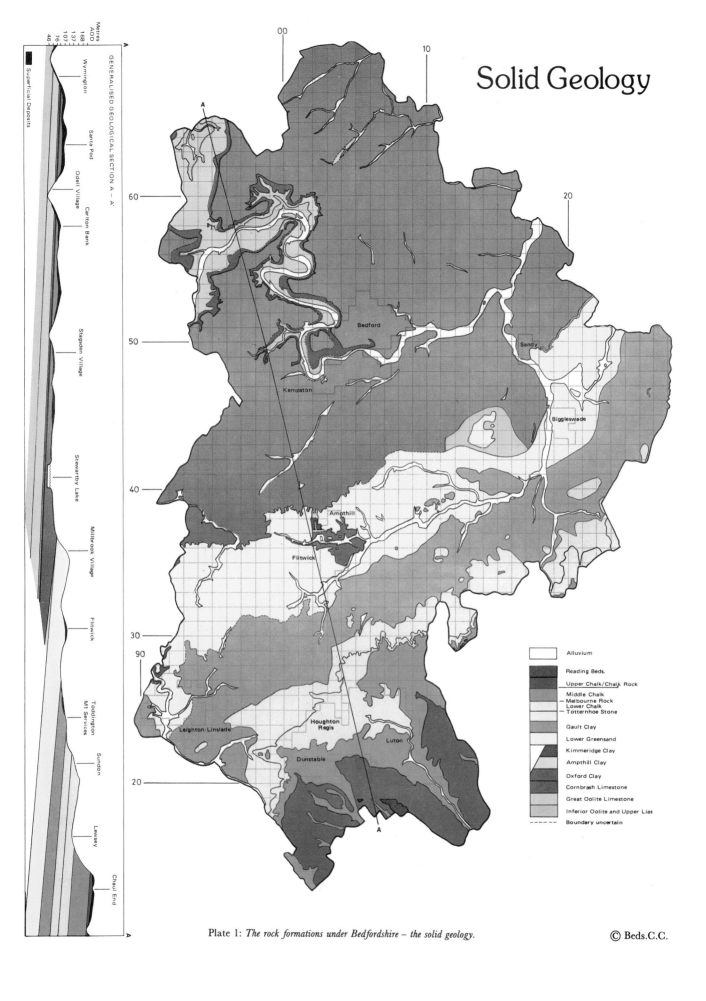

Solid Geology

GENERALISED GEOLOGICAL SECTION A — A'

Metres AOD: 168, 137, 107, 76, 46

A — Wymington — Santa Pod — Odell Village — Carlton Bank — Stagden Village — Stewartby Lake — Millbrook Village — Flitwick — Toddington M1 Services — Sundon — Lewsey — Chaul End — A'

Superficial Deposits

Bedford · Sandy · Kempston · Biggleswade · Ampthill · Flitwick · Leighton-Linslade · Houghton Regis · Luton · Dunstable

Legend:

Alluvium
Reading Beds.
Upper Chalk/Chalk Rock
Middle Chalk
Melbourne Rock
Lower Chalk
Totternhoe Stone
Gault Clay
Lower Greensand
Kimmeridge Clay
Ampthill Clay
Oxford Clay
Cornbrash Limestone
Great Oolite Limestone
Inferior Oolite and Upper Lias
Boundary uncertain

Plate 1: *The rock formations under Bedfordshire – the solid geology.*

© Beds.C.C.

heathland was lost to forestry plantation during the late 19th and early 20th centuries; then in the last few decades increasing areas of downland were lost to scrub when sheep-grazing ceased to be economic. This long period of relative habitat stability enabled the great diversity of the flora and fauna of the downland habitat to evolve into an irreplaceable treasure. Many rarities have been able to maintain themselves here because of the peculiar suitability of the habitat, often on the edge of their climatic range. Such ecosystems are, like Stonehenge, a gift from ancient man.

Impact of the Plough

About 2500 years ago, the climate became damper and more equable, and this was reflected in an upsurge in abundance of Alder trees and marshland. At the same time, perhaps due to Man's influence, Beech and Hornbeam trees greatly increased in abundance. Both just reached Britain before the Channel land-link was broken, and now exist at the natural limit of their range in south Bedfordshire.

However, these changes pale into insignificance compared with the effect of Man's development of the technology for making iron ploughs. With this and the use of chalk as fertiliser, land could be kept in continuous cultivation around settlements and even heavy clay soils could be tilled. The extensive areas of disturbed soil produced by cultivation would have provided habitat, once again, for what were now 'arable weeds' – the mugworts, docks and cornflowers amongst others. When the Romans arrived cereals were already being grown in the county. At this time the only areas not fully settled were the inhospitable Gault and Oxford Clay.

The Roman occupation had little impact on the Bedfordshire landscape but the increased trade helped plants of cultivated ground to spread rapidly and increased traffic with the Continent helped more plants and animals to colonise Britain. Fallow Deer probably arrived at this time as well as such plants as Corn Marigold, Ground-elder, Alexanders, Corncockle and Scarlet Pimpernel. These were all imported deliberately or accidentally by Man.

The verges of the new roads would also have provided extensive new wayside-verge habitat, not least in Bedfordshire which is traversed by such Roman roads as Watling Street and the Great North Road.

When the Normans came they found that much of the primaeval forest had already been cleared to create farmland – although there had been some regrowth on cleared land since Roman times. During the next two-hundred years clearance continued until the woodland remaining was mainly on intractable heavy soils, such as the wetter parts of the Boulder Clay, which is where our present-day broad-leaved woods are now concentrated. By A.D. 1300 almost all suitable land was being cultivated and the larger Bedfordshire woods would have been not too different in size from what we see today. The biggest contribution about this time, to the creation of the modern countryside, was the introduction of an animal which was to have an enormous impact right down to the present day – the Rabbit. This was introduced in the 12th century.

Sheep were being farmed in Britain in Norman times, perhaps on our downland. They were to be an important factor in maintaining chalk grassland in a condition favouring the finer grasses and the more specialised flowers. Sheep numbers increased steadily, peaking in the

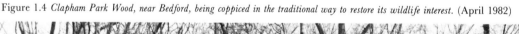

Figure 1.4 *Clapham Park Wood, near Bedford, being coppiced in the traditional way to restore its wildlife interest.* (April 1982)   © Beds. C. C.

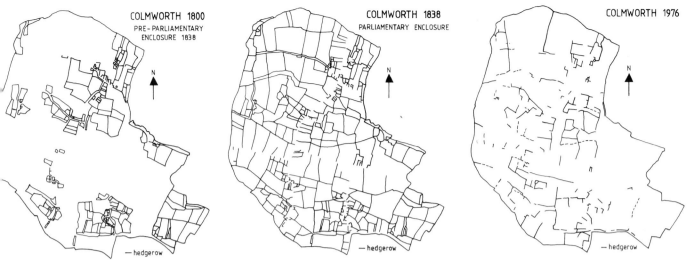

| COLMWORTH 1800 | COLMWORTH 1838 | COLMWORTH 1976 |
| PRE-PARLIAMENTARY ENCLOSURE 1838 | PARLIAMENTARY ENCLOSURE | |

Figure 1.5 Colmworth, in the north of the county, illustrates the changing fortunes of hedgerows in a traditionally arable farming area. In this parish the traditional open fields were enclosed between 1800 and 1838; since the Second World War many of the 'new' hedges, as well as more ancient ones, have been removed to form larger fields.
© Beds, C. C.

14th–17th centuries. In such large numbers their grazing would have prevented the showy displays of downland flowers we sometimes see where grazing is light. More recently, during the past hundred years, sheep pasturing has declined, leading to the virtual extinction of traditional sheep-walks in Bedfordshire.

Woodland Coppice

An important technique practised during the Middle Ages was the management of woodland by the system known as coppice-with-standards. This was to continue until economics forced its replacement by the planting of softwood, Scots Pine, European Larch and various alien conifers. Coppice-with-standards was based on a ten to fifteen year cycle of cutting the brushwood understory of Hazel, Field Maple and Ash just above ground level (coppicing) and allowing it to regenerate and produce repeated crops (Figure 1.4). In addition, scattered Oaks and Ash were left to grow to maturity as 'standards', for use as constructional timber. The advantage of this system for wildlife was that there was always a wide range of woodland habitats within a wood, from open glade to closed leaf canopy. Glades are a particularly important habitat for butterflies, birds and the masses of spring flowers. Being labour-intensive this system has now fallen into disuse in Britain, except in a few nature reserves.

Hedgerows

In much the same way as ancient woodland, an ancient hedgerow is very much richer than one planted in recent centuries. The earliest hedges were probably formed in Saxon times, and some still survive as boundaries between properties, parishes or counties. These early hedges were formed directly from woodland by the simple expedient of leaving a strip when the wood was cleared. This naturally resulted in a cross-section of the woodland flora and fauna being incorporated in the hedge. However, many hedges are of more recent origin.

Field systems through the Middle Ages and up to the 18th and 19th centuries often comprised large communal fields, with smaller hedged closes around settlements. More than half of Bedfordshire had been enclosed by a piecemeal process by about the 16th century. Ownership of the remaining areas was eventually rearranged with the aid of various Acts of Parliament between 1603 and 1903, particularly around 1800. Enclosure resulted in the formation of smaller fields bounded by newly planted hedges (Figure 1.5). Thus many hedges date from the times of the Enclosure Acts and are therefore relatively modern by ecological timescales. Detailed studies of Bedfordshire hedgerows have been made, showing how the richness and variety of hedgerow shrubs and trees varies across the county. This is affected both by the age of the hedge and the soil type, the hedges on our limey soils being richer than those on sand, for instance.

Trees from Abroad

As communications with distant lands improved over the centuries, so more and more trees have been introduced to Britain. These have made a considerable impact on both the wildlife and the landscape. Some early introductions which now form woodland in the county are Sycamore (15th–16th century); Norway Spruce (16th century); European Larch (17th century); and Corsican Pine (18th century). Individual planted specimens of other species are quite frequent in hedgerows near habitation.

9

The Sycamore is able to propagate itself with great ease, becoming a 'weed' in places and a particular nuisance when competing with the more desirable native species. The Corsican Pine and European Larch are widely planted for timber in the county, as, to a lesser extent, is the Norway Spruce, though the climate is probably too dry for this and some alien conifers planted extensively in other parts of Britain.

It is interesting that the richness of the insect fauna on trees and shrubs, and hence of insect-eating birds, is very dependent on the antiquity of the plant in Britain. Even late natural immigrants, such as Beech and Hornbeam, have nothing like the richness of the older natives, such as oaks, willows and birches. Man's recent introductions are even poorer.

Wetlands

The history of the wetlands of Bedfordshire is not well documented. Until the 17th century the wetlands of the Great Ouse valley would have provided continuity of marshland habitat between the county and the vast marshland area of the Fens. Then the large-scale drainage of the Fens and canalisation of the rivers began to isolate our marshland into ever smaller fragments, until now they are almost totally destroyed. As recently as the past decade, further work has been under way to lower, even further, the water tables in the county's river valleys. Our few small remaining marshes are very precious since we could easily see the last of these disappear within a generation, unless a conscious effort is made to preserve what is left.

Clay Grasslands

Away from the ancient sheep-walks of the Chilterns, the history of our grasslands is not well recorded. We know that some of today's pasture was ploughed in earlier times, and this is indicated by a 'ridge-and-furrow' pattern. But, although the existence of this pattern often indicates a field which has not been ploughed in modern times, nearly all such fields have now been treated with herbicides and fertilisers to increase the agricultural yield. When this is done the traditional flora is destroyed.

In the past few years, a surfeit of milk production in Europe has resulted in dairy farmers being encouraged to turn to other activities. This has resulted in a sharp reduction in the amount of the remaining grassland in some parts of the county.

The most ancient grassland will not, of course, show a ridge-and-furrow pattern, never having been ploughed. When cropped as hay-meadows such grassland was rich in abundance and variety of flowers in spring and early summer: Meadowsweet, Cowslip, Meadow Saxifrage, buttercups, vetches, bedstraws and a multitude of others were a common sight within living memory. Even the now rare Green-winged Orchid and even rarer Fritillary were often abundant. Butterflies were present in numbers now only a memory to a few.

The damper pastures and water-meadows of river valleys were further enriched by such moisture-loving species as Marsh-marigold, marsh-orchids and Cuckooflower. But, surprisingly to people from more humid regions of Britain, the Primrose is only a woodland glade and hedgerow species with us.

This would have been the picture for many centuries, from the earliest days of farming in Britain until recent technical advances made possible cheap effective land-drainage and near total control over native plants competing with crops. Today, most of our grassland has been subjected to such treatment so that only small pockets of traditional grassland survive, where it is still possible to see flowers as our forefathers knew them. Among these rare survivors are a field beside Maulden Church and a section of Biggleswade Common, near the railway; the few other sites are small and inaccessible.

Flowers of arable fields have also disappeared within the last generation. Fields of poppies were once an everyday sight. Now, arable 'weeds' such as Cornflower, Corncockle and other attractive species have become great rarities.

A quite different type of grassland evolved in the large country parks so characteristic of the 18th century. This grassland was planted with well spaced-out trees and is often regarded as 'woodland' from a strictly ecological viewpoint; parts of Woburn Park are classic examples of such habitat (Figure 1.6).

Climate Evolved

The climate today might sometimes seem damp but, compared with the rest of Britain, Bedfordshire is in a region of particularly low rainfall. Data from Cardington for the period 1847–1871 show an annual average rainfall of 525 mm (21.45 in). A hundred years later the annual rainfall had not changed significantly; between 1947 and 1971 the average was 531 mm (21.68 in). The differences across the county are much greater, rainfall being about 25 per cent greater on the high ground of the Chilterns than in the centre of the county. This is most noticeable with summer thunderstorms, but in winter too the snow lies longer on this high ground.

Climatically, the county has more in common with East Anglia than with other parts of southern England. East Anglia has the most continental climate in Britain. In winter the temperatures are a degree or two lower and in summer a degree or two higher than elsewhere in

southern England. It is not surprising, therefore, that we have a number of plants and animals at the limit of their British range in the county.

Figure 1.6 *The north-east corner of Woburn Park: a classic English parkland habitat with ancient oaks and deer-grazed rough pasture.* (November 1985)

© B. S. Nau

11

THE FINAL SCENE?

The changes and influences described above have brought the countryside to what we see today – predominantly arable farmland, with some pasture, mainly in the north-west (Figure 1.7); a modest amount of woodland, span 10 000 years. These changes in habitat, fauna and flora were evolutionary rather than revolutionary. The timescales were slow enough for the wildlife to adapt. In the last hundred years the pace has changed dramati-

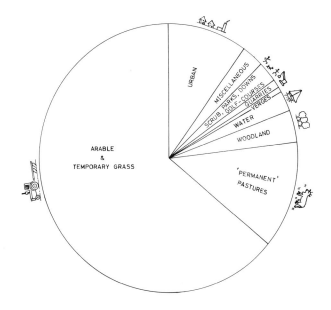

Figure 1.7 *Land use: most of the county is farmland growing cereals, oil-seed rape, or other arable crops; few counties have a lower proportion of woodland.*

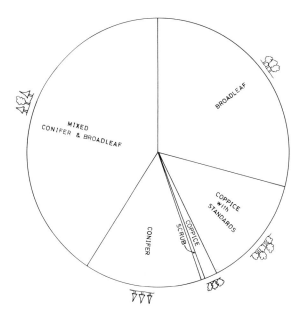

Figure 1.8 *Woodland types: most of the woods have now been planted with conifers; surviving traditional 'coppice-with-standards' woods are mostly neglected and overgrown.*

much of it plantations of alien conifers (Figure 1.8); and quite extensive urban development.

Many of the changes outlined in this chapter took place slowly, over centuries, or even longer timescales which are hard to appreciate. Even the events since the Ice Age

cally. Man has brought into service resources of energy and technology which have made possible changes at a rate, and of an extent, never previously experienced by our wildlife.

Chapter 2

Naturalists in the Past

First Awakenings

Our early ancestors were only interested in the wildlife around them in so far as it had a use to them. They knew that some trees were more useful than others for building, making poles or baskets, that some wild animals and birds were useful for food but others just vermin to be destroyed. Churchwardens' accounts during the 16th to 19th centuries list vermin destroyed. These records show that at one time we had Polecats (Figure 2.2) and Pine Martens in the county.

A wider interest began to develop in the 16th and 17th centuries. At this time herbalist John Gerard made the first recorded natural history observations in the county. He reported Purple Milk-vetch and Elecampane (Figure 2.1). These had been seen by him growing on downland between Barton-le-Clay and Luton some time before 1596. In the following 200 years other observations appeared in print, but always of the unusual. It was left to Charles Abbot in his *Flora Bedfordiensis* in 1798 to attempt to provide a comprehensive account of all the members of the plant kingdom known to grow in the county, down to the commonplace daisy and buttercup. In the rest of this chapter the developing interest in natural history will be chronicled up to the explosion of activity following the Second World War.

Abbot: The First Naturalist

Charles Abbot (1761 to 1817) was a remarkable man. He was a Doctor of Divinity of Oxford University and Fellow of New College before coming to Bedford as a young man of 24 to be under-master at the Grammar School. He was, at the same time, vicar of Oakley, vicar of Goldington, and curate of St Marys and, for a period, of St Pauls, in

Figure 2.1 *Purple Milk-vetch (left), Elecampane (centre), and Sainfoin were among the first wild flowers recorded from the county, in* The Herball, or General Historie of Plantes, etc. Gathered by John Gerarde. *Published in London in 1597.* © P. Walton

Bedford. Notwithstanding this, his duties were so slight that he still found time to travel on horseback throughout the county studying its wild flowers and butterflies.

The publication of his *Flora* was a splendid achievement, the first work of its kind in English. A copy in which he listed later additions is in Luton Museum. Another copy in which he listed the butterflies of the county cannot now be traced. He also collected plants. These specimens were preserved as an herbarium and still survive in six bound volumes. To our lasting regret there is no indication of where or when the plants were found. A smaller, four-volume, collection, his *Flora Selecta*, does give localities for a few specimens. Both herbaria are now at Luton Museum but his butterfly collection is lost.

Abbot was an avid collector and was always hopeful that he would find something new, even something new to science. He made the noteworthy discovery of the Large Blue butterfly in the county, near Bromham, a species which recently became extinct in Britain (Figure 2.6); he was indeed the first to report the Chequered Skipper butterfly as a British insect, from Clapham, north of Bedford (Figure 2.3). But he was disappointed that his fellow lepidopterists, Aurelians, would not adopt his name, 'the Duke of York Fritillary', in honour of the king's favourite son and commander-in-chief. He was more successful in persuading J. E. Smith to name a new willow he had found *Salix russelliana* (the Bedford Willow), in honour of the 5th Duke of Bedford (of the Russell family), whose extensive library he was allowed to use. Unfortunately for Abbot this 'new' willow is now only considered to be a hybrid. A plant he found growing in the Ouse, which he thought was entirely new to science, proved to be the roots of a willow. One hopes that it was not a Bedford Willow! He also drew Smith's attention to a strange orchid he found growing under trees at Woburn. He had an excellent drawing of it made by James Forbes, the Duke's botanical artist. It was indeed unusual as it lacked green pigment, yet did not appear to be either a parasite or saprophyte. In 1833, after the death of both Abbot and Smith, Forbes's illustration appeared in the

Figure 2.2 *The Polecat was amongst the 'vermin' listed in churchwarden accounts from the county. Like the Pine Marten (also once in Bedfordshire) it was long ago driven from lowland Britain.* © P. Walton

Supplement to British Botany as a new species with a description by Smith. It is now known that Abbot had found an abnormal form of Violet Helleborine which usually has green pigment.

The task Abbot set himself, of accounting for so much of the natural history of the county, had been simplified by Linnaeus's introduction in 1753 of binomial Latin names for organisms. The 3rd Earl of Bute, who acquired Luton Hoo in 1763, put forward a rival system of classification of plants in one of the most costly publications of all time. It mentioned just one plant, Blue Anemone, growing at Luton Hoo! Bute, whose main reputation otherwise was as Britain's most unpopular prime minister, was largely responsible for the founding of Kew Gardens.

The Russell family's interest in natural history continued and the time of the 6th Duke saw the publication by him of George Sinclair's superb *Hortus Gramineus Woburnensis* (1816). This was a limited edition which contained the actual specimens of the plants instead of their illustrations. A copy is in Luton Museum. This was

Figure 2.3 *The Chequered Skipper butterfly was first found in Britain at Clapham. Once widespread in the East Midlands it has declined to the point of extinction in England in recent decades.* © R. Revels

followed by James Forbes's *Salictum Woburnense* in 1828 and *Pinetum Woburnense* in the following year. Both were lavish publications.

Botanists and Collectors

Abbot had around him others interested in the natural history of the county but none of his stature. Plant life continued to be the main interest, with little evidence of attention to other branches of natural history until the end of the century. It was a time when it was considered that natural history was a suitable interest for ladies of gentle birth. One such was Frederica Sebright who lived a little over the county boundary, as it then was, at Beechwood near Markyate. In 1820 she began to make a collection of delightfully prepared specimens of wild flowers, some collected in Bedfordshire. This gave the dates and places of collection, and is the first such local herbarium known. She knew other excellent botanists who no doubt gave her assistance. The collecting ceased in 1823 when she married her deceased sister's husband – an action then considered sinful. The greater part of the remainder of her life was spent in Geneva.

Another early 19th century botanist was Caroline Gaye, daughter of a Shefford doctor. In 1831 she began to draw wild flowers with considerable skill, and later extended her range to include fungi and mosses. She eventually filled ten volumes with her drawings. Caroline became a private governess, staying for long periods in other parts of the country, and continuing to draw whenever she had time, or during her visits to Shefford. Her drawings are now with Frederica Sebright's specimens at Luton Museum. Like Abbot she longed to discover something new and almost succeeded in persuading Henslow, professor of botany at Cambridge, to describe as a new species a violet she had found. She hoped it would be named Cary's Violet, *Viola gayeana*, but it was only a form of Common Dog-violet.

Two contemporaries of Caroline Gaye, Emma and Caroline Alston, made a small collection of delightful drawings of plants from Odell Great Wood in about 1830. This is now at the County Record Office in Bedford.

William Crouch (1818–46) made a collection of plants which were mainly from around his Cainhoe (Clophill) home, with many from Cainhoepark Wood, which no longer exists, having been felled some years ago. It was bound into four volumes, possibly after his death. He apparently knew Caroline Gaye, fourteen years his senior, as there are a few plants in his herbarium collected by her. This may be the solution of the mystery of the Alternate-leaved Golden-saxifrage credited to him. He had a correctly named specimen with its locality improbably given as Lidlington, where he was curate. It is just possible that Caroline sent him the specimen and that he saw the very closely allied Opposite-leaved Golden-saxifrage, well known in his part of the county, and thought it to be the same.

A few years later another more extensive collection of plants was made by John McLaren (1815–1886), a gardener to Samuel Whitbread at Cardington. It was compiled as the result of medals being awarded by the Royal Horticultural Society for the best collections of wild flowers made in 1864 in one county. McLaren's entry amounted to about 700 well presented specimens. He was

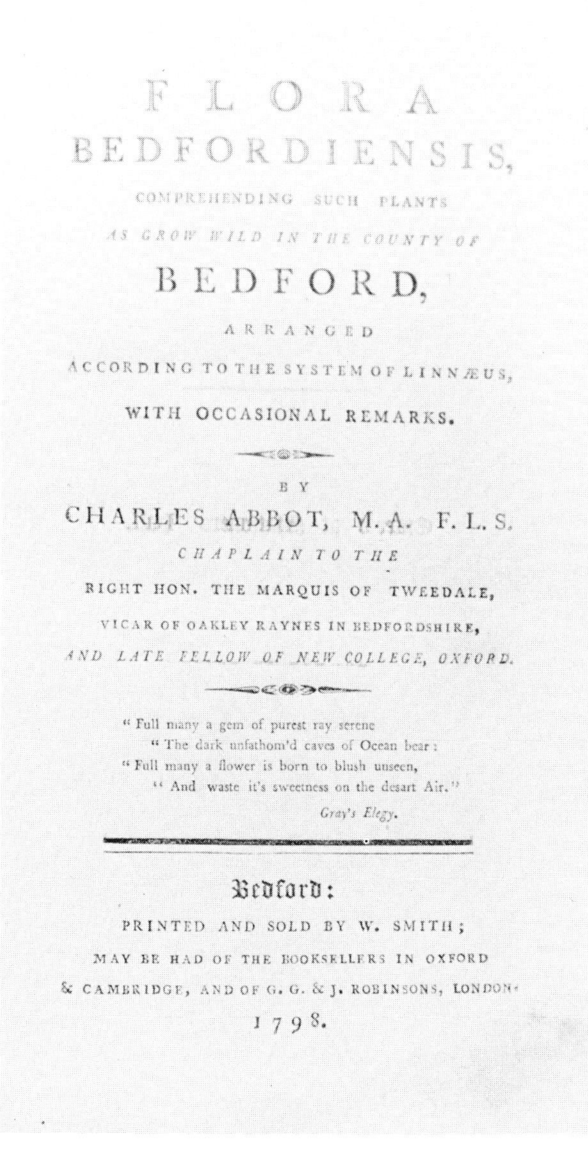
FLORA
BEDFORDIENSIS,
COMPREHENDING SUCH PLANTS
AS GROW WILD IN THE COUNTY OF
BEDFORD,
ARRANGED
ACCORDING TO THE SYSTEM OF LINNÆUS,
WITH OCCASIONAL REMARKS.

BY
CHARLES ABBOT, M.A. F.L.S.
CHAPLAIN TO THE
RIGHT HON. THE MARQUIS OF TWEEDALE,
VICAR OF OAKLEY RAYNES IN BEDFORDSHIRE,
AND LATE FELLOW OF NEW COLLEGE, OXFORD.

"Full many a gem of purest ray serene
"The dark unfathom'd caves of Ocean bear:
"Full many a flower is born to blush unseen,
"And waste it's sweetness on the desart Air."
Gray's Elegy.

Bedford:
PRINTED AND SOLD BY W. SMITH;
MAY BE HAD OF THE BOOKSELLERS IN OXFORD
& CAMBRIDGE, AND OF G. G. & J. ROBINSONS, LONDON.
1798.

Figure 2.4 *The title page of Abbot's* Flora Bedfordiensis, *the first work of its kind in English.* © R. Revels

Figure 2.5 *Two Bedfordshire museums hold collections of plants and animals from the county. (Left) Bedford Museum holds the historic Steele Elliott collection of birds and animals.* © R. Brind. *(Right) Luton Museum is the home of several collections of Bedfordshire plants, some made in the county a hundred years or more ago.*

© E. Meadows

awarded a silver medal which is now with his collection at Luton Museum. He then made an even larger herbarium, given to the British Museum (Natural History), the only Bedfordshire collection of its kind not still in the county. McLaren was also a pioneer in meteorological recording, maintaining a weather station at Cardington for forty years.

Collecting was very popular in the middle years of the 19th century and so, with bird egg collecting respectable and mounted insects beautiful in display, there were many mute inglorious Abbots around. A little is known of some of them, but their collections have long since disintegrated and what they may have known of the natural history of the county often died with them. Above all there was no ready means of communication between them.

The First Natural History Society

In August 1874 a long correspondence began in the *Bedfordshire Times* on the status in the county of Sweet-flag,

a not uncommon plant by the Ouse. The many letters published prompted Thomas Elgar to suggest that a local natural history society should be formed. There was a considerable response, perhaps not surprisingly since there was at about this time a national increase in interest in natural history, causing many local societies to be founded.

On 16th April 1875 the Bedfordshire Natural History Society came into being, with William Hillhouse (1850–1910), an assistant master at Bedford Modern School, its most active member. He had a great desire to see another Flora of the county, as it was then a long time since Abbot's monumental work had appeared. In the hope of achieving this he secured a donation from the 9th Duke of Bedford to assist in its preparation. The Society itself began well by publishing a journal, the hallmark of the better societies. In this appeared three long papers by Hillhouse showing that some progress was being made with the new Flora. Then, in 1877, he left Bedford to take up a scholarship at Cambridge where he remained until

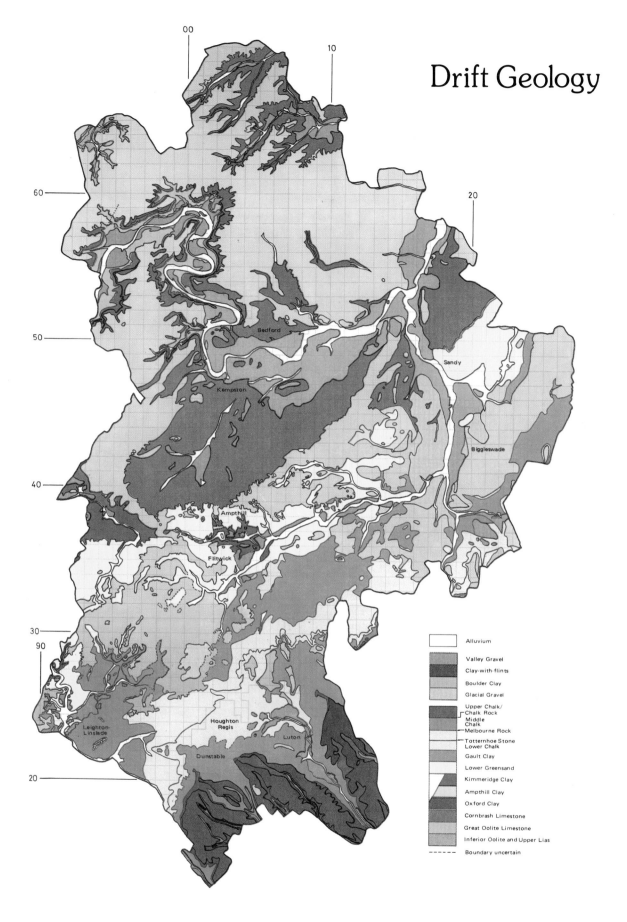

Drift Geology

00

10

20

60

50

40

30

90

20

Bedford

Sandy

Kempston

Biggleswade

Ampthill

Flitwick

Houghton
Regis

Luton

Leighton-
Linslade

Dunstable

	Alluvium
	Valley Gravel
	Clay-with-flints
	Boulder Clay
	Glacial Gravel
	Upper Chalk/ Chalk Rock
	Middle Chalk
	Melbourne Rock
	Totternhoe Stone Lower Chalk
	Gault Clay
	Lower Greensand
	Kimmeridge Clay
	Ampthill Clay
	Oxford Clay
	Cornbrash Limestone
	Great Oolite Limestone
	Inferior Oolite and Upper Lias
- - - - -	Boundary uncertain

Plate 2: *The surface deposits of Bedfordshire – the drift geology.*

© Beds.C.C.

he became the first professor of botany at Birmingham. It is difficult to speculate what would have resulted had he remained in the county as he was not a good field botanist. Probably his main achievement was to bring John McLaren into closer touch with younger men such as John Hamson and James Saunders, of whom we shall have more to say. The Society did not last long, coming to an end about 1885. It failed because it was not a truly county society. All its meetings were in Bedford where almost all its members lived, and those among them with a genuine interest in natural history were too few to make a viable society. The only useful work it did was botanical, most of the papers read at its meetings, some of which it also published, had little relevance to other aspects of natural history in the county and many not to natural history at all.

Before the Society came to an end, an herbarium apparently begun by Hillhouse was taken over by Arthur Ransome, who had recently come to Bedford to be editor of the *Bedfordshire Times*. He was not a botanist but was anxious to see the herbarium grow. Specimens came from McLaren and Saunders until it was finally taken over by John Hamson, who added more. In 1948 it was found in Bedford Library, almost completely destroyed by insects. It cannot now be found. It is a great pity that this collection no longer exists as it was undoubtedly the best of its kind made in the county in the 19th century.

Naturalists into the 20th Century

In 1859 James Saunders (1839–1925) came from Salisbury to Luton, soon to go into the expanding straw-hat industry. He had little education but an interest in geology, his carefully documented specimens being at Luton Museum. About 1877 a series of tragic domestic disasters caused him to pass through a period of mental strain. According to Charles Crouch, who had a great respect for Saunders, a Quaker friend urged Saunders to find a life interest in something bigger than himself. This Saunders did, eventually to become one of the foremost botanists of his day. He soon joined the Bedfordshire Natural History Society, its only Luton member! In a few years he had mastered the higher plants, contributing papers to the Society's journal on the wild flowers of South Bedfordshire and *Notes on Characeae (stoneworts) gathered in Bedfordshire*. By 1882, after he had worked through the mosses and liverworts he finally turned his attention to the slime fungi on which he became an authority. In 1897–98 he contributed a series of articles to a local newspaper on *The wild flowers of Bedfordshire* which, with a few additions and emendations, was later published as *The Field Flowers of Bedfordshire* (1911), his only independent published work.

Saunders probably wrote more than any previous Bedfordshire naturalist and he always wrote well. He was among the first to attempt some interpretation of nature, in a paper 'On the shrinkage of the sources of the upper Lea', in the journal of the Hertfordshire Natural History Society which he joined when the Bedfordshire Society failed. His approach to the study of nature would now be called 'ecology', a term which was scarcely known in 1903.

According to Crouch, Saunders lacked a visual memory, which meant that almost every plant he saw had to be identified as if he had not met it before. I knew him in his later years, and had attributed his inability to name the plants shown to him to his advanced age, but Crouch's theory would explain why he was happier dealing with the lower plants, the specimens of which always demand a close examination. It is possible that he missed seeing many plants. This would account for some unusual entries in his book, for example '*Veronica montana* ... Eversholt (Abbot). A recent record is desirable'. This species is plentiful enough in woods near Luton which he is known to have visited.

John Hamson (1858–1930) was an equally remarkable man. With a minimum of formal education he studied geology, chemistry, history, archaeology, Greek, French, German and Esperanto and taught shorthand and botany for many years to evening classes in Bedford. He came to that town in 1883 to be with Ransome, with whom he had previously worked, joining the staff of the *Bedfordshire Times*. His interests were more in fungi than the flowering plants but he was in an excellent position to receive records of the latter as his weekly item in the paper had frequent notes on nature. In 1906, following Saunders' example, he contributed a series of articles later collected together in a booklet *An Account of The Flora of Bedfordshire*, which it scarcely was. Hamson did not, as Saunders did, send specimens of plants to experts for correct determination with the result that his own were sometimes in error. Worse still, he doubted the correct identification of others, such as Ada Stimson's Southern Wood-rush at Marston Thrift. Between them Hamson and Saunders knew all the plant kingdom in Bedfordshire but appear to have worked little together.

Any neglect of the plants of the middle of the county was remedied by Charles Crouch (1855–1944), nephew of William and one of few of the family to live to old age. He was an excellent botanist and close friend of Saunders. It is a pity that he wrote so little. I knew him well in the last few years of his life, when I came to realise his affection for the Ampthill area and its wild flowers. 'You can go to the chalk for specimens but you must come to the greensand for the species.' How right he was. He had definite views on everything and four strong objections: to farmers who failed but became professors of agriculture; to Anglo Catholics (although, staunch Anglican as he was, he respected Catholics); to Sir Albert Richardson the architect; and to anybody who did not read *The Times*! His most cherished possession was his uncle's herbarium and the day before he died he insisted on my taking it. 'Take it now my boy, or . . . you will never have it.' It is now at Luton Museum with all Saunders' collections.

Invertebrates and other groups

In the early years of the century, facing the daunting task of preparing an account of the beetle fauna of the county for the *Victoria History*, Canon W. W. Fowler, the national authority on this group and author of a five-volume standard work, admitted that 'at first it appeared hopeless to draw up any list at all'. It could have helped if Dr J. A. Power, a celebrated coleopterist who lived in retirement in Bedford for three years until his death in 1883, had been able to get out into the field to collect. Fowler himself was a frequent visitor to Bedford, owning a house next-door to Power though not apparently engaging in any fieldwork in the county. However, subsequently a Warwickshire coleopterist, W. Ellis of Knowle, visited Bedfordshire with the purpose of establishing a basic list of beetles for the county and Fowler was able to provide him with a list of seven or eight hundred species. This was not impressive compared with that of the adjoining county of Hertfordshire where over fifteen-hundred species had been listed two years earlier. (The British list of that time was about 2000 species.) During the next few decades, following publication of Fowler's list, work on beetles was mainly done by visitors to the county.

The Natural History of the Hitchin Region reveals how little work of any kind was done on the fauna and flora in the decades following the *Victoria History*, other than in popular groups such as flowering plants, vertebrates and butterflies and moths. Collections continued to be made of birds' eggs, insects and plants, but most of these seem to have disappeared without trace – perhaps no great loss in the absence of detailed documentation on the origins of the specimens. Some collections do survive; Luton Museum has the collections of butterflies and moths made by H. A. Tebbs and by Mrs S. Taylor, both of Bedford, and by W. B. Munns, R. E. R. Sanderson and others of Luton. It also holds collections of beetles made by E. Milne-Redhead in the county between 1939 and 1945, their identifications confirmed by H. K. Airy Shaw, and of local Hymenoptera and Mollusca made by B. Verdcourt.

Bedford Museum holds an excellent collection of many insect groups made by Ray Palmer between the late 1920s and the 1940s, and includes some Bedfordshire material. The museum also has his notebooks for the same period, which document the origin of many of the specimens and make fascinating reading.

Two visitors to Bedfordshire made limited but signifi-

cant contributions to the knowledge of beetles in the county between the wars. B. S. Williams of Harpenden (Hertfordshire) and F. H. Day of Carlisle (Cumberland). Day diffidently reports finding about two hundred species of beetle at Tempsford, during a visit of a few days in early June 1922. During the 1920s Williams concentrated on the downland, adding about 150 species to the county list. His records were published posthumously by Dr P. L. Roche of Northwood (Middlesex) in one of several short papers he published on the beetles of the county in the early 1940s. This was followed by an upsurge of interest in a number of groups of insects in the county, involving several entomologists active during the 1940s.

C. Mackechnie Jarvis, who lived in Bedford for a short time, paid special attention to the beetles. Jarvis's enthusiasm must have had few equals. Anxious to find a particular beetle species resident in the nests of the Wood Ant, he visited the southern part of Maulden Woods early one morning, at a time when the ants could be presumed to be least active. Determined not to leave with 'ants in his pants' he stripped himself of clothing before plunging a bare arm into the depths of the chosen nest. The exercise completed he had no difficulty in removing those ants still clinging to his body, but not without being stung from head to foot so severely as to be seriously ill for some days! With help from another active fieldworker, Bernard

Figure 2.6 *The Large Blue: this attractive butterfly, once quite widespread in the country became extinct in Britain in recent years; it was known from a site near Bromham in the early 1800s.* © R. Revels

Plate 3: *Some less familiar examples of the county's rich and varied fauna. (Left) An Alder-fly laying eggs on a riverside sedge.* © Mary Sheridan. (*Bottom right*) *The Wasp Beetle,* Clytus arietus, *mimics a wasp in colour, shape and movements.* © B. S. Nau. (*Top right*) *The attractive spindle-shaped shell of a snail,* Macrogastra rolphii, *among lichens on a Beech tree at Streatley; this is a southern species rare in the county.* © D. G. Rands

Verdcourt, Jarvis raised the beetle list to a more respectable total, in excess of 1100 species, before leaving the county to live for a few years at Harpenden – he had married Williams' daughter – and then moving further afield, losing interest in both Bedfordshire and beetles.

There are some 19th century records of beetles from the county. Dawson in his work on ground beetles, *Geodephaga Britannica*, published in 1854, mentions *Harpalus smaragdinus* (then called *H. discoideus*) which had been found at Sandy and was considered a great prize, and *Broscus cephalotes*, a sand-dune species, which had been found at Woburn. Ninety years later, in the 1940s, Jarvis refound the former in the same area, while more recently the sand-dune beetle has been refound at Clophill.

Other insects were not entirely neglected between the wars. In 1931 Victor Chambers (1911–1984) began his outstanding work on the Hymenoptera, a very large group of four-winged insects comprising ants, bees, wasps, ichneumons and sawflies. Born in Luton, he spent much of his life in the county and this is where his entomological fieldwork was done; he had a genuine affection for Bedfordshire. In the course of time he was to become a national authority on the ants, bees and wasps and, later, on an obscure group of small wasp-like *Parasitica* (*Belytinae*). He described species new to science and was himself honoured with species named after him. He concentrated on the unravelling of the life cycle of these insects and on the discovery of unknown male, female or larval stages. He wrote a great deal, mainly in the scientific journals, his 1949 paper 'Aculeate Hymenoptera of Bedfordshire' being described as 'probably the best example of a synopsis of the Aculeata of a single county'.

Needless to say, Chambers had wider interests too, which he was ready to share with others. He knew the whole county well, his favourite area being the Greensand Ridge, rich in his bees and wasps, and the chalk downland, the conservation of which became an additional interest. Bedfordshire had not known his like before. On his death, Chambers' entomological collections went to the British Museum (Natural History), where many of his Hymenoptera have been incorporated into the national collection while others were passed on to Leicestershire Museum and The Royal Scottish Museum in Edinburgh.

Another fine field naturalist who concentrated on the invertebrates is Bernard Verdcourt, active in the county during the 1940s and still a regular visitor. During the Second World War, while a scholar at Luton Grammar School, he became interested in molluscs (snails, slugs and mussels), which had previously been inadequately studied in the county. The account in the *Victoria History* had been based on records from the Luton area made by Saunders, whose marginal interest was no doubt due to his earlier interest in geology. In 1888, Saunders' son,

Edgar, published a short list in the *Midland Naturalist*, which Saunders himself supplemented with occasional records sent to the Conchological Society of Great Britain and Ireland. Otherwise all that was known of the molluscs of the county depended on casual observations made mainly by visitors. Verdcourt, however, laid a sound foundation to the study of this group in the county.

Verdcourt also took an interest in insects, such as Water-bugs, Lacewings and Mayflies, as well as Harvestmen. His records on these were published in *The Bedfordshire Naturalist*. He left the county to pursue a career as a botanist based at the Royal Botanic Gardens, Kew. Fellow scholars were Brian Laurence, who made pioneering studies of flies around Fancott, and Geoffrey Nicholls, who updated what was known of the geological structure of the county.

The war years brought other naturalists to the county. The entomologist Ray Palmer, who moved to Flitwick from Hitchin, and the Kew botanist Edgar Milne-Redhead, whose military service brought him to Dunstable. Milne-Redhead's unique contribution was the interest he took and the encouragement he gave to others in tasks they were undertaking.

In 1945 the British Trust for Ornithology initiated, on a county basis, a survey of rookeries. The simple nature of this survey meant that one did not have to be a specialist ornithologist to participate, thereby doing much to bring together naturalists who hitherto had worked in isolation. This pointed the way for the future study of wildlife in Bedfordshire.

During the past twenty years the invertebrates have been well served: molluscs, woodlice, centipedes, millipedes, spiders and harvestmen, grasshoppers and crickets, hoverflies and bugs, not to mention butterflies, moths and dragonflies have all been subjected to an intensity of detailed study by enthusiastic amateurs matched in few, if any, other counties. The same can be said of the various groups of vertebrates and the more primitive plant groups such as mosses, lichens and fungi.

Steele Elliott and the Vertebrates

Until the closing years of the 19th century almost all the lasting work on the natural history of Bedfordshire was limited to the study of its flora but a refreshing exception came then with the contribution made by Jannion Steele Elliott (1871–1942) to our knowledge of its birds and mammals. Born at Bedford and educated at Bedford Modern School his enthusiasm at an early age for egg collecting developed into a determination to learn all he could about the birds in the county. Little had hitherto come to light – only a few notes in national journals, occasional unverified references in local newspapers, and an unreliable list in a history of Luton published in 1855.

Steele Elliott, who had considerable physical energy (he once walked from London to Bedford in one day, just for the fun of it) tramped the Bedfordshire countryside to extend his knowledge. He became friendly with gamekeepers, taxidermists (of whom there appear to have been many in the county) and birdcatchers (of whom there were even more in those days). He gathered much information on the mammals and rural life. Reference has already been made to Steele Elliott's examination of churchwardens' accounts for some Bedfordshire parishes in the 16th to 19th centuries to try to discover what birds and animals, considered to be vermin, then existed. His work was eventually published in 1936 by Luton Museum. His collection of eggs, to which he later added skins of birds and mammals, is now housed in Bedford Museum (Figure 2.7).

Although he left the county in 1896 his interest was maintained with frequent visits and correspondence. His departure prompted him to put on record what he knew in his *Vertebrate Fauna of Bedfordshire*. The first part appeared in 1897 with only 150 copies printed, giving some indication of the limited interest at that time in natural history. It ended in 1901 with the fifth part and only the birds so far dealt with. There can be no doubt that Steele

Elliott originally intended to complete his *Fauna* with accounts of the mammals, reptiles, amphibians and fishes. The reason for his failure to do so was that *The Victoria History of the County of Bedford* was being planned and he had been invited to be a contributor.

The Victoria History

The Victoria History of the County of Bedford was published in 1904. As its name suggests this dealt primarily with the history of Man in the county but gave as full an account as possible of its wildlife. The excellent treatment of birds by Steele Elliott is fuller than that in his *Fauna* so that anyone who has not ready access to this, the rarest published work on the natural history of the county, is not at any great disadvantage. His account of the mammals was equally good. The reptiles and amphibians were entrusted to J. Lacey Fishwick and the fish to A. R. Thompson, both outsiders who depended on Steele Elliott for much of their information. The account of fishes was limited, sometimes only to details of the weights of specimen fish caught by anglers.

Probably to achieve some uniformity with the histories of other counties the responsibility of presenting an account of the flowering plants was given to G. C. Druce, the foremost British botanist at that time who was, however, not without some knowledge of the county as he came originally from neighbouring Northamptonshire. He received much of his information from J. Hamson, who had full responsibility for the fungi, J. Saunders, responsible for the mosses, liverworts and stoneworts and C. Crouch. James Saunders also assisted John Hopkinson, president of the Hertfordshire Natural History Society, in presenting an account of the geology.

The accounts of the other organisms were all entrusted to outsiders, national authorities on their subjects, the slugs and snails to B. B. Woodward, beetles to W. W. Fowler and spiders to F. O. Picard-Cambridge, all revealing very little work done in the county. Some exception must be made for the butterflies and moths dealt with by C. G. Barrett. This account included a long list compiled by A. E. Gibbs, of St Albans. It makes many references to local collectors, making us regret that not one was apparently sufficiently informed to be entrusted with its compilation. There was finally an account of the Bedfordshire crustaceans with much of the information provided by Saunders who put on record the occurrence of crayfish in the county.

The natural history of the county as presented in the *Victoria History* is a landmark, the only full account so

Figure 2.7 Peregrine falcons shot in the county in the 19th century, at Broom in 1895 (left) and Old Warden in 1881 (right). Part of the Steele Elliott collection in the Bedford Museum.   © R. Revels

so far presented. It reveals that much still needed to be done but in the following forty years little progress was made.

The Flying Duchess

The interest of the Russell family continued and in the time of the 11th Duke, who held the title from 1893 to 1940, Muntjac Deer and Chinese Water Deer were introduced to Woburn Park (Figure 2.8). The former escaped and spread widely in Bedfordshire and neighbouring counties. The latter is also now at large but has been less successful. The Duke's wife, Mary, well known as 'the Flying Duchess', was a keen birdwatcher in a changing world of bird protection when the observation of bird behaviour began to replace egg collecting and birdcatching. Her favourite site on the estate appears to have been the secluded Battlesden Lake. After her untimely death her ornithological diary was published, but unfortunately it contains few references to Bedfordshire birds.

The Hitchin and Letchworth groups

The apparent lack of interest within Bedfordshire in the study of its natural history resulted in some Hertfordshire naturalists turning their attentions to the county. This was already evident in the *Victoria History*. It was very much the case with Hitchin, which over a long time produced a succession of active naturalists, and with Letchworth Garden City, where natural history seemed to be an essential part of the new way of life its pioneers were seeking. Both were so near to the county boundary that the naturalists in each took a radius of twelve miles from the centre of their respective towns as their area of study. In each case this included a large part of Bedfordshire.

J. E. Little (1861–1935), for a time headmaster of Hitchin Grammar School, was one of the leading field botanists of his day and made a detailed study of the Ivel basin. His study *The Ivel district of Bedfordshire*, published in the year of his death, is a valuable addition to our knowledge of the flora of the county. The previous year had seen the publication by the Hitchin and District Regional Survey Association of the magnificent work entitled *The Natural History of the Hitchin Region*, the result of some years of investigation and planning. Almost all branches of natural history were covered, in addition to archaeology, geology, meteorology and aromatic and medicinal herbs, the last of local interest, there being a flourishing firm of herbalists in the town. J. E. Little, probably feeling that he had put all he knew of plants on record elsewhere, contented himself with a bibliography, but the sections on butterflies and moths, fishes, reptiles, amphibians, birds and mammals, all the work of A. H. Foster, were excellent. Apart from the fleas and flies dealt

Figure 2.8 *The Chinese Water Deer is a small deer of open country which has become established in small numbers in south-west Bedfordshire since escaping from Woburn Park.* © R. Revels

with by F. W. Edwards, a national authority who lived at Letchworth, the rest of the animal kingdom was covered by Ray Palmer. Among the many organisms which received his consideration were worms, centipedes and millipedes, earwigs, bugs, lacewings, caddis flies and ants. The Hitchin survey contained some Bedfordshire records but, if nothing else, it drew attention to many branches of natural history.

The Second Natural History Society

As the Second World War approached there was a national upsurge of interest in natural history, which may have had many causes, including the coming of broadcasting, the awarding of scout's badges for proficiency in natural history and a broader approach to the teaching of biology in schools. From time to time there were short-lived groups in the county bent on further study. One such was formed for young people at Woburn by Mary, Duchess of Bedford. The war years saw the setting up of nature reserve investigation committees with the anticipation that, when peace came, some machinery would be brought into being to conserve nature in Britain.

Naturalists in the county, of whom there were now more although they were still few in number, could well be brought together again. The moving spirit in achieving this was Henry Key, a pharmaceutical chemist in Bedford, who, though primarily an ornithologist, had a wider knowledge and appreciation of nature. He was to prove a supreme organiser. Scholars at Bedford School, where there was an interest in birdwatching for many years, invariably went to Key, the expert, to discuss their problems. He invited the other naturalists he knew in the county to meet in Bedford on a Sunday afternoon in September 1946. The response was so promising that it was decided to form the Bedfordshire Natural History Society which still flourishes today. The main objective was to be the study of the natural history of the county. The members who joined the new society this time came from all parts of the county, which was promising, but even more strength came from the youthfulness of the more active members. An exception was Oliver Pike, the first president, who lived near Leighton Buzzard and was well known as a nature photographer (Figure 2.9). Aged 69, he seemed much older.

The most important decision was to publish a journal – that records made in the past had not been committed to print was seen as a serious deficiency. The Society's journal *The Bedfordshire Naturalist* began with Ra Palmer, living at Flitwick, an ideal choice as its first editor.

To achieve one of its main objects the Society appointed an expert panel of 'recorders'. Palmer himself took over the recording of grasshoppers and crickets, amphibians and the mammals, Key, who was also secretary, the birds (there could be no other choice), Fred Soper, then living at Bedford, the fishes, Victor Chambers, then in Luton, the sawflies, bees, wasps and ants while Arthur Guppy, then living at Bromham, made himself responsible for a meteorological report, which he continued to do until 1980. The remaining early recorders appointed were able young men, Geoffrey Nicholls, then at Cambridge but from Westoning, for geology, Bernard West, of Bedford, for butterflies and moths, C. MacKechnie Jarvis, also of Bedford, for beetles, and three Lutonians, Bernard Verdcourt for lacewings, Brian Laurence for flies (of which he had made a special study) and Peter Taylor, shortly to go to Kew, for ferns, mosses and liverworts. My preparation of the *Flora of Bedfordshire* (1953) was well advanced and so I became recorder for flowering plants. We were soon joined by Derek Reid, who was at Kew but had come from Leighton Buzzard, for the recording of the fungi.

Figure 2.9 Oliver Pike was one of the early wildlife photographers of national reputation; he lived at Leighton Buzzard and was the first President of the Bedfordshire Natural History Society. The high standard of his work is shown by these Badgers photographed in the early years of the century.

Courtesy of H. A. S. Key

It made a good team but mention needs also to be made of the contribution of Elsie Proctor, one of the most active members in the early days. She was training teachers in environmental studies at the Froebel Training College in Bedford. The nature study room there was home for the Society in those early days.

A distinguished pioneer member was the 12th Duke of Bedford. He was an authority on parrots and deer as well as having a wider natural history knowledge. He was without doubt the best naturalist of his family. He was later to be the Society's President, delivering a memorable address on deer. But there can be no doubt that he was happier to be just an ordinary member, coming at times to meetings to sit in the back row – not a little to the consternation of more than one speaker, lest he ask a question to which an appropriate answer was not known!

There were field meetings as well as lectures. The very first was to Great Hayes Wood led by Edgar Milne-Redhead, who had been temporarily domiciled at Dunstable during the war and had much affection for the county. In the course of this meeting he found a plant species on the railway nearby that was new to the British flora, the Grey Mouse-ear. It is still there!

As with most other societies of its kind the interest of the greater number of its members was in birds, prompting Henry Key to organise a series of one-day ornithological conferences at Bedford at which many of the leading British ornithologists of the time took a prominent part. They were a tremendous success, attracting visitors from a wide area, leaving little doubt that they paved the way for national conferences of a similar nature. There was, however, no danger in those early days that an interest in birds would dominate the Society, as may be seen by an examination of the contents of the early numbers of its journal, *The Bedfordshire Naturalist*, which had a good balance of almost all branches of natural history study.

Changes were inevitable. Ray Palmer left the county in 1952 to be succeeded as editor by H. F. Barnes, who had a particular interest in plant galls and continued until his untimely death in 1955, when Arthur Guppy became editor. Some of the active younger members left the county to begin successful careers elsewhere and there were not always others to carry on the work they had begun. The Society went through a quiet period in the 1960s to flourish again in the ensuing decades. However, over its forty years existence, the Society has been remarkably well served by a series of recorders, often of national reputation. Their enthusiastic efforts have made Bedfordshire one of the most thoroughly studied of counties.

Conservation

The study of natural history in the county had been the main aim of the society and in its early days it succeeded well. But another of its objectives was to endeavour to conserve the flora and fauna of the county. With much thought, therefore, a list of sites of natural history importance was prepared and when the Nature Conservancy was formed it was grateful for this groundwork. This list became the basis for the first schedule of Sites of Special Scientific Interest. We were overjoyed when Knocking Hoe, which we considered to be one of the two most important sites, was made a National Nature Reserve in 1955.

Notwithstanding this apparent progress, sites in the county known to have a considerable natural history interest were lost at an alarming rate. Naturalists' trusts were being formed in other counties leading some to think that the formation of a similar trust would be of benefit to Bedfordshire. In 1959 the Natural History Society asked other bodies likely to be interested to meet and it was decided at this meeting that a trust should be formed. I was President of the Society at that time and had also an interest in Huntingdonshire which, although more than well provided for with nature reserves, had at most not more than half a dozen naturalists in the whole county. I pressed for and succeeded in getting the trust to include Huntingdonshire which at that time so obviously needed any help Bedfordshire could give. Who was to know that there would soon be the Monks Wood Experimental Station with a regiment of professional biologists well able to press for, and succeed in getting, still more reserves in Huntingdonshire to the neglect of Bedfordshire.

There were fears as to whether the Society and the newly-formed Trust could both survive and these were to some extent justified when for a time the Society became weak. Fortunately it recovered and for some years now the Bedfordshire Natural History Society and the Bedfordshire and Huntingdonshire Naturalists' Trust (now Wildlife Trust) have worked side by side, the Society continuing to foster the study of wildlife and its conservation, and the Trust acquiring and managing nature reserves.

Chapter 3

The Variety of Wildlife

Variety of Species

Bedfordshire still has a surprising variety of plants and animals. Many of these need a very specific habitat and are therefore not at all common in the county, but they do add greatly to the interest of our wildlife. In this chapter the variety within the various groups will be outlined and the way in which it is changing will be indicated.

To give an impression of this variety, the numbers of species known from Bedfordshire in a selection of groups are listed in Table 3.1. In those groups which have been studied fairly thoroughly about 50–60 per cent of the species known from Britain as a whole are to be found in Bedfordshire. From this can be estimated how many may be found in some of the less studied groups. In the table such estimates are shown in italics.

Although the table is not complete, in particular many lower forms of life are not listed, the rich variety of species in the county shows very clearly. This richness is quite surprising in view of how little wildlife habitat is left in the county.

It might be thought that so many different species must include many pests and weeds. This is not really the case; many of the species occur only in small numbers and are so particular about their habitat and food that they are not even a potential threat.

Birds, Farmland and Wetlands

Birds are a convenient group with which to begin, because they have been studied more thoroughly than most others. They also show up some of the problems affecting other forms.

A few years ago, a register of important bird sites in Britain was put together by the British Trust for Ornith-

Table 3.1 Examples of the numbers of species in various groups in Bedfordshire and Britain

Group	Bedfordshire	Britain
Plants		
Flowers	983	2137
Mosses and Liverworts	294	987
Lichens	149	1400
Fungi (large)	*1000*	3000+
Vertebrate animals		
Birds (breeding)	113	192
Mammals	34	56
Amphibians and Reptiles	9	15
Fish	27	42
Invertebrate animals		
Butterflies	33	55
Moths (large)	515	900
Dragonflies	18	45
Beetles	*2000*	4000
Bees, Wasps, Ants, etc	*3000*	6100
Bugs (true)	310	537
Aphids and leafhoppers	*550*	1111
Lacewings	24	60
Flies	*2500*	5200
Caddis-, May-, and Stone-flies	*130*	269
Thrips	*80*	159
Woodlice	23	39
Centipedes	24	41
Millipedes	32	53
Snails, slugs and mussels	135	200

Totals in italics are estimates

ology. Sites in Bedfordshire, representing several different habitat types, are listed in Table 3.2. This also shows the number of species of bird using each habitat in the breeding season and in winter. This shows that most sites are at least as important for the wintering species as for the breeding species. This is very noticeable for the open water of the flooded clay and gravel quarries. Both gulls and waterfowl are very dependent on these, the gulls for roosting and the waterfowl for feeding and resting.

A comparison of the two farms in the list is very revealing too – one is top of the list for variety of breeding

Figure 3.1 *A red and black froghopper (*Cercopis vulnerata*)–seen here on horsetail–is a conspicuous insect of hedgerows and verges in the spring.* (Dropshort Nature Reserve, June 1983).   © B. S. Nau

Table 3.2   The richness and variety of birdlife, shown by Bedfordshire survey data from the British Trust for Ornithology

(a)   Numbers of species in various habitats

Habitat	Site	Area (ha)	Nesting	Winter
Mixed farm and woodland	Old Warden	74	64	—
Arable farm and golfcourse	Streatley	122	36	—
Pasture	Biggleswade Common	160	43	62
Downland and scrub	Dunstable Downs	100	43	45
Primary woodland	Maulden Woods	200	63	62
Secondary woodland	Warden Warren	70	51	45
Gravel pits	Harrold/Odell	55	55	93
Clay-pit	Brogborough	125	51	70

(b)   Farmland breeding populations, pairs per 100 hectares

Feeding mode	Mixed farm (Old Warden)	Arable farm (Streatley)
Seed-eaters	261	106
Insect-eaters	339	65
Predators and scavengers	15	2
All	*615*	*173*

(c)   Waterway breeding populations in east of England, pairs per 10 km

Habitat	Waterfowl	Other wetland species
Rivers	107	47
Canalised waterways	50	57

species, the other is at the bottom – showing the difference between a traditional farm and one devoted to intensive cereal growing (Figure 3.2). This comparison reflects the losses which can occur as a result of the destruction of semi-natural habitat on farmland.

The contrast is even more vivid when one compares the number of breeding birds on the two farms. Table 3.2b shows the figures for equal areas. The intensive cereal farm has only about one quarter of the number of birds, with the insect-eating species affected particularly badly. In view of the considerably greater acreage of cereals now grown in the county it must be concluded that the farmland of Bedfordshire today has only a fraction of the songbird population it had even a few decades ago.

A similar contrast shows up between the more-or-less natural and the canalised waterways. The results of bird counts made in the east of England are shown in Table 3.2c. Canalised rivers and canals have far fewer pairs of waterfowl than do natural rivers. Unfortunately, in Bedfordshire much of the length of our rivers has been canalised, reducing the quality of the riverside habitats and, one must assume, the variety and numbers of birds.

This canalisation has been done for several reasons. Because of an increased rate of rainwater run-off, due to the many new roads and houses, and because agricultural land-drainage has been a profitable undertaking aided by government grants, rainwater has been finding its way into the rivers much more quickly than in the past. So, to prevent flooding, water authorities have dredged and straightened and otherwise manipulated our rivers. The alternative is to provide temporary storage for stormwater. This concept has rarely been applied, but exceptions are a retention lagoon built in Cowslip meadow on the north edge of Luton and the balancing lake for the Ouse, just out of the county at Willen Lake (Milton Keynes) – very popular with birdwatchers. This approach puts the cost where the problem is created and does not require the destruction of the natural features of our rivers.

Another pressure on our river valleys has been that riverside farmland values can be increased if periodic flooding can be prevented by lowering the water table. This has been the stimulus for major river engineering schemes in the county in the past two decades. It has had a drastic effect on birds and other wildlife dependent on the wetlands in river valleys.

Finally, the Great Ouse was 'rebuilt' downstream from Bedford in the course of engineering works to make the river navigable by pleasure-craft. The river had been made navigable in the distant past but after years of neglect had returned to an attractively varied semi-natural state.

It was only late in the day that the extent of the effects on wildlife of all these changes to our rivers was realised. The river authorities are only now beginning to consider the possibility of conservation of some of the wildlife habitat which would be affected by proposed river engineering works. The evident effects noted on bird life are bound to apply to other forms of animals and plant life along our rivers.

Recording Wildlife Populations

Whilst there is still a rich variety of species in the county, most are scarce and only a few are really common. Table 3.3 shows that in four of the more attractive families of flowers, only two species are very widespread in the county whilst twenty-two are very localised. Others fall between these extremes.

The distribution of these flowers was measured by the

Figure 3.2 *(Top) Open farmland bird census area with few hedges or other cover, in the south of the county near Warden Hill, Streatley. (TL 078275, July 1986) (Bottom) Mixed farmland with well developed hedges and scattered woodland, in mid-Bedfordshire at Old Warden. (TL 136444, July 1986)*

© B. S. Nau

number of 2 × 2 km grid squares – tetrads – in which each had been found. If a species was found anywhere in a tetrad, even if there was only one plant, then this tetrad was included in the total. This means that even though a species may be found in a good number of tetrads, it may still be very vulnerable and could easily be lost from the county if the total population is small. The situation can be even more delicate because the sites where scarce species are found are often themselves small and easily destroyed.

These are the two main kinds of information on the wild-life populations of Bedfordshire. In a few groups we are fortunate in having actual population counts for certain species, although sometimes only at special sites, for example, the Man Orchid at Totternhoe Knolls Nature Reserve. More often the geographical distribution has been mapped in Bedfordshire using the tetrad method mentioned above. As previously noted, this approach does have shortcomings, but it is relatively quick and practical compared with the alternatives and it does indicate something about the status of the species.

A list of the groups which have been mapped by the Bedfordshire Natural History Society is given in Table 3.4.

A rare example of actual population counts for insects and some other invertebrates is a study of chalk grassland

28

Table 3.3 The distribution of members of the orchid, gentian, primrose, and bellflower families in Bedfordshire

Distribution type	No. of species	% of tetrads
Very widespread	2	over 50
Widespread	4	26 to 50
Fairly widespread	5	11 to 25
Local	8	6 to 10
Very local	22	under 5

A *tetrad* is a 2 × 2 km Ordnance Survey grid square

fauna on Barton Hills. This was carried out by ecologists from the Nature Conservancy Council in the 1960s. They used various sampling methods over several years to investigate how grazing affects populations. The remains of wire-netting exclosures used in this study can still be seen.

Some of the results of the NCC study are shown in Table 3.5. This summarises counts of various animals in one square foot of turf. These large populations are unnoticed by the casual visitor to our downland. The study showed that the populations are very dependent on the tussocky structure of the turf. When grazing stops there is an increase in the animal populations for a couple of years before they begin to decline. This suggests that intermittent grazing would be a good way to maintain the interest of downland turf. In fact, during 1986, sheep grazing has been taking place once again on Barton Hills, Sharpenhoe Clappers and Bison Hill, Whipsnade, as a habitat conservation measure. Intermittent management would probably be beneficial to other types of grassland too, such as roadside verges and marshland. The tussocks are important because of the effect they have on the micro-

Table 3.4 Groups for which Bedfordshire distribution maps have been prepared by Bedfordshire Natural History Society official recorders

Species group	Pub'n date	Recorder
Flowers and Ferns	1976	Dr J. G. Dony
Mosses and Liverworts	—	A. R. Outen
Lichens	1981	F. B. M. Davies
Birds (breeding)	1979	B. D. Harding
Mammals	—	D. Anderson
Amphibians and Reptiles	—	H. M. Muir-Howrie
Butterflies	—	A. J. Martin
Moths (large)	—	V. W. Arnold
Dragonflies	—	Dr N. Dawson
Grasshoppers and Crickets	—	D. G. Rands
Bugs (true)	—	Dr B. S. Nau
Woodlice	—	Dr A. J. Rundle
Centipedes	—	Dr A. J. Rundle
Millipedes	—	Dr A. J. Rundle
Snails, Slugs and Mussels	—	E. B. Rands

Table 3.5 Numbers of invertebrate animals per square foot (approx.) found in downland turf on Barton Hills in 1966–67 in grazed land and in land not grazed for two years

Species group	Grazed	Ungrazed
Butterflies and Moths	21	20
Beetles	317	629
Grasshoppers	—	3
Bees, Sawflies, etc	25	68
Bugs	71	520
Spiders etc	45	507
Centipedes and Millipedes	281	1002
Woodlice	5	149
Snails and Slugs	21	42

(Based on Morris, M. G., 1968, *J.appl.Ecol.* **5**, 601–611)

climate and the protection they provide from large predators. When they are allowed to develop too much, however, many less robust plants are squeezed out, with the loss of essential foodplants for some of the insect species.

To illustrate the results obtained by mapping Figure 3.4 shows some examples. The maps are for the Primrose, the Nightingale and a marsh snail (*Ashfordia granulata*) and are shown beside national 10 × 10 km grid-maps, for comparison.

Figure 3.3 *The Clustered Bellflower: a common Campanula of downland.*

© R. Revels

Plate 4: *Two of the county's varied waterways. (Top) Mute Swans feeding on the River Great Ouse at Odell.* (SP 965575, May 1985) © D. G. Rands. (*Bottom*) *The Grand Union Canal at Linslade.*

© Mary Sheridan

County Distribution   National Distribution

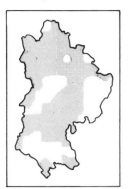 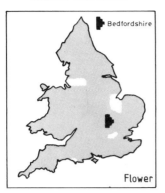

Primrose

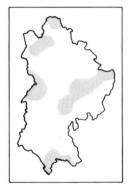 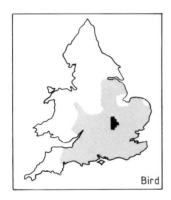

Nightingale

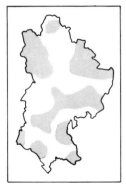 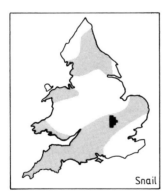

Ashfordia granulata

Figure 3.4 *The distribution of species of animals and plants can be very different within the county than is suggested by national distribution maps; this is illustrated here by three examples: Primroses need high humidity, the Nightingale is a bird of dense thickets, and the snail shown is a marshland species.*
Courtesy of BTO, ITE(NERC)

Figure 3.5 *The White-legged Damselfly: a river dragonfly on the edge of its British range in the county; its broad white legs are well shown.*   © B. S. Nau

This illustrates the very different impression given by the more detailed local map. Species which are widely distributed nationally may be very localised within the county, and therefore more vulnerable. The Chalk-hill Blue butterfly and the White-legged Damselfly, a dragonfly, are just two examples of species near the edge of their British range in Bedfordshire. Such species are a particular conservation problem since their loss from Bedfordshire would be a reduction of their range in Britain, and possibly significant even on a European scale.

Population Changes

Having considered the great variety of wildlife to be found in the county, attention will now be given to the population changes taking place.

Most naturalists who study wildlife in this part of Britain form the impression that, on the whole, both variety and abundance are declining. This has been remarked upon by naturalists over many years but only recently has there been a systematic approach to its study.

The lack of data from the past became particularly evident in the 1960s when bird populations declined drastically as a result of poisoning by agricultural pesticides; but earlier, from the 1950s, observers were noting that butterfly populations were in decline. In the case of the various species of fritillary butterfly the decline was so severe in this part of Britain that the woodland species have been lost completely. In general, however, it is not possible to be precise about the extent of decline because there is a lack of historic data with which comparison could be made. Crude as the mapping method is, it may fail to reveal quite massive *population* changes, but when it does show a change in the *distribution* of a species, this is probably very significant.

Bird population changes will again be discussed in detail first since these are quite well documented.

Changing Bird Populations

This is perhaps the only group for which the picture is fairly optimistic. Even though we have lost species from the county in recent decades, species gained perhaps more than compensate. Good national and Bedfordshire data are available from the 1960s onwards due to the activities of the British Trust for Ornithology.

Probably the most important loss has been the Red-backed Shrike, which used to be well established as a breeding species, notably on the steep slopes of the Chiltern escarpment. This is an example of a loss through natural causes. An unfavourable climatic trend towards cooler, damper summers seems to have caused the decline of the population which was established in south-east England.

Among the gains in Bedfordshire in recent decades can be counted the Collared Dove, now verging on pest status having first arrived in Britain about 30 years ago, the Little Ringed Plover, dependent for its nest site on gravel temporarily exposed during quarrying, and the Common Tern which finds nesting beaches in flooded quarries. The Black-headed Gull was a temporary gain for a few years, nesting on islets in flooded claypits. Other examples of bird population trends can be found in the *Bedfordshire Bird Atlas* compiled and published by the Bedfordshire Natural History Society in 1979.

Nationally, rather few bird species declined during the decade 1967–76, for which good census data is available. A considerable number actually increased. A conspicuous exception is the Whitethroat; this species suffered a dramatically sudden decline in the late sixties. It is believed that this was due to a severe drought in its winter quarters in the African Sahel region. Three resident farmland species have also declined quite seriously nationally, the Corn Bunting, Grey Partridge and Rook; although in Bedfordshire the Corn Bunting has followed a different trend, possibly even increasing. Changes in farming practice seem a likely cause of these changes. Loss of insect food for the young in the case of the Grey Partridge, loss of grassland for feeding and trees for nesting in the case of the Rook. Other farmland species in decline are insectivorous migrants which have probably suffered habitat loss here and may also have suffered from the trans-Saharan droughts of recent years.

Woodland birds in decline include insect feeding migrants, as well as one resident insectivore, the Willow Tit. Climatic factors may be at work but the changes in woodland habitat are probably also a factor, in particular, replacement of native hardwoods, such as Pedunculate Oak and Ash, by conifer plantations. This has been a particular feature in Bedfordshire and neighbouring counties. The upsurge of replanting in the last two or three decades resulted in birds of scrub or grassland temporarily flourishing. These take advantage of favourable conditions while the plantations are young but are forced out as the conifers close in and shade out all shrubs, flowering plants and grasses. The Tree Pipit and Grasshopper Warbler are notable examples. The Nightjar also benefited temporarily but is now hardly to be found in Bedfordshire; here too climatic factors may be partly responsible, cooler, damper summers affecting its insect prey.

Wetland birds follow a somewhat similar cycle in quarries. Most of our gravel and clay pits are worked in a flooded state, or with extensive shallow pools, in any case being allowed to flood when worked out. The new habitats formed by flooded gravel or clay pits are quickly colonised by waterfowl and attract many migrant waders, particularly Green and Common Sandpiper, Redshank, Greenshank, Lapwing, Ringed and Little Ringed Plover. Since the 1960s over thirty species of migrant waders have been observed in such quarries. When working ceases the current practice is for recreational activities to take over – fishing, sailing, water skiing, etc. These often cause considerable disturbance and bird numbers fall. At the same time vegetation rapidly colonises the beaches, which are attractive feeding places for the waders as well as providing resting sites for ducks. The changes as the vegetation develops attract a somewhat commonplace community of song birds, replacing the wetland species.

Mineral workings have certainly enriched the birdlife of the county but, at the same time, have been responsible for the loss of damp meadows and marshes which have a rich flora and fauna of their own. These habitats are now so scarce in Bedfordshire that the 'trade-off' is no longer adequate compensation for their loss.

Changing Butterfly Populations

The butterfly situation is far from satisfactory. The species of butterfly declining or lost from Bedfordshire in recent decades are set out in Table 3.6. This information is based on *national* distribution maps showing species ranges.

As explained before, distribution maps do not give a totally accurate picture of trends, especially for species whose numbers are falling but whose overall range has not yet changed appreciably. Never the less it can be seen that several species have been lost from the county over recent decades and many now have a reduced range in our region. Two species whose regional ranges have not

Figure 3.6 *(Top) The Collared Dove: first arrived in Britain about 30 years ago and is now common.* © R. Revels. *(Bottom) The Nightjar at nest in Rowney Warren about 1950, since then conifers have grown up and the habitat is no longer suitable.*
© H. A. S. Key

changed very much but which are believed to have de-clined quite considerably in numbers within the county are the two downland blues, the Chalk-hill Blue and the Small Blue. The habitat for these has certainly been greatly reduced by the spread of Hawthorn scrub since sheep grazing on the downland went into decline. The Adonis Blue and the Silver-spotted Skipper have been lost already, whilst the Brown Argus Blue and the Duke of Burgundy have a reduced range. However, very recently

the Silver-spotted Skipper has been seen again in the county so perhaps it may yet become re-established.

Although loss of habitat is probably the most important cause of the decline of these butterflies, the downland species are rather sensitive to climatic changes since they are mostly species near the limit of their range in Britain and in recent decades summers have tended to be cooler and damper.

There are also some woodland butterflies amongst

33

Table 3.6   The changing status of butterflies in the Bedfordshire region
Species in decline in the region are listed with nationally most local species first. Species already lost from Bedfordshire are in italics

Black Hairstreak	White Admiral
Chequered Skipper	Brown Argus Blue
Silver-spotted Skipper	Marbled White
Large Tortoiseshell	Purple Hairstreak
Adonis Blue	White-letter Hairstreak
Brown Hairstreak	Grizzled Skipper
Small Blue	*Small Pearl-bordered Fritillary*
Wood White	*Pearl-bordered Fritillary*
Chalk-hill Blue	*Silver-washed Fritillary*
Duke of Burgundy	Dark-green Fritillary
High Brown Fritillary	Green Hairstreak

(Based on pre-1960 and 1960–1975 distribution maps published by the National Biological Records Centre)

those in general decline, for instance, the hairstreaks (Table 3.7), Wood White and White Admiral. In Bedfordshire, however, the Wood White has possibly been increasing its range in recent years, having been found in a number of new localities. The picture for the Marbled White is similar, the species showing signs of becoming established away from its traditional Chiltern stronghold.

The woodland species of fritillary butterfly have been completely lost from the county in recent decades, in common with much of this part of England (Table 3.8). In the case of these declining woodland species the changes in forestry methods are likely to have been an important factor, greatly reducing the extent of suitable habitat, glades and open rides, leaving small fragmented popula-

tions which are very sensitive to other pressures, such as adverse weather conditions.

The undocumented release of captive-bred butterfly stock, of varying place and origin, is a factor causing some confusion. The desirability of such uncontrolled introductions is questionable.

Moths and Mothing

By contrast with butterflies, little is known of the populations of our moths and the way these have changed over the years. Entomologists have taken an interest in the moths of Bedfordshire for over a hundred years but this has rarely extended beyond the amassing of collections of specimens. Most of these collections have been lost and, in any case, very little information was recorded about the origin of specimens; even place names were vague or non-existent. In the absence of reference specimens for checking against modern identification criteria many of these older records have now to be disregarded.

Since the post-war revival of interest however, the respectable total of over five hundred species has been recorded for the county. This total refers to the larger moths, a large number are known as 'micros' and are usually ignored by lepidopterists, being more difficult to identify. In the following discussion we refer to the large moths, unless otherwise stated.

In Bedfordshire, in recent years, work has begun on the micros too and 640 species are now known from the county. The micro moths include the very attractive Plume Moths with their feather-like wings, and many micros have larvae which are leaf-miners. The leaf-miner species can often be named by noting the combination of the host-plant and the appearance of the 'mines'.

Table 3.7   Changes in the status of hairstreak butterflies in Bedfordshire

Hairstreak species	*1940–50*	*1950–60*	*1970–*
Black	Small numbers in north	Two woods in north	One wood, 1984–
Brown	Small numbers in south	Status unknown	Extinct
Green	Widespread on limey soils	Unchanged	Confined mainly to Chilterns
Purple	Common and widespread	Unchanged	Widespread in fair numbers
White-letter	Widespread	Widespread	Much scarcer due to Dutch elm disease

Table 3.8   The decline of fritillary butterflies in Bedfordshire

Fritillary species	*1940–50*	*1950–60*	*1970–*
Dark Green	Small numbers, lime-rich grassland	Present	Three sites
Silver-washed	Common and widespread, woods	Present	Extinct
High Brown	Widespread, woods	Present	Extinct
Pearl-bordered	Widespread, woods	Present	Extinct
Small Pearl-bordered	Reduced numbers, woods	Present	Extinct
Marsh	Sewell (lost elsewhere), meadow	Status unknown	Extinct
Heath	Extinct (1854 only record, wood)	Extinct	Extinct

In the last decade or so the availability of portable electrical generators and a variety of special lamps has revolutionised the study of moths. It is now possible to take the very effective ultra-violet lamps out into the countryside to build-up a picture of the distribution of moths throughout the county. Usually a mercury-discharge lamp is used, which gives out an intense visible and ultra-violet light, being a very powerful attraction to moths. On a warm, cloudy, summer's night, moths may arrive by the hundred (Plate 5). Unfortunately it is not usually possible to assess the size of the population because the numbers attracted vary so much with species, season, type of light-source, habitat and weather conditions; however, light-traps are invaluable for showing what species are present and giving a general idea of their abundance.

Several types of trap are in use in the county. The simplest involves hanging the lamp over a white bed-sheet laid on the ground. The moths usually fly round the lamp a few times and then drop down to alight on the sheet where they can be boxed for closer inspection. For unattended use the lamp is mounted above a collecting drum with baffles and a funnel to direct the moths down into the drum from which they can be extracted later. With either of these methods the moths are later released, during hours of darkness to avoid predation by birds. For systematic long-term censusing of moths a national network of low-power 'Rothamsted' light-traps is in use, these kill the moths so that they can be sent away for counting and identification. Several of these have been located in the county for periods of years. They have the advantage that they do not need an entomologist on the spot and, being operated on a long term basis, they do provide a measure of population changes.

In the more distant past the relatively inefficient hurricane lamp was used and the 'sugaring' of trees was popular too. Hunting and rearing caterpillars was also productive.

Among the changes which have been observed over the years, the large and fascinating Goat Moth (wing-span about 80 mm) appears to have declined. At one time it was considered widespread through the county but this is

no longer the case. Why this should be happening is not known, the larvae burrow in willow and other trees, feeding on the wood, so there is no obvious loss of habitat. On the positive side, Blair's Shoulder-knot is a recent addition to our fauna. Discovered for the first time in Britain on the Isle of Wight in 1951 it now seems well established in southern England. It was first found in Bedfordshire at Clifton in 1985. Its caterpillar feeds on flowers and leaves of Cypress trees, particularly the Californian Monterey Cypress (*Cupressus macrocarpus*) and the popular hybrid Leyland Cypress, very widely planted in gardens. Presumably the widespread availability of the food-plants has helped this moth to spread.

In general, over the last thirty years the moths do not seem to have suffered quite as badly as butterflies. Perhaps they are less affected by climatic factors and often have a broader range of food plants. However, some moth caterpillars are very specific in their requirements for food-plants, and this itself may have a restricted distribution. For example, the Beautiful Snout is restricted to Bilberry, which in Bedfordshire is found only on the Greensand and is gradually declining there through shading by conifer plantations; again, the larval food-plant of the Feathered Rustic is Thyme and this is almost restricted to the chalk.

The richest habitats for moths are on the Chalk Downs and the Greensand Ridge; we will return to these in later chapters. Locally, there are good sites too on the clays and limestone. Table 3.9 illustrates the numbers of species which have been found at different sites around the county. These sites have not all been worked equally thoroughly but the figures do give a general indication of their richness.

Sometimes quite surprising species occur in private gardens, for instance the Royal Mantle is a chalk downland species which had not been seen in the county for fifty years until it turned up in a light-trap in a Luton garden. Gardens can also attract large numbers of species, revealed by running a moth trap. A 'Rothamsted' trap run in a garden surrounded by arable farmland near Cockayne Hatley has produced no fewer than 288 species over a period of ten years' continuous operation.

Table 3.9 Numbers of moth species recorded from various light-trap sites, 1974–1986

Chalk		Greensand		Clays	
Barton Hills–Pegsdon Hills	150	Aspley Heath	260	Cranfield Airfield	230
Bison Hill, Whipsnade	147	Cooper's Hill, Ampthill	169	Hardwick Spinney, Stagsden	134
Sewell Cutting	185	Flitwick Moor	275	Kings Wood, Heath and Reach*	176
Totternhoe Knolls	125	Old Warden	268	Marston Thrift	253
		Rowney Warren, near Shefford	98	Maulden Wood*	353
River valley		Sandy Warren	331	Potton Wood	133
				Putnoe Wood, Bedford	90
Felmersham Gravel Pits	130			Coppice Wood, Melchbourne	183

*Denotes clay sites partly on Greensand

Table 3.10   The hawk-moths of Bedfordshire

Resident species:

Privet Hawk-moth	Widespread in small numbers
Pine Hawk-moth	The larvae feed on leaves of Scots Pine and Norway Spruce on the Greensand Ridge; most common in the Aspley Heath and Woburn area
Lime Hawk-moth	Common throughout the county and often attracted to light; the larvae feed on leaves of other trees as well as the many Lime trees planted in urban areas
Eyed Hawk-moth	Widespread though not common, most records are of larvae feeding on garden apple trees
Poplar Hawk-moth	Common throughout the county and often attracted to light
Elephant Hawk-moth	A common and attractive moth widespread in the county, often attracted to light. The larvae not infrequently found on willowherbs, bedstraws and garden fuchsias; its striking appearance makes it one of the most-easily recognised caterpillars
Small Elephant Hawk-moth	Local and uncommon, it appears at light in June and July in the heathy and chalky areas where bedstraws, its larval foodplants, grow

Migrant species:

Convolvulus Hawk-moth	Last recorded in 1983
Deaths-head Hawk-moth	Last recorded in 1982
Humming-bird Hawk-moth	A regular migrant in varying numbers
Silver-striped Hawk-moth	Very rare in Bedfordshire, not seen since 1948

The most impressive moths belong to the Hawk-moth family. These include our largest and most spectacular species as well as exotic migrants which are amongst the rarest. In Bedfordshire seven resident species are known (listed in Table 3.10) and four migrant species have been recorded over the past forty years.

The Changing Flora

This subject will be given a chapter to itself. Here, it will suffice to say that this group has suffered many losses, and populations of many species continue to decline.

The greatest losses have been among the plants of marsh, damp meadow, heath and acid grassland. Many species will have been affected by damage to aquatic habitats, especially those riverside species vulnerable to dredging and grading of rivers.

Few of the lower plants, such as fungi, mosses and lichens, have been studied in sufficient detail to measure population changes in the county, though these have undoubtedly occurred. However, in the case of the lichens

Table 3.11   Distribution of some Bedfordshire lichens in relation to their tolerance of air-pollution (sulphur dioxide)

Species	Tolerance $\mu g/m^3$	Occurrence, % of tetrads
Lecanora conizaeoides	170+	100
Xanthoria parietina	125	76
Parmelia saxatilis	100	23
Evernia prunastri	40	8
Usnea subfloridana	40	3

From B. M. Davis, *The Bedfordshire Naturalist* **33**

and those mosses which grow on trees, recent studies suggest that atmospheric pollution has probably caused the loss of those species which are not tolerant of sulphur dioxide in the air (Table 3.11). This may seem surprising to those who think of Bedfordshire as a non-industrial county, but mapping of lichens has shown that the species which are widespread in Bedfordshire are those most tolerant of air pollution whilst those which are less tolerant are scarce.

Population Changes of Other Invertebrates

Study of insects, molluscs and other invertebrates has been much less extensive than that of plants and the vertebrate animals. There have, however, been some studies, and these give evidence of a few species expanding and rather more in decline. The grasshoppers are one group which have suffered nationally from the deterioration and loss of heathland and 'natural' grassland, through cultivation and afforestation. Some of the rarer species are becoming dangerously restricted in distribution and one or two could even be lost from Britain if current trends of habitat loss were to continue.

In Bedfordshire the distribution of grasshoppers has been studied quite thoroughly in recent years. This work shows that the Mottled Grasshopper is limited to a few sites, mainly on the Greensand where sandy open heathland survives. The Stripe-winged Grasshopper can now no longer be found in the county. A third species at risk in the county is a marshland species, the Short-winged Cone-head. This is known from only a single colony, fortunately within the nature reserve at Flitwick Moor.

The dragonflies present a more complicated picture.

Farm ponds have been lost and river habitats damaged, but there has been much new dragonfly breeding habitat created by flooded quarry workings and garden ponds. One cannot of course assume that these habitats are equally suitable for all species.

Quite a few dragonflies are near the limit of their British range in Bedfordshire and at least three are declining generally, White-legged Damselfly, Ruddy Darter and Broad-bodied Chaser. Some others are more widely distributed but appear to be absent in the Bedfordshire region – Variable Damselfly and Black Darter. A small green damselfly, the Scarce Emerald Damselfly, used to be found in Bedfordshire, at Heath and Reach, but has not been seen in the county for decades and has been lost from most other sites in Britain. On the brighter side, two of the larger dragonflies seem to have become much more common in Bedfordshire in recent decades, Black-tailed Skimmer and Migrant Hawker, the latter formerly bearing the unfortunate contrived English name 'Scarce Aeshna', but now one of the commonest large dragonflies!

The Mollusca (snails, slugs and mussels) have been better studied than most of the less familiar groups. The evidence of distribution maps shows a national decline for a few species but no clear trend for most. A wetland snail, *Aplexa hypnorum*, has suffered particularly from loss of habitat and is known from only a few sites in the county. The largest British slug *Limax cinereoniger*, which in lowland Britain is found only in ancient woodland, survives in four of our larger woods in Bedfordshire although it is in decline nationally and is on the edge of its range in the county.

Several species are experiencing long-term national decline for reasons unknown. One is the tiny snail *Acicula fusca*, which used to be widespread but the northern limit of its range has retreated southwards so that now this lies across mid-Bedfordshire. Another is *Pomatias elegans*, which resembles a winkle, it lives only in lime-rich places.

As with the butterflies, there are insects in other orders which have very specialised habitat requirements which restrict them to the warmer drier habitats offered by chalk downland, heath or sandy grassland. Such insects are found among the true bugs (Heteroptera), bees and ants (Hymenoptera), and beetles (Coleoptera). Such species are often found to be at the edge of their national or European range on the Chiltern Hills or the Lower Greensand, and have suffered from the same loss of habitat and climatic effects as described above in the case of butterflies, grasshoppers, and flowers.

Turning to the aquatic life of our rivers one can only conjecture what changes must have taken place as a result of the engineering works and changes in water quality over the years. River engineering works have certainly

Figure 3.7 *The Sand wasp (*Ammophila sabulosa*) on Cooper's Hill: very dependent on open sandy habitat, shown here digging its nest-hole where it will store caterpillars for its larvae to feed on.* (TL 027375, September 1986)
© B. S. Nau

eliminated much habitat favoured by species requiring fast-flowing stony shallows or quiet muddy margins.

Population Changes of Other Vertebrates

The situation with mammals is unusual in that a quarter of our British species have been introduced into the country by Man at one time or another. More particularly, the Muntjac Deer and the Chinese Water Deer were both introduced to Britain in Bedfordshire, escaping from Woburn Park.

The Muntjac Deer has been particularly successful, filling an ecological niche which was vacant in our woodlands. This deer flourishes in the shrubby understory of woods and feeds on green shoots of Bramble and coppiced trees, and thistles. It seems likely that it will modify this habitat in the way that the Rabbit, another introduced species, modifies grassland. It has already presented a problem where coppicing has been reintroduced for the management of woodland. The Muntjac Deer severely 'prune' the shoots sprouting from the coppice stools, preventing their natural growth to reform the shrub layer. This is a problem at Marston Thrift for instance.

Two other introduced species, which just reach Bedfordshire, are the Fat Dormouse, which flourishes in the Whipsnade area, and the Mink which is spreading rapidly in Britain and is now establishing itself in the county. The Mink is a riverside animal with a voracious appetite for birds and anything else it can catch. This is one species which we could well do without.

As far as most of our mammals are concerned, the situation is not one of conspicuous change in population. Even the Rabbit appears now to have reached a new stable level, since the onslaught of the disease myxomatosis decimated the population. On farmland it is kept well in check but where the Rabbit is uncontrolled by Man its pressure on any edible vegetation is almost total. This can be seen in places on the Chiltern downland, such as around Sharpenhoe Clappers and parts of Barton Hills.

A mammal whose population has been studied in detail in Bedfordshire is the Badger. With experience it is easy to identify a Badger's burrow or sett and suitable habitat is readily recognised. These factors made it possible to census occupied setts in the county and in 1979 there were fifty-four occupied setts known, Figure 3.8. Badgers prefer a well-drained position, the chalk in the south and the sands of mid-Bedfordshire are particularly favoured.

Most setts are in banks or fairly steeply sloping sites, hedgerows being the most frequently used habitat. However, rather strange sites are sometimes used; for instance, a former anti-aircraft gun emplacement near Leighton Buzzard has been used, another sett was dug under a

concrete road in the far north of the county, and occasionally land drains are used. It seems that only flat low-lying country is shunned, in particular the clays of the Gault and the Marston Vale, and the valleys of the lower Ouse and the Ivel.

Disturbance by Man is a frequent occurrence. Illegal Badger digging does occur and not infrequently Badgers are dug out and removed from a sett where the farmer or landowner finds their presence undesirable, the animals being released anywhere that looks suitable. Perhaps most disturbance is a consequence of the frequent presence of Foxes in Badger setts. This often results in the sett being gassed, poison bait being laid, or other assaults on the sett in the course of attempts to dispose of the Foxes; also setts are often blocked by fox-hunters.

Despite these adversities the Badger thrives remarkably well and the population appears reasonably stable in the county at present. It seems that it is only in areas of the county which are intensively managed for game by unsympathetic gamekeepers or landowners that the Badger has been more or less eliminated. This may account for some of the blank areas on the distribution map in otherwise apparently suitable areas. It must be said, however, that the presence of Badgers is more often viewed sympathetically and they are usually allowed to live in relative peace.

More details of the studies of Badgers in the county are to be found in *The Bedfordshire Naturalist* (**33**, 1979).

One mammal lost to the county in recent decades is the Otter. A recent thorough search of the county revealed no sign of this species. The various species of bat are also under much pressure, being insectivorous and dependent on the shelter of old trees and buildings. Insects are scarcer than they used to be, there are fewer old trees in the county and buildings are now generally too well maintained. Evidence from other parts of Britain points to a general decline of bat populations.

By contrast with the Otter and bat situation that of the Harvest Mouse is much more encouraging. It had been thought that this, our smallest mouse, had become rare but in fact this was because it was not realised that its primary habitat was no longer cornfields. Steele Elliott in 1916 commented that it had not been recorded 'in recent times'. In 1946 Ray Palmer could add nothing further. However, in the winter of 1972–73 local naturalists happened to visit a site in east Hertfordshire where Harvest Mice had been known for some years in a marshy habitat; they saw a nest and this stimulated a search for nests in similar sites in Bedfordshire. This search was quickly rewarded, and during the next two years it was established that this inconspicuous animal is actually widespread in

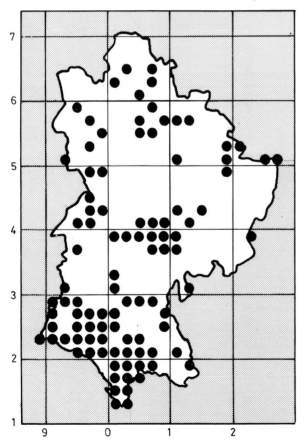

Figure 3.8 *Badger distribution in Bedfordshire: dots mark 'tetrads' (2 × 2km squares) where a sett is known, most are on the Chilterns or the Greensand Ridge.*

Figure 3.9 *Daubenton's Bat, the 'water bat' feeds low over water. There are few known localities in the county. Ampthill Park Lake is a typical feeding site. This individual was tangled in a discarded fishing line by the Ouse at Great Barford.*
© D. G. Rands

Bedfordshire. It seems to be scarce or absent in only two areas, the Gault and Chalk of the south-east and in the Marston Vale.

The Harvest Mouse is often found in damp areas but the availability of suitable grasses seems more important. The mouse builds a spherical nest, about the size of a tennis ball, by shredding grass leaves lengthwise and weaving them to form the nest. The mouse needs reasonably stiff plant stems to support the nest and a supply of suitable grasses. The Bedfordshire survey showed that most nests are built in Reed Canary-grass or Common Reed, although occasionally other tall grasses are used. Favoured nest-sites are roadside verges, ditch banks, marshes and waste ground. In such sites the grasses form dense clumps which persist through the winter, and it is here that the nests can be found most easily. The presence of overhanging trees seems to discourage the Harvest Mouse. Interestingly only one nest was found in a cereal crop, even though this is the site most people imagine to be the typical habitat.

The Harvest Mouse does seem able to take advantage of newly created habitat. For example in clear-felled compartments in Maulden Woods the mouse has regularly been caught in live-traps used for studies of small mammals. In one area seventeen were caught in four nights. This site had been clear-felled two years previously and had developed a dense growth of Tufted Hair-grass, mixed with Bramble and Bracken. Twelve years later there were still Harvest Mice in this compartment, there still being considerable open areas with suitable grasses.

In the course of the study of the distribution of Harvest Mice in the county, the opportunity was taken to check nests for presence of fleas, since it had been thought that this was one rodent not a host to fleas. In fact R. S. George found eight species of fleas in these samples!

All amphibians and reptiles in Britain are under pressure from loss of habitat and not least in Bedforshire. In the county the Grass Snake, Common Lizard and Slow Worm all seem to have become scarcer, while the Adder is a great rarity now, though perhaps it was never common. The trend to construct farm irrigation lagoons may be helpful in providing breeding sites for frogs and toads as, too, may be the proliferation of garden pools.

Figure 3.10 *Harvest Mice: no longer a cornfield species they are found almost anywhere there are dense tussocks of grass suitable for its nest.*
© D. G. Rands

One toad, the Midwife Toad, was introduced into Britain at Bedford where it has become established. It has never shown signs of spreading of its own accord, although it has been transported by enthusiasts to other parts of the county and beyond, as far as Sheffield at least.

Like mammals, fish have been introduced extensively into Britain and not infrequently Bedfordshire has been the site of the initial introduction. In 1880 the European Catfish was introduced into the lakes in Woburn Park.

39

This is an omnivorous bottom-dweller which can reach a metre in length over about ten years. They have flourished at Woburn and since 1947 fish from here have been introduced into other waters in the county, and beyond. Another Woburn introduction is the Zander, a large member of the Perch family. This was first introduced in 1878, with additional stocking in 1910. In 1947 and 1950 fish from Woburn were netted and moved to other lakes in the county. It was when ninety-seven fish from Woburn were moved to the Great Ouse Relief Channel, in The Fens, in 1963, that this species really began to increase rapidly and spread. Within five years Zander were widespread in the Relief Channel. By 1969 they were found in the River Wissey, the Cam, the Nene, and the Old Bedford River. This story mirrors that of the Muntjac Deer, which also became established from Woburn stock, if unintentionally in this case.

The status of other species of river fish of interest to anglers is well illustrated by figures obtained by the Anglian Water Authority, by electro-fishing and netting. The diagrams in Figure 3.11 show the comparative numbers of different species in the Ouzel, Grand Union Canal, Great Ouse above and below Bedford, and the Ivel. Clearly the Roach is the most numerous species and the Gudgeon second. Other species occur in more modest numbers. In terms of total weight, the Common Bream was top of the list in the sluggish waters of the Grand Union Canal and the lower Great Ouse, the Roach in the faster flowing waters of the Ouzel and the Ivel. Further details will be found in *The Bedfordshire Naturalist* (**38,** 1983, **39,** 1984 and **40,** 1985).

The smaller species of fish, such as the Minnow, the Stone Loach, the Bullhead and the two sticklebacks are less affected by Man's manipulations but have not been studied enough to form a clear picture of their status today compared with that in the past. All five species, however, seem to occur in good numbers around the county, the first three in flowing water with stony shallows – a habitat which has shrunk in recent decades – and the sticklebacks in almost any permanent water, not least in the many flooded quarries.

Over-view

The trend of wildlife populations in Bedfordshire is, perhaps more than in most other counties, one of depressing decline – both in variety and in numbers. The county is under exceptional pressure for intensive exploitation for agriculture and urban development, and leisure activities. Between these pincers, the most extensive areas of wildlife habitat have already been lost and surviving fragments are vanishing steadily. The best that can be hoped for is that the recent upsurge of awareness of these pressures may slow the rate of loss.

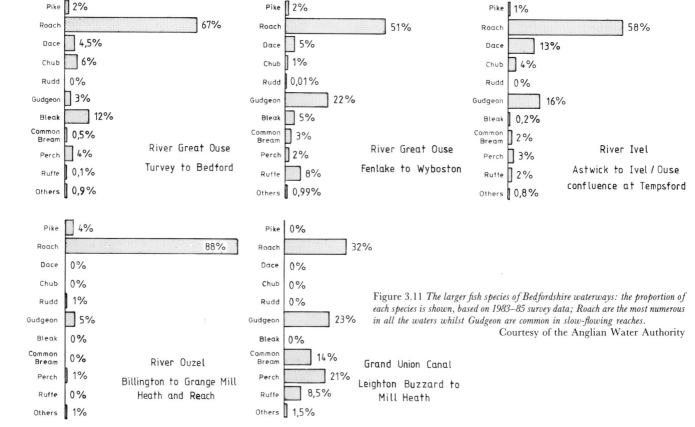

Figure 3.11 *The larger fish species of Bedfordshire waterways: the proportion of each species is shown, based on 1983–85 survey data; Roach are the most numerous in all the waters whilst Gudgeon are common in slow-flowing reaches.*
Courtesy of the Anglian Water Authority

Chapter 4

Wildlife Habitats

Chapter 1 explained how wildlife habitats developed from the laying down of geological deposits, through the Ice Age and through prehistoric times to the making of the modern landscape by Man in recent historic times. This chapter will consider these habitats as they are today.

Habitat and Geology

Wildlife habitats strongly reflect the underlying geology. This can be seen very well by comparing the geology maps in Plates 1 and 2 with Figures 4.1 and 4.2 which show how the variety of wild flower species and hedgerow shrubs vary over the county. It is easy to see how the distribution of lime-rich soils – formed from chalk, limestone or the chalky Boulder Clay – matches the distribution of the areas richest in wild flowers or hedgerow shrubs. This variety of plant life is also reflected in the diversity of other forms of wildlife, making these areas particularly interesting to naturalists.

Occasionally, as at Maulden and Heath and Reach for instance, lime-rich soils are found close to the very different soils formed from the sands of the Lower Greensand. This greatly increases the variety of plants and animals to be found within a very small area. At the two localities mentioned, Boulder Clay was deposited on the Greensand Ridge and eroded from parts of the south-facing slopes. So, close to wet limy clays there are warm dry soils, leached of soluble minerals and supporting very different wildlife communities.

Surprisingly, the plateau formed by the chalk also has soils which are rather poor in lime. The reason for this is the deep layer of Clay-with-Flints on top of the Chalk itself. This layer was formed by the leaching of the chalk over long periods of time, dissolving most of the soluble salts and leaving behind the insoluble residue seen today, the Clay-with-Flints. So it is that one finds here patches of grass heathland (at Whipsnade and Studham), and such plants as Gorse, Bracken and Rowan, which avoid limy soils yet flourish here, where the solid geology map shows chalk. In places the clay has been heavy enough to discourage agriculture, and a number of woods have survived to make this one of the more wooded regions of the county. It is here that the native Common Dormouse has been seen occasionally and here too is one of the few woods in the county where one can admire Wild Daffodils in profusion.

The habitats provided by the Chalk itself and by the Greensand Ridge are so important that they will each have a chapter of their own. The importance of the Chalk lies in the rich flora and fauna of the downland turf whilst that of the Greensand lies in the relics of heathland and the hill-slope marshes where sand meets clay.

Between the Chalk and the sand of the Greensand Ridge, there is a low-lying vale of Gault Clay. These marine clay deposits were of desert origin and poor in nutrients, the soils of the Gault therefore lack the interest of the limy soils of the chalk or the warm dry soils of the sands. They form few attractive habitats for the naturalist. Surprisingly, it is even quite difficult to find a hedgerow oak in the Gault vale!

Running parallel with the Greensand Ridge, to its

Figure 4.1 *The richness of flower and fern species varies over the county, depending on geology and other factors. Shading on the map shows the richest regions (over 260 species in a 2×2 km square). The Greensand Ridge, diagonally across the middle, the Ouse valley in the north and the chalk country in the south are especially rich.*

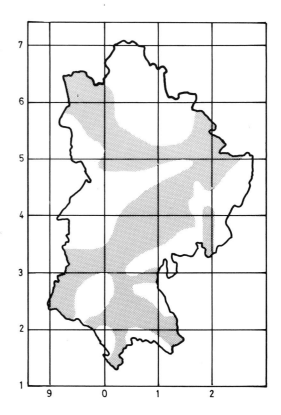

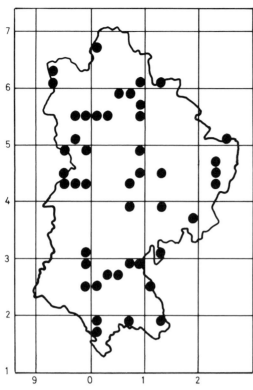

Figure 4.2 *The richness of hedges and trees, shrubs and climbers is greatest in ancient hedges and is also affected by the geology; hedges on sandy soils are poor compared with those on limy-clay. Hedges have been lost from intensive arable farmland, in north-east Bedfordshire for instance. The dots show where hedges in the tetrads sampled averaged seven or more species.*

Courtesy of B. S. Nau and E. B. Rands

north, is the Marston Vale, notable for its Oxford Clay, used extensively for brick-making. This activity is responsible for one of the county's notable wildlife habitats, the flooded clay-pits in the area between Houghton Conquest to the east and Ridgmont to the west. Because the pits have very extensive sheets of open water they attract many interesting birds, vagrants and regular migrants; gull roosts and waterfowl are particular features in winter.

Whilst the clay-pits have their special interest, the Marston Vale in general is rather lacking in notable wildlife habitats, there are few woods and rather mono-

Figure 4.3 *This quarry at the margin of King's Wood (Heath and Reach) epitomises the wildlife interest of the Greensand Ridge, which provides some of the most interesting wildlife habitats in the county. These include ancient oakwoods, sandy heathlands and, where groundwater reaches the surface, boggy wetlands. The Greensand itself ranges from almost pure white to deep red, as in the centre of the cliff in the photo.* © Mary Sheridan

tonous hawthorn hedges with few other shrubs. In this it resembles the Gault Vale.

The Oxford Clay of the Marston Vale also extends northwards, forming a plateau covering most of the northern half of the county. Fortunately it is overlain by limy glacial Boulder Clay, which gives this part of the county its particular character and considerable wildlife interest. This is shown up well by the floral richness map, Figure 4.1, and is reflected too in the fauna.

Being good for wild flowers this clay plateau is also high-grade agricultural land. This has caused loss of much interesting habitat over the centuries, and increasingly in recent decades. The hedgerows are particularly rich in variety of shrubs and it is all the more sad that so many have been, and continue to be, destroyed.

Because the Boulder Clay of the plateau often forms wet heavy soils some areas were left as woodland when the rest of the area was cleared for farming in centuries past. This happy chance provides us with some of the best of our remaining oak woods. Among these are Odell Great Wood with its broad rides, West Wood, once coppiced and now partly converted to conifers, and smaller woods such as Great Hayes Wood, which has suffered less adverse interference than most, Forty Acre Wood north of Harrold, and Lady Wood at Melchbourne.

From the solid-geology map one might expect that limestone would play an important role in the natural history of the county, as it does in other parts of Britain, the Cotswolds for instance. However, in Bedfordshire the Great Oolite Limestone is mostly deeply buried beneath glacial clay and can have little direct effect on wildlife. On the other hand, one cannot ignore the use of limestone in walls in the north-west of the county, since, whilst they are normally bonded with mortar or cement, many have developed a fascinating flora in the crevices. Typical flowers of the limestone walls are Stonecrops and Ivy-leaved Toadflax. A particularly interesting exposure of

Table 4.1 Proportions of different habitats in the county

Habitat	% of county area
Woodland (including scrub, hedges etc)	4.5
Grassland (including fen etc)	20.0
Open ground (including arable, quarries, gardens, etc)	60.0
'Developed'	15.5

the limestone occurs in the cutting of an abandoned railway south of Turvey. This is one of the best localities for mosses in Bedfordshire.

Finally, there are the alluvial deposits of the river valleys, sand and gravel with their overburden of loam. In the valley of the Great Ouse and its tributaries the Ivel and Ouzel, these have been quarried extensively. This has almost completely changed the character of the wildlife interest of these river valleys. The gravel-pits are particularly concentrated along the valleys of the Ouse and Ivel.

Habitat and Land Use

Although geology is the basis of most wildlife habitats, it is Man's use of the land which moulds them to their present form. Sadly, many of the best habitats are shrinking as Man's requirements change. The approximate proportion of each main habitat in the county today is shown in Table 4.1.

WOODLAND
The term 'woodland' will be used here in a very broad sense, including not only woods as such but also those shrubby habitats which are intermediate between grassland and high forest in the natural succession of habitats. So hedges are included here, as well as green lanes, scrub, and wetland 'carr'. The inclusion of hedges is justified on the basis that the original hedges are believed to have been formed from remnant strips of woodland when fields

Table 4.2 The occurence of woodland habitats in Bedfordshire

Woodland type	Occurrence in Bedfordshire		
	Decreasing	Stable	Increasing
Primary deciduous	Surviving ancient woods		
Secondary deciduous		Woods planted on former farmland	
Conifer, ex primary deciduous			Clear felled and replanted ancient woods
'Wood-edge'	Hedges and green lanes	Rides and edges of woods	
Scrub		Neglected farmland (very little)	Ungrazed downland disused quarries and disused railways
Carr (fen scrub)	River margins	Wet peatland	

were first carved from the ancient forests which covered the countryside. Green lanes are included as they have the character of a woodland-edge habitat, an untarred track enclosed by a pair of hedges. Table 4.2 lists the woodland habitats of the county and indicates for each whether it is increasing, decreasing or stable. This discussion of woodland habitats will begin with woods in the strict sense of the word.

Woods

Bedfordshire is one of the least wooded of English counties; only 4.5 per cent of its area is woodland and much of this is conifer plantation. Table 4.3 summarises the main statistics for the county's woods.

Most of the conifers have been planted since the Second World War, 56 per cent between 1951 and 1980. Another feature of Bedfordshire woods is their fragmented nature. Few are of appreciable size, only seventeen are larger than fifty hectares. This presents a problem since the rarer woodland animals and plants have small fragmented populations and this makes them very vulnerable to fluctuations in numbers caused by climatic factors or Man's activities.

In woods the greatest wildlife interest is usually concentrated in warm sheltered 'wood-edge' habitats, such as rides, glades and the woodland margin itself. These edge

Table 4.3   The size and nature of Bedfordshire woodlands

(a)   Form of management

Woodland type	%	Area (ha)
Broadleaf		
Standards	29.0	1456
Coppice-with-standards	13.5	678
Coppice	1.7	85
Scrub	0.3	15
Total broadleaf	*44.5*	*2234*
Conifer		
Mixed conifer-broadleaf plantation	41.0	2060
Conifer plantation	14.5	728
Total conifer	*55.5*	*2788*
Total area of woodland	*100.0*	*5022*

(b)   Size distribution

Size range (ha)	No. of woods	Total area (ha)
at least 1, less than 2	155	209
at least 2, less than 5	161	482
at least 5, less than 10	83	557
at least 10, less than 25	75	1086
at least 25, less than 50	31	1065
at least 50	17	1623
Total	*522*	*5022*

(Based on Bedfordshire CC, *Forestry Aspect Report 1973*)

Figure 4.4 *Some 'woodland' habitats in the county. On the facing page (lower) Odell Great Wood: an Oak-Hazel wood with broad rides, on Boulder Clay in the north-west of the county,* © *Mary Sheridan, (upper) Spanoak Wood (Swineshead): an ancient broadleaved wood now replanted with Norway Spruce; at this stage Tufted Hair-grass (centre) and Wood Small-reed (left) are flourishing, with many other flowering plants, but in about ten years the conifers will shade out the ground vegetation. (TL 068673, September 1986)* © *B. S. Nau (Above) Dunton Green Lane, south-east of Biggleswade: this is the best surviving example of a green lane in the county. Its well-grown hedges provide shelter to attract a diversity of butterflies in summer. It forms both a parish and a county boundary and is probably of very ancient origin. (TL 233421, May 1986).* © *B. S. Nau*

habitats are best when there is a gradual transition from tall trees, through a variety of shrubs of graded height to a flowery verge or ride. In Bedfordshire, the best examples of such habitats are in Maulden Wood, Odell Great Wood, and Potton Wood. In Chapter 7 'The Greensand Ridge' some of our woodlands will be discussed in more detail.

Woods which have a continuous history back to the primaeval forest are known as 'primary woodland' to distinguish them from woods of more recent origin, 'secondary woodland'. The distinction is important because primary woodland is much richer in wildlife than is secondary woodland.

Looking at a map of the county it can be seen that the Greensand Ridge has many areas of woodland but only by visiting these does one discover that most are plantations of conifers, planted during the past hundred years or so. Closer inspection fails to reveal much wildlife interest in plantations more than a few years old. The trees are so closely spaced that no natural vegetation can survive in the dense shade, and where vegetation is lacking so are most other forms of life.

Elsewhere in the county broad-leaved plantations have sometimes been planted. For instance, poplar or willow plantations are not infrequent in marshy fields. These form a typically uninteresting form of woodland, often at the expense of marsh which had a rich and varied flora and fauna.

Beech too has been planted. Interestingly, all of the few Bedfordshire beechwoods are believed to be fairly recent plantations, unlike some in neighbouring counties, further west along the Chiltern Hills, which are of more ancient origin. This perhaps accounts for the relatively modest interest of Sharpenhoe Clappers, Leete Wood at Barton, and Streatley Firs, when one compares them with more famous beechwoods out of the county, those of the Buckinghamshire and Oxfordshire Chilterns in particular. Never the less, some treasures are to be found within the county, such as Fly Orchid (Plate 6), White Helleborine, and Yellow Bird's-nest – all to be found in some of the smaller of our Chiltern beechwoods.

In the past, most of the woodland in this part of England would have been managed as coppice-with-standards, in the traditional way described in Chapter 1. These coppice-with-standards woods can still be recognised by the neglected coppice stools, with multiple stems growing up almost as tall as mature standard trees. Coppicing produced a patchwork of sheltered, lightly shaded, glades alternating with more mature woodland and creates a particularly rich flora and fauna.

Usually the coppiced understory was Hazel, with varying amounts of Midland Hawthorn, Field Maple, and Ash; while the standards allowed to grow to maturity were Pedunculate Oak and Ash.

Since such woodland was rarely if ever planted anew, any wood showing signs of management as coppice-with-standards is probably very ancient and may have direct lineage back to the primaeval forest. The flora and fauna of such continuous primary woodland is incomparably richer in variety and quantity than it is where the continuity has been broken (Plates 10 and 11).

During the present century, most of the ancient woods in the county have been clear-felled and replanted with conifers or have deteriorated through neglect. Either way, they now form even-aged stands which lack the variety of old-fashioned woods. As a result it is no longer possible to see the great spring explosion of woodland flowers which used to follow the influx of sunlight, as the coppicing followed its regular cycle. Violets, Primroses, Wood Anemones and Early-purple Orchids were among the most spectacular of these flowers. To see what Bedfordshire woods would have been like for many centuries one must now go out of the county, to such woods as Waresley, in Cambridgeshire, or even better to Bradfield Woods near Bury St Edmunds in Suffolk. The drifts of spring flowers are quite breathtaking in these woods, now restored to active coppice-with-standards management. How sad it is that such sights are no longer to be seen and enjoyed in Bedfordshire!

It has been suggested that this change in woodland management also contributed to the loss of the attractive fritillary butterflies which once graced our local woods.

Recently small-scale reintroduction of coppicing has begun in two Bedfordshire woods, Marston Thrift (near Marston Mortaine) and Bramingham Wood (on the north edge of Luton). One day perhaps the full glory of spring woodland flowers will be seen again in Bedfordshire.

Hedges and Green Lanes
The origin of early hedges from the primaeval woodland has already been mentioned. Green lanes are ancient rights of way which were never tarred. They are typically bounded on each side by a rich well-developed hedge, which makes a sunny sheltered habitat with a rich variety of plant, insect and bird life. Sometimes the neglected hedges dominate the lane, Blackthorn scrub creeping out from either side until it threatens to engulf the lane completely.

Green lanes are a particular feature of the clays of eastern England but in Bedfordshire few survive in good condition. The best, by far, is one between Edworth and Dunton, in the east of the county. It runs eastwards for nearly two miles, to end at the River Rhee, a tiny tributary of the Cam. Along half of its length it actually forms the county boundary with Hertfordshire. There are few better places in the county to see butterflies than along this green lane on a summer's day. In fact hedgerows in general are

Plate 5: *Moth trapping with an ultra-violet lamp reveals the many moths which are normally never seen. (Left) An exceptional mothing event in Maulden Woods on a hot night in 1976 when moths were attracted to the light in thousands. This member of the Bedfordshire Natural History Society is 'dripping' with moths.* © D. G. Rands. *(Top right) Merveille du Jour – one of our most attractive moths, and (bottom right) Poplar Hawk-moth – one of the commonest hawk-moths.*

© V. W. Martin

amongst our best habitats for butterflies, providing shelter as well as flowers to attract them. Three species in particular are associated with hedgerows: the Orange-tip, attracted by the white flowers of Garlic Mustard which are abundant in spring, the Gatekeeper, common on Bramble flowers in high summer, and the Ringlet, which flitters around shady hedgerow shrubs.

It is sad that so many green lanes have been lost to the cause of agriculture. Usually the hedges have been removed; in other cases dumping of hardcore or clay spoil from ditching activities on adjacent farms has changed the character overnight, after centuries of gradual evolution. Two green lanes in the north of the county have suffered particularly, Yelnow Lane, which runs west from Sharnbrook, and Forty Foot Lane to the north-west of Souldrop. Another, running north-east from Swineshead, has also suffered considerably. One hopes that what survives will be preserved.

Hedges themselves can be very ancient, especially those marking land boundaries between farms, estates, parishes or counties. Like mediaeval buildings, these very old hedges are truly ancient monuments. Not all are ancient of course, many date from parliamentary Enclosure Acts, especially between 1760 and 1820 when the old open field systems were enclosed by hedges. In Bedfordshire about half of the open fields were enclosed in this way.

It is possible to recognise the oldest hedges by the large number of shrub species. New species colonise a hedge very slowly; roughly one species per century in a thirty-metre length of hedge. It is now recognised that hedgerow shrubs can be very long lived; individual plants may be centuries old, which is probably why new species find it difficult to get a foothold in an established hedge. Naturally, there must also be a source of plants when an opportunity does present itself; a hedge running out from a wood will often be richer than one in open country. The richness in plant species is matched by a richness in the insects dependent on them and the birds dependent on these. A good hedge is to be treasured!

The hedges of the county have been studied in detail by members of the Bedfordshire Natural History Society, in whose journal the results were published (*The Bedfordshire Naturalist*, **30** and **32**). It was found that the richness of hedges varied between the geological regions. A study of 1130 hedgerows revealed over sixty species of tree, shrub, and woody climber. Table 4.4 lists these. The richest hedges are on the Boulder Clay and Clay-with-Flints, as can be seen by comparing the hedgerow-richness map, Figure 4.2, with the geology map, Plate 2.

Another survey, by the Bedfordshire County Planning Department, used aerial photographs to compare the hedges in sample areas in 1945 with those surviving in 1976. This showed that 24 per cent of the 1945 hedges had

been destroyed by 1976. The Boulder Clay areas were worst affected; they had lost 37 per cent, reducing the length of hedgerow from 5.8 to 3.7 km/square kilometre. The south and west of the county were least affected, having lost only 11 per cent. Some areas already had rather little hedgerow even in 1945 and so today these areas still have least: the valleys of the lower Ouse and the Ivel, the Marston Vale, and the east Bedfordshire clay uplands. These now average only three kilometres of hedge per square kilometre.

Trees are a feature of hedges; they used to be encouraged as a traditional source of timber. In 1980 the Forestry Commission estimated there were still about 103 000 trees in the hedgerows of the county. Ash is the commonest hedgerow tree, although Pedunculate Oak is also very common. Hedgerow trees being exposed to sun and rain provide good habitats for a variety of lichen species.

Hedgerow (and other) elms suffered a very severe setback during the terrible epidemic of Dutch elm disease. This was at its worst during the 1970s. In the clay vales and along the river valleys where the elms were such a feature of the landscape the sight of rows of dead elms became commonplace. By 1980 the Forestry Commission estimated that there were only 9700 live elms in the county, of which only 30 per cent were in good health. Even now, in the mid-1980s, some dead elms still stand like sentinels. The disease is lingering on.

The English Elm was worst affected by Dutch elm disease, but the Wych Elms too have gradually succumbed and one still sees specimen trees dying back. Often, too, one sees clumps of suckers of the English Elm attempting a comeback, but in early summer the telltale appearance of dying leaves reveals the presence of the disease.

The 1980 Forestry Commission survey of 'non-woodland' trees gives a breakdown of tree species by location, this is summarised in Table 4.5. These figures are for all trees not actually in woodland.

Scrub

During the post-war decades impenetrable Hawthorn scrub has become a familiar feature of the steep downland slopes of the Chilterns. Once kept in check by grazing Sheep and Rabbits it has spread remorselessly across the downland. Sheep farming on the downs became increasingly uneconomic and Rabbits were decimated by the disease myxomatosis. The maps in Figure 4.6 show how extensive the scrub has become.

Once it was believed that Hawthorn scrub was just a stage in the natural succession by which grassland transforms to high forest. More recently it has been suggested that the scrub itself can be a stable climax vegetation. What is certain is that, as it spreads, the scrub shades and

Table 4.4   The trees, shrubs, and woody climbers of Bedfordshire hedgerows

Trees	Shrubs	Climbers
Common and Widespread (*in 10% or more of hedges in most geological areas*)		
Ash	Hawthorn	Bramble (species)
Field Maple	Blackthorn	Black Bryony
English Elm	Dog-rose	Ivy
Pedunculate Oak	Elder	Bittersweet
Wych Elm	Hazel	Field-rose
Sycamore	Dogwood	Dewberry
	Wild Privet	
Occasional (*in at least 1% of hedges, but fewer than 10% in most areas*)		
Apple (species)	Midland Hawthorn	Traveller's-joy
Holly	Wayfaring-tree	White Bryony
Wild Cherry	Spindle	Honeysuckle
White Willow	Willow (species)	Hop
Crack Willow	Buckthorn	
Hornbeam	Guelder-rose	
Small-leaved Elm		
Infrequent (*in fewer than 1% of hedges studied*)		
Aspen	Raspberry	
Beech	Wild Plum	
Lombardy Poplar	Cherry Plum	
Lime (species)	Barberry	
Silver Birch	Broom	
Yew	Currant (species)	
Scots Pine	Lilac	
Norway Maple	Gorse	
Grey Poplar	Gooseberry	
Black Poplar	Spurge-laurel	
Corsican Pine	Duke of Argyll's Teaplant	
Horse-chestnut	Forsythia	
Rowan		
Common Whitebeam		
Wild Service-tree		
Downy Birch		
Alder		
Sweet Chestnut		
Turkey Oak		

Table 4.5   Non-woodland trees in Bedfordshire

	Individual	Clumps	Belts	Total
Conifer				
Pines	560	840	6150	7550
Spruces	1840	280	1480	3600
Larches	90	—	—	90
Cypresses	5960	190	—	6150
Other conifer	7290	2590	190	10070
All conifers	*15740*	*3900*	*7820*	*27460*
Broadleaf				
Ash	46410	25540	49320	121270
Sycamore	24020	14990	38300	77310
Pedunculate Oak	21680	13670	20100	55450
Beech	2680	90	29540	32310
Birches	10790	10240	6130	27160
Willows	10400	7660	7270	25330
Poplars	6260	13720	2180	22160
Alder	840	4370	11810	17020
Horse-chestnut	12120	2220	1020	15360
Sweet Chestnut	190	—	11720	11910
Lime	9830	830	280	10940
Elms	2310	—	7380	9690
Other broadleaf	41880	62880	51240	156000
All broadleaf	*189410*	*156210*	*236290*	*581910*

Only trees 70 mm diameter or more at chest height were counted. Forestry Commission Survey, 1980

Figure 4.5 *On the facing page, Sharpenhoe: Between 1947 and 1980 the country-side has changed considerably, with the removal of hedgegrows, death of elms due to Dutch elm disease, and residential development. These two photographs from Sharpenhoe Clappers strikingly illustrate the changes, the loss of elms is particularly noticeable.* © Beds. C. C.

kills the rich flora so typical of open downland, and with it the foodplants of the larvae of the Chalk-hill Blue, Duke of Burgundy and other attractive downland butterflies. It might be thought that the scrub would benefit birds. However, once the scrub approaches maturity its main attraction to birds is as a refuge, for roosting or nesting, particularly for Woodpigeons annd Magpies. Ground feeders and seed-eaters find the absence of plant life under the scrub holds little attraction, although the haws in autumn do provide food for immigrant thrushes. Only when the scrub is still sparse is it attractive to a wider range of species, especially finches and buntings.

In one or two places attempts have been made to clear encroaching scrub but this is labour intensive and must be followed up every few years to keep the Hawthorn permanently in check. Sites where clearance has been undertaken in recent years include Sharpenhoe Clappers, Totternhoe Knolls, Whipsnade Downs, and Warden Hill (Streatley). Curiously, the one area which has been kept under control by grazing is that within the boundaries of Whipsnade Zoo. Here the Red-necked Wallabies have taken on the function of Sheep! Viewed from the vale to the north, the contrasting appearance of the scrub cover of Dunstable Downs stands out very clearly compared with the open grassy slopes within the zoo.

An interesting aspect of the scrub in Bedfordshire is just how uniformly it is made up of Hawthorn. Along the Chilterns to the southwest, through Buckinghamshire and into Oxfordshire, more and more shrub species are to be found in the scrub. Beyond the Tring Gap, species which are rare or non-existent in Bedfordshire scrub, such as Box, Yew, Juniper, and Common Whitebeam are conspicuous members of the scrub flora. Even quite common hedgerow species in Bedfordshire are infrequent in the downland scrub, although less so to the southwest. The reason for this contrast is a puzzle still awaiting an answer. Anyone interested in this should make the journey to the National Nature Reserve at Aston Rowant, where the M40 motorway crosses the Chiltern escarpment, and see for themselves just how different the scrub is there compared with Dunstable Downs or Barton Hills. In June or July there is the added pleasure of seeing

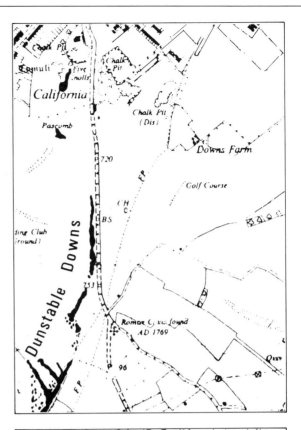

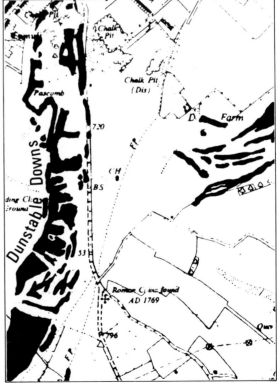

Figure 4.6 *Hawthorn scrub is rapidly spreading over the flowery downland turf of the Chilterns, 'sterilising' large areas. The maps (based on study of aerial photographs) show the increase of scrub on Dunstable Downs over the 34 year period 1947 to 1981.* © Beds, C. C.

butterflies which are not to be found on the Bedfordshire downs either.

The control of downland scrub must be one of the biggest countryside conservation problems in Bedfordshire today. Not just for the loss of the rich flora and fauna of chalk grassland, sad though this is for naturalists, but also for the hundreds of acres of land which are 'sterilised' by impenetrable scrub. Because so much land cannot be used for recreation, there is all the more pressure on the few open grassland areas which do remain.

Carr

What scrub is to chalk downland, carr is to fen. Historically, in this part of England marshes and fens were maintained, like downland, by Man's activities – in this case the grazing of cattle and the cutting of reeds and sedges. However, in modern times these activities have become uneconomic and such wetlands have been neglected. Scrub then quickly develops, eventually becoming wet woodland. These wet-scrub habitats are termed 'carr' and their typical woody plants in Bedfordshire are Rusty

and Goat Willow, and Alder. Later in the evolution of the habitat the ground dries out and litter builds up and other trees and shrubs appear, particularly Downy Birch and eventually even Pedunculate Oak.

Carr is one of the scarcer habitats in the county, most fens and marshes having been drained and converted to agricultural use. The remaining examples are mostly concentrated along the valley of the River Flit, in mid-Bedfordshire. The most notable example is Flitwick Moor. This has evolved to its present very woodland-like state within living memory (Figure 4.7). Recently some welcome attempts to restore some of its former interest have been made by work parties of the Bedfordshire and Huntingdonshire Wildlife Trust, who manage a large part of the site as a nature reserve.

Elsewhere, carr only exists as fragmented sites, mostly bordering waterways, as between Bromham Mill and Bromham Park, for instance. Sutton Fen in the east of the county is larger, but there the carr has evolved to give a rather dense woodland habitat which has largely dried out.

Just as downland scrub eventually eliminates the rich and varied flora and fauna of chalk grassland, so does carr reduce and eventually eliminate the interest of fen. In the

Figure 4.7 *Evolution of wetland to woodland at Flitwick Moor. (Below) Alder carr is a habitat which has replaced open wetland where some of Flitwick Moor's choicest flowers once grew, moribund stools of Greater Tussock-sedge have also suffered from the shade. (TL 045347, January 1986) (Left) As leaf debris builds up wet peat-cuttings gradually dry to become first birchwood and later oakwood. This shows well in the north section of Flitwick Moor where this photograph was taken, the Birch trees are growing on ridges left by the peat working, the hollows are still boggy under a veneer of dead leaves and moss. (TL 047354, September 1986)* © B. S. Nau

last few decades Flitwick Moor has lost such Bedfordshire rarities as the Marsh Violet, Bogbean and Marsh Cinquefoil. These have been shaded out from the wet areas near the Flitwick to Greenfield road.

On this sad note, this account of the wooded habitats of the county is concluded.

GRASSLANDS

Taking an ecologically oriented viewpoint, Table 4.6 classifies our grasslands by soil characteristics and vegetation type. From a slightly different standpoint Table 4.7 shows the situations in which our grassland habitats arise and shows whether the area of each is increasing, decreasing or fairly stable.

In discussion about woodland the evolution of grassland was touched upon. It is not a naturally stable habitat in the English climate – although it is in countries where there is an extreme continental climate, as in prairie or steppe. In Britain, grazing or mowing is necessary to arrest the natural sequence of events, to prevent grassland changing quite rapidly into scrub or woodland. In fact it is centuries of such management that has allowed the rich flora and fauna to develop on our best, most ancient, grasslands – about 3000 years in fact. As with woodlands, it is the oldest, managed the same way over long periods of time, which have the most varied and interesting species. In Bedfordshire the oldest grassland is chalk downland and because of its great interest a separate chapter is devoted to it (Chapter 6, 'The Chalk Downs').

Limestone Grassland

Limestone grassland is a very scarce habitat in the county because most of the Bedfordshire limestone is overlain by Boulder Clay. However, here and there small areas may be found, usually on valley slopes where the River Great Ouse has cut into the limestone. Examples occur at Pavenham and north of Milton Ernest, where the river runs close to the Bedford to Rushden road. These sites often combine limestone grassland with marshy spring-lines, adding further interest. The flora of the limestone grassland resembles that of chalky Boulder Clay, characteristic species of both include Quaking-grass, Hoary Plantain and Cowslip.

Neutral Grassland

Amongst the neutral grassland habitats, river flood-plain meadows and ridge-and-furrow pasture elsewhere have much in common. The former are often better drained,

Figure 4.8 *A flowery meadow in springtime was a sight of great beauty with the abundance and diversity of flowers, some of these are shown here: Cowslip, tall stems of white Meadow Saxifrage, the white and green flowers of the Star-of-Bethlehem, and the inconspicuous spikes of Marsh Arrowgrass and (lower left) the Adders-tongue Fern.* © P. Walton

Table 4.6   A classification of Bedfordshire grasslands

Lime-rich grassland	Neutral grassland	Heath
Chalk grassland Downland Chalk quarries Road verges and cuttings on chalk	*Flood meadows* River flood-plain meadows	*Lowland grass heath* Pasture on Lower Greensand
Limestone grassland Old pasture in NW. Beds	*Old clay pasture* Heavy pastureland Ridge-and-furrow fields	*Southern heath* Uncultivated areas on sand
	Tussocky grassland Clear-felled woods on clay Gravel or clay-pit margins with poor drainage	
	Reverted farmland Neglected pasture Quarry margins Unused building land	

(Based on *Grassland ecology and wildlife management*, Duffey *et al.*, Chapman and Hall, London, 1974)

but may still be well watered, whilst the latter are often poorly drained clay.

Former water-meadows are a special category of the flood-plain grasslands. These may still have the remains of the ditch network once used for controlled flooding in spring. The hay crop could be appreciably increased by this means. Typically, there would be two interleaved ditch networks, one fed from the river and one draining back into the river. An example can still be seen beside the River Ivel, where the Henlow to Biggleswade road crosses the river. A winding dyke here is also notable for the display of the alien Water Fern; free-floating fronds turn pink in winter and form sheets of colour. Elsewhere in the county this strange fern is found intermittently on ponds, as at Biddenham, Keysoe Row and Bedford Park.

One of the best remaining flood-plain meadows is a section of Biggleswade Common which has escaped destruction by agricultural 'improvement'. This is the area in the vicinity of a dyke just west of the railway. Here, in spring, one can still see drifts of Cowslips and, a little later, the white Meadow Saxifrage. Among the rarer Bedfordshire flowers to be found here are the Star of Beth-

Table 4.7   The occurrence of major grassland habitats in Bedfordshire

Habitat type	Occurrence in Bedfordshire		
	Decreasing	Stable	Increasing
Traditional meadow	Unimproved pasture and water meadow	Commons, greens, road and railway verges	
Intensive grass crops		Pasture, leys	
Downland	Chalk escarpment	Chalk quarry margins, disused chalk/limestone quarries, road and railway cuttings in chalk	
Marsh	River flood-plain depressions, spring-lines	Road verges in poorly drained places	Margins of flooded quarries
Fen	Waterlogged valley sedge peat (alkaline)		
Bog	Waterlogged peat (acid), very rare habitat		
Heath	Uncultivated land on sand	Road and rail verges on Greensand, especially cuttings	Sand quarry margins, disused sand quarries
Lawn		Urban parks	Urban gardens and road verges, sportsfields

Figure 4.9 *Springtime in Maulden Church Meadow, one of our best surviving unspoilt pastures. The upper part of the meadow is lime-rich Boulder Clay whilst the lower part is on Greensand; this diversity is reflected in the flora.*

© B. S. Nau

lehem, a white member of the lily family, the Marsh Arrowgrass, not a grass but an obscure little plant which is a relative of the pondweeds, and, in the dyke itself, one of the rarer Bedfordshire pondweeds, Opposite-leaved Pondweed.

One of the most interesting grassland sites is Maulden Church Meadow (Figure 4.9). This combines plants of the chalky Boulder Clay, at its northern end, with those of the Lower Greensand, at its lower, southern, end. There is the added bonus of an excellent field pond.

This field also provides interesting historical clues. Examination of Figure 4.10 shows that the boundaries of this field do not conform with those of the surrounding fields. The latter line up with the present boundary of Maulden Wood, suggesting that they were formed by clearance of a former extension of the Wood to the west. The Church Meadow disrupts the pattern in a way which suggests that it was created at an earlier date than the other fields. There have been, however, some later changes to its boundaries. The enclosures map of 1797

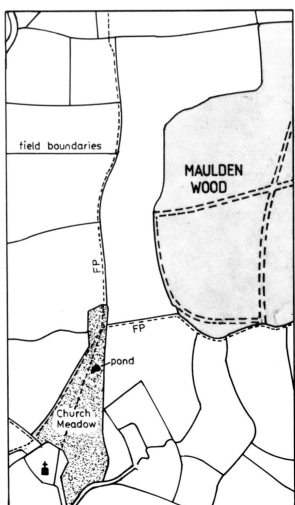

Figure 4.10 *The field boundaries around the west end of Maulden Wood suggest how the wood probably extended further west in early times: the fields near the church disrupt the pattern, perhaps cut from the primaeval forest earlier than the fields closer to the wood.*

shows a long narrow field formed by the north end of the present field. It also shows a strip running south-west to the rear of the churchyard, called 'The Slipe'. The rest of the present field was part of a larger oval field, which also included what is now a paddock in the grounds of the Grange. The pond was in this larger field.

A visit to the field reveals traces of the old boundary of The Slipe, and a ditch and bank running diagonally south-west from the pond. This well drained bank is favoured by mining bees, whose spoil heaps can be seen beside their pencil-thick burrows in early summer. Traces of a former hedgerow can also be seen running north from the pond and regenerating shrubs have to be cut down regularly to prevent the hedge reforming.

In what was The Slipe, just below the pond, the botanist today can find a profusion of the strange little Adder's-tongue fern. In The Slipe too, there used to be an abundance of the nest mounds of the subterranean yellow ant *Lasius flavus*, together with its usual lodger, the little white woodlouse *Platyarthrus hoffmanseggi*. Unfortunately these have been levelled, removing an interesting micro-habitat with a characteristic zoning of vegetation. The clay soil of the upper end of Church Meadow has a characteristically calcareous flora. This contrasts strikingly with the lower part of the meadow, where the sand makes itself felt. The meadow has an unusual assemblage of trefoil species (Table 4.8).

The characteristic 'ridge-and-furrow' pattern formed by mediaeval ploughing is a feature of many old pastures in the county, categorised here as 'neutral grassland'. They can still be seen quite commonly around the county where cattle or sheep are pastured. Unfortunately, although such fields are often examples of very old grassland, most have been subjected to agricultural 'improvement' by application of fertilisers and weedkillers. Together these eliminate the natural history interest.

Pastures which are good neutral grassland from the naturalist's viewpoint are extremely few and far between in the county today although just a few decades ago they must have been a common sight. Cowslip, Cuckooflower and Green-winged Orchid (Plate 6) are typical flowers of such habitats. Those examples surviving are often isolated 'secret' fields in sympathetic ownership. Some idea of the

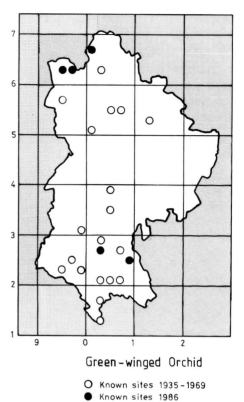

Green-winged Orchid

○ Known sites 1935–1969
● Known sites 1986

Figure 4.11 *The Green-winged Orchid is an attractive flower of ancient pasture, declining due to the effects of agricultural sprays and fertiliser application. Solid circles show surviving sites, open circles where the habitat has been destroyed.*

© J. G. Dony

recent loss of such habitats can be gained by comparing the distribution of the Green-winged Orchid prior to 1970 with that today (Figure 4.11).

A plant which has probably benefited from habitat changes in recent decades is a rather attractive grass with silvery feather-like flower-heads, Tufted Hair-grass. This flourishes in damp soils. When broadleaf woodland is thinned, felled or coppiced, a dense growth of this grass forms within a couple of years. Such attractive woodland flowers as Primrose or Wood Anemone are quickly overwhelmed by it after a season or two of flowery abundance. In the river valleys too, neglected grassland around gravel excavations are quickly taken over by this grass. In such sites, as in the woodland, it forms 'tussocky grassland', which is sufficiently distinctive to be regarded as a special sub-category of the neutral grassland habitat. This is a particularly useful habitat for birds. Characteristic breeding species are Meadow Pipit, Grasshopper Warbler and Reed Bunting. In winter it can be a favoured roosting site for Meadow Pipits, Yellowhammers, Corn Buntings and Reed Buntings. The occasional Short-eared Owl may also be seen.

Table 4.8 The trefoils of Maulden Church Meadow

Species	County status
Subterranean Clover	rare
Knotted Clover	scarce
Slender Trefoil	scarce
Strawberry Clover	uncommon
Lesser Trefoil	widespread
Red Clover	widespread
White Clover	widespread

Plate 6: *The county is rich in orchids although some are very scarce. (Centre) Burnt Orchid – very local on the Chalk.* © Mary Sheridan. *(Top right) Fly Orchid – under Beech on the Chilterns, and (top left) Green-winged Orchid – now scarce, found in damp meadows.*

© R. Revels

Reverted Farmland

This is a habitat particularly characteristic of the suburban fringes of towns. Land which is temporarily neglected, pending future building development, can develop considerable wildlife interest. There is often a fine floral display of what would normally be termed 'weeds' but which, nevertheless, can provide a very attractive show of colour, together with butterflies attracted by the flowers. As such sites mature, quite surprising species can appear, apparently from nowhere. One such site, given the name 'Cowslip Meadow', lies beside the Bedford road in the northern suburbs of Luton. This site has additional variety due to the presence of springs. In 1981 it produced Southern Marsh-orchids and in the winter of 1979–80, two pairs of Bearded Tits found a home. Other wetland plants to appear include a number of sedges (Brown, Hairy, Distant and Long-stalked Yellow) and Bristle Club-rush. This particular field has now been encroached upon by new houses and the creation of a drainage-water retention lagoon, but most still survives.

Grass Heath

This habitat must once have been widespread across the middle of the county on the Greensand Ridge. During the last hundred years or so most of the dry, acid, sandy soils have been planted with conifers and turned into woodland. Prior to this it is likely that sheep would have grazed the grass heaths. Of the sandy pastures which remain some have been agriculturally 'improved' but the best of those remaining are two meadows in an enclave of Maulden Woods, although in Woburn Park too there is some good grass heath, in the north-east of the park.

Characteristic plants of this habitat include more or less extensive areas of moss or lichen 'lawn'. The typical mosses are

> *Polytrichum* species
> *Brachythecium albicans*
> *Ceratodon purpureus*

and the most conspicuous lichens are pixy-cup lichens

> *Cladonia coccifera*
> *Cladonia chlorophaea*

Typical grasses are the tiny Early Hair-grass and the Wavy Hair-grass. Despite their names they are not closely related; the latter is in the same genus as the Tufted Hair-grass of tussocky grassland, mentioned above.

The flowering plants include much Sheep's Sorrel and various hawkweeds, but the delicate blue Harebell and golden drifts of Common Bird's-foot-trefoil are also conspicuous. The trefoil and sorrel are responsible for the abundance of Common Blue and Small Copper butterflies in such meadows.

When grazing and mowing are discontinued, woody shrubs in the form of Gorse and Broom quickly shoot up, and Bracken may move in too. Interestingly, in one of the Maulden Woods meadows oak saplings are quite numerous even in the middle of the field, well away from the wood. It appears that Jays are responsible for this, burying acorns for the winter and then forgetting to retrieve them.

Apart from the main sites mentioned there are fragments of grass heath elsewhere on the Greensand. The periphery of sand quarries and verges of railway tracks often provide good examples. One of the best of the latter is the disused track which runs along the foot of Sandy Warren and here there are Bugs to be found nowhere else in the county, the long thin *Chorosoma schillingi* and the Bishop's Mitre Shield-bug. Both of these are abundant on the Suffolk Brecklands and might perhaps have been more common in Bedfordshire when heathy grassland was more extensive. Interestingly, there are a number of other Bugs which are quite common in the Brecks but which have not been found in the county at all. Perhaps the more continental climate of the Brecks is sufficiently distinct from that of the Bedfordshire Greensand that 'continental' species, near the limit of their range, cannot survive in the county.

Southern Heath

Bedfordshire is virtually at the northern limit of the habitat known as Southern Heath, characteristic of Dorset, Hampshire and Surrey. What is left in the county is very fragmented. The best examples are scattered along the Greensand Ridge – at Shire Oak (Heath and Reach), Cooper's Hill (Ampthill), Figure 4.12, and part of Sandy Warren. At these sites Heather can still be seen flowering in late summer, and with it an interesting fauna which is characteristic of this habitat.

Unfortunately, in Bedfordshire there is not the rich variety of reptiles found on the heaths of more southern counties. The Common Lizard is indeed to be found occasionally, but is so inconspicuous as hardly to warrant the adjective 'common'. The Adder, a typical heathland snake is a rarity in the county, years passing with no sightings. Neither the Sand Lizard nor the Smooth Snake reach Bedfordshire.

For the reader wishing to see what Bedfordshire heaths might have been like in centuries past, it is recommended that a visit be made to the heaths of the Isle of Purbeck, in Dorset.

This habitat will be referred to again in Chapter 7 ('The Greensand Ridge').

VERGES

The 1316 km of roadside verge in rural Bedfordshire is the largest body of wildlife habitat in public ownership in the county. Table 4.9 shows how the 1062 hectares of rural

Figure 4.12 *A sandy bank on Cooper's Hill (Ampthill), an area of Southern Heath regenerated from pine plantation. Heather (right), Bracken (top left) and a sparse growth of fine grasses such as Wavy Hair-grass, with much warm bare sand are typical of such habitat, as too are the tiny burrows of Solitary Wasps and Mining Bees.* (TL 027375 September 1986)   © B. S. Nau

verge are distributed among different types of road.

Not all verges are of equal interest; some are narrow and border busy roads, so that mud, salt and vehicle slip-streams have an impact on the habitat. However, there is one plant which has flourished under these conditions, even though, or perhaps one should say because, its normal habitat is coastal salt marsh. This is the little Reflexed Saltmarsh-grass. In 1978 it was found by Dr and Mrs Dony established along 20 km of the Great North Road (A1) in the county. It was absent from the St Neots by-pass, then only eight years old. Salt has apparently been in use for de-icing the A1 since 1950, and so presumably this plant has arrived since that time. The grass is very selective, being found only within one metre of the carriageway.

Road verges provide a variety of habitats, ranging from various types of grassland to scrub. A particular feature is the absence of treatment with herbicides or fertilisers – so often the death of farm grasslands. The wider verges are usually the more interesting ones, and those in cuttings can be of particular interest because erosion thins the soil layer so that the usual coarse fast-growing common plants give way to less common species. The best of all are those 'bare' verges, where little or no top soil has been added, and clay, sand or chalk are left more or less exposed at the surface. Such habitats are gradually colonised by a colourful display of slow-growing plants (which should appeal to those responsible for mowing verges!). Table 4.10 lists some of the best examples of such verges.

Bare verges on Boulder Clay are often favoured by an abundance of Common Spotted-orchids and Bee Orchids, and many butterflies including Common Blues, Small Coppers and various Browns. Grasshoppers are to be found in abundance, especially the Common Field Grass-

hopper but also the Common Green Grasshopper and the rarely noticed Common Ground-hopper which seems to be attracted by the sun-warmed clay (Figure 4.13). Such Boulder Clay verges also have a very characteristic group of bug species (Heteroptera), most of which are particularly associated with the plants characteristic of these sites. Table 4.11 lists some of these and their host plants. Another feature in summer is the profusion of day-flying burnet moths, whose blond-coloured pupal cases can be seen on grass stems by the dozen.

Table 4.9   Rural road verges in Bedfordshire

Class of road	Length, km	Verge–width, metres	Area (ha)
Motorway	24.7	2 × 10.4	50
Trunk road	89.1	2 × 5.2	89
Principal road (A)	112.7	2 × 5.2	112
Other classified (B and C)	472.0	2 × 4.0	378
Unclassified	618.1	2 × 3.4	433
Total	*1316.6*	—	*1062*

The verge widths are based on Way, J. M., 'Roads and the conservation of wildlife.' *J. Inst. Highway Engrs.* XVII, 7 July 1970

Plate 7: *Verges are now a last refuge of many attractive flowers. (Top) O*
Daisy flowering in profusion on a roadside bank near Thurleigh. © R. Rev
(Bottom) Field Cow-wheat taking advantage of temporarily suitable habitat at
edge of a clay-pit in the Marston Vale.   © A. J. Ma

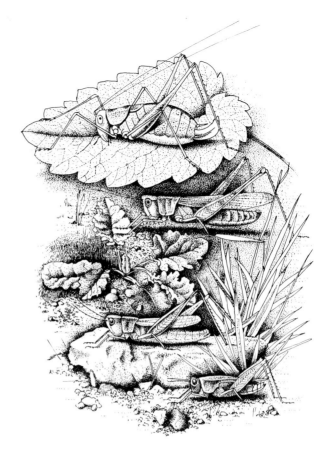

Figure 4.13 *Some 'grasshoppers' of roadside verges: the Speckled Bush-cricket (top) is a species of tall vegetation, the Common Field Grasshopper (upper middle) is our commonest species and like the Meadow Grasshopper (lower middle) is a grassland species. The Common Green Grasshopper (bottom) prefers bare or mossy ground with little grass.* © P. Walton

On chalk, bare verges provide an excellent habitat for many of the most attractive chalk flowers, Common Rock-rose, Sainfoin, Clustered Bellflower, Common Spotted-orchid, Fragrant, Pyramidal and Bee Orchids, and the Kidney Vetch and Horseshoe Vetch beloved by some of the special downland butterflies, including the Chalk-hill Blue and the Small Blue.

The bare verges of the Greensand also have their characteristic flora. Eventually these sandy verges develop a dense shrubbery of Broom and Gorse, but in the early years flowers predominate. Very typical are patches of Mouse-ear Hawkweed, each miniature dandelion-like plant having a rosette of silvery leaves pressed flat to the ground, and the yellow flowers of Lady's Bedstraw and blue Harebells are common. A particular feature are the patches of moss and pixy-cup lichens, *Cladonia* species. Specialities include the blue, scabious-like Sheep's-bit (actually a member of the bellflower family!) and the

Table 4.10 Some examples of 'bare' verges on various sub-soils

Geological type	Grid reference	Location
Boulder Clay	SP979514	A428 at Stevington turn
	TL032580	Bletsoe, Thurleigh T-junction
	TL218403	A1, Langford turn
	TL073393	A6, Maulden Woods picnic site
Lower Greensand	SP926290	Fox Corner, Heath and Reach
	TL082372	A6, Warren Wood, Silsoe
	TL229496	Potton Church
Chalk	TL064298	Sharpenhoe Cutting
	TL076293	A6, Barton Cutting
	TL005234	A5, Puddlehill
	TL000183	Bison Hill, Whipsnade

Table 4.11 Typical bug community of 'bare' verges on Boulder Clay in Bedfordshire

Family	Species	Host plant
Berytinidae	Cymus glandicolar	Glaucous Sedge
	Cymus melanocephalus	Hard Rush
	Gampsocoris punctipes	Spiny Restharrow
Nabidae	Nabis ferus	(predacious)
Miridae	Macrotylus paykulli	Spiny Restharrow
	Adelphocoris lineolatus	Spiny Restharrow
	Dicyphus annulatus	Spiny Restharrow
	Oncotylus viridiflavus	Common Knapweed
	Orthops campestris	Wild Carrot
	Calocoris roseomaculatus	Oxeye Daisy
	Leptopterna ferrugata	Grasses (drier areas)
	Leptopterna dolobrata	Grasses (damper areas)

native Goldenrod, which flowers in late summer. Interesting insects abound in such places and there are few things more pleasant on a sunny day than to lie on a warm sandy flowery verge and study at close quarters the profusion of plants and insects.

The wealth of wildlife interest of these bare verges is in such contrast to the poverty of the cultivated grasslands of the countryside that it must be hoped that the highway authorities can be persuaded to allow more such verges to develop. Most have arisen by accident but when the Silsoe by-pass was built in 1983 areas of verge were left free of topsoil intentionally. Already the wildlife interest of these areas is markedly richer than where the verges were topsoiled and grassed over. Although vegetation is slow to develop on such sites it is incomparably more attractive in the longer term (Plate 7) – and being slow-growing requires little if any mowing for road safety reasons.

Here and there a special marker-post may be seen on a verge. These were erected under an arrangement between the Bedfordshire and Huntingdonshire Naturalist's Trust (as it was called at the time) and the County Surveyor's Department, to indicate a verge having some special wildlife interest which requires consideration in the management of the site.

Bog, Fen and Marsh

Although all three of these are terrestrial wetland habitats, there is, strictly speaking, a clear distinction between marsh, fen and bog in terms of alkalinity/acidity and soil composition. Marsh and fen both tend to be alkaline, bog to be acid. Marsh soil is mainly formed of mineral matter, while fen and bog soils are formed from organic debris, peat formed by the incomplete decay of plant remains, usually sedge or reed.

Bog

In Bedfordshire bogs are to be seen at only two sites and both exist as a result of Man's recent intervention. The smaller and more recent bog is on the southern slopes of Wavendon Heath (now conifer plantations), south-west of Woburn Sands. A series of three ponds was formed in 1914 by damming a stream and springs (Figures 4.14 and 4.15). As the catchment of the water is Greensand acid conditions have built up until now the ponds are bogs with floating beds of *Sphagnum* mosses. These mosses are a rarity in the county because of the lack of suitable habitat. It is likely that the moss was present around the natural acidic springs before the ponds were made. This is also our only locality for a uniquely acid-loving 'glass-snail', *Zonitoides excavatus*. When, in the early 1980s, a very deep fuller's-earth quarry was opened up on the Heath, it was feared that this might disrupt the flow of ground-water supplying the ponds. Happily, so far the fears have proved groundless, despite the considerable flow of water

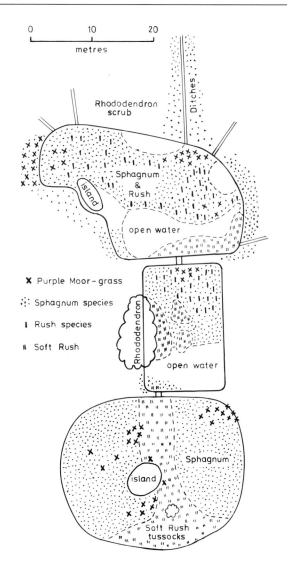

Figure 4.14 *Wavendon Heath Ponds is a 'Site of Special Scientific Interest' notable as a rare example of bog habitat in this part of England. Acidic springs, rising from the Greensand, were channelled into artificial ponds which now have an interesting flora, which includes Sphagnum mosses and Purple Moor-grass, as well as one of the only snails of acid habitat (Zonitoides excavatus), all of which are regional rarities.*

pumped from the quarry into a drain flowing away to the east. Already exhausted areas of the quarry are being backfilled and returned to forestry.

The larger of our two bog sites is that part of Flitwick Moor where peat has been excavated. Excavation of peat extended over many years, from at least as early as 1718 when the peat was used as fuel, to the period 1910–1967 when it was used as a filtration medium for town gas. The peat cuttings became flooded with acidic spring water and were then colonised by bog vegetation (Figure 4.16).

Figure 4.15 *New Wavendon Heath Ponds: the upper pond viewed from the north-west corner is a mosaic of Sphagnum moss, rushes and Purple Moor-grass.* (SP 931338, May 1986)

© B. S. Nau

As bogs go, Flitwick Moor is not particularly acid; less acid-tolerant plants such as Bulrush and Common Reed are able to thrive in many areas, particularly near the main west-to-east Mid Drain. In fact these species are in danger of dominating some areas and squeezing out the more unusual species.

At Flitwick Moor, as at Wavendon Heath, communities of *Sphagnum* mosses have become established. There are no fewer than nine species at Flitwick Moor and five at Wavendon Heath. Table 4.12 shows the species at each site. At Flitwick the survival of these attractive plants has been threatened by 'poaching' for horticultural use, commercial and otherwise, but it is to be hoped that the Bedfordshire and Huntingdonshire Wildlife Trust can now give them the protection they deserve.

A feature of the water in the peaty pools of the Moor is the presence of extensive 'rust' deposits. These originate from iron in the underlying Greensand which is dissolved

Table 4.12   Sphagnum mosses in Bedfordshire

Sphagnum species	Flitwick Moor	Wavendon Heath Ponds	Elsewhere	Notes
recurvum	common	fairly common	–	undemanding, forms hummocks
squarrosum	common	–	–	waterlogged peat
fimbriatum	fairly common	–	Ampthill Park	pH tolerant
auriculatum	–	fairly common	–	water margin, forms 'lawns'
cuspidatum	uncommon	uncommon	–	pools, pH tolerant
palustre	uncommon	uncommon	–	pH tolerant, forms hummocks
capillifolium	scarce	scarce	–	forms hummocks
subnitens	scarce	–	Stockgrove Park	forms low cushions
girgensohnii	scarce	–	–	peat banks
russowii	very rare	–	–	scarce in SE England

by acidic water permeating from below (made acid by dissolved carbon dioxide of biological origin) and is deposited on exposure to air, when it is converted to insoluble ferric oxide. These chalybeate springs are marked as such on large scale Ordnance Survey maps. The iron-rich water was at one time marketed for medicinal use by the Flitwick Chalybeate Co. Interestingly, it was also the high iron content of the peat which made it suitable for gas purification.

The original fen peat at Flitwick Moor was typically about a metre thick (over three metres in places) and was formed from Common Reed, fragments of which can still be found in the peat. It has been laid down since Roman times, probably under lake conditions initially, but by the 15th century it was dry enough to have formed fen able to yield 'hay' and to be used for grazing cattle. In more recent times it is likely that the Moor has become progressively more acidic within the peat cuttings, but the situation is complicated by the effect of more alkaline water which spills into the old cuttings from ditches fed by the River Flit. In recent decades there has been progressive drying out of the Moor, as the water table has been

Figure 4.16 *The evolution of peat cutting at Flitwick Moor. (Top) Peat cutting when still in use in the late 1940s, looking north-east towards Flitton. Such fen peat is alkaline but becomes acid as lime is dissolved and washed away, it can then develop a bog flora.* (TL 048352) © H. A. S. Key. *(Bottom) The same area today is a dense swamp of sallows, reeds and sedges.* (TL 049353, May 1981)

© B. S. Nau

lowered to improve drainage in the surrounding farmland. This is reflected in the increasing tree cover, particularly in much of the former bog areas. The aerial photograph in Chapter 7 (Figure 7.8) shows the predominance of trees.

This important site will be discussed again in Chapter 7 ('The Greensand Ridge'); further historical details of the Moor can be found in an account by the late Dr V. H. Chambers in the Bedfordshire and Huntingdonshire Naturalists' Trust's journal *Ardea* for 1979–80.

Fen

Peatland habitat with either a base-rich or neutral soil is fen; its vegetation is typically dominated by sedges and marsh grasses. It is also favoured by a unique community of specialised flowering plants, insects and birds. Not surprisingly the best fens have been renowned among naturalists over the centuries.

Fen forms naturally in river flood-plain areas with poor drainage and, like downland, was traditionally managed by Man to maintain a grassland habitat. This involved cropping the sedges as fodder and cattle bedding, so preventing its evolution to scrub (carr) and thence to woodland. Fen was probably extensive in Bedfordshire centuries ago but now most has been lost, through either drainage and cultivation or neglect and evolution to carr.

The largest remaining examples of fen are in the Flit valley. The most notable is part of Flitwick Moor, which still contains some fen, as well as bog, and much carr and woodland habitat. Another remnant survives in the Flit valley at Pennyfathers Moor, near Clophill. This is rapidly becoming encroached upon by commercial developments, having become more accessible with the opening of the Ampthill–Maulden By-pass. A few small areas of fen survive in other river valleys. Since the fen habitat once covered a huge area between Bedfordshire and The Wash, from which The Fens in East Anglia derives its name, it is particularly sad that so little fen now remains in Britain in general and in Bedfordshire in particular. Even those fragments which are managed as wildlife reserves are threatened by drainage of surrounding areas and the resulting lowering of the water table.

The naturalist wishing to get the feel of an extensive fen must now travel out of the county, to Wicken Fen in Cambridgeshire or Redgrave Fen on the Norfolk-Suffolk border.

Marsh

Like other terrestrial wetland habitats in Bedfordshire, the total area of marsh is small. However, there are more marshes than fens or bogs and they can be grouped into several categories, as in Table 4.13. The map in Figure

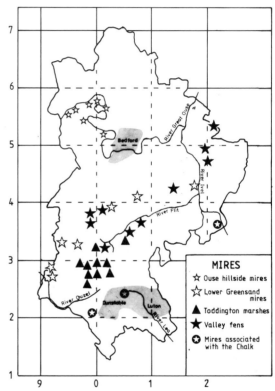

Figure 4.17 *Bedfordshire mires (marshes, fens and bogs): along the upper Ouse valley marshy springs form where the river valley cuts into the limestone; others form round springs where water flows from the Chiltern chalk, from the sands of the Greensand Ridge, or as at Toddington from glacial gravel overlying clay. Fens are mainly on river-valley flood-plains where generations of sedges build up an alkaline peat.*

Table 4.13   Types of marsh in Bedfordshire

Type	Associated geology	Location and nature
Chiltern marshes	Chalk over marl	Springs at the base of the chalk, now very scarce, most drained, very base-rich
Toddington hill marshes	Glacial gravel cap over Gault clay	Hillside springs; a series of about ten, ranging from acid to base-rich
Greensand hill marshes	Impermeable strata in sand	Hillside springs, mostly base-poor
Flood-plain marshes	Alluvium	Springs or high water-table, base-rich or neutral, including Flitwick Moor and other fens
Ouse hillside marshes	Impermeable strata in limestone etc.	Springs on slopes near river, on outside of river-meander bends, neutral or base-rich

Based on survey by Dr J. G. Dony (1983, unpublished)

Table 4.14 Sedges (Cyperaceae) of Bedfordshire marshes

Marsh type:	Chiltern	Toddington	Greensand	Flood-plain	Ouse hillside
No. of sites studied:	3	10	7	10	7
(1) Rare Bedfordshire species					
Common Cottongrass	–	1	–	1	–
Wood Club-rush	–	1	–	1	–
Flat-sedge	1	–	–	–	–
Pale Sedge	–	–	–	1	–
Star Sedge	–	1	1	–	–
Long-stalked Yellow-sedge	–	1	–	–	–
Carnation Sedge	1	4	1	–	–
Bottle Sedge	–	1	–	1	–
(2) Commoner Bedfordshire species					
Common Spike-rush	1	4	4	–	3
Bristle Club-rush	1	5	1	–	–
Lesser Pond-sedge	1	7	2	5	4
Distant Sedge	1	2	–	–	1
Brown Sedge	1	8	2	–	2
Hairy Sedge	2	9	7	–	7
Common Sedge	–	3	7	1	–
Oval Sedge	–	1	5	2	–
Greater Tussock-sedge	1	4	1	5	1
Number of species	*9*	*15*	*10*	*8*	*6*

Numbers in the body of the table are the number of sites at which a species was recorded by Dr J. G. Dony in 1983; the 'rare' species are those known from fewer than ten tetrads in the county.

4.17, which is based on a study by Dr J. G. Dony in 1983, shows the distribution of the different types over the county. The Chiltern marshes have all but totally disappeared and three studied by Dr Dony in 1983 were only a shadow of their former selves.

Perhaps the most interesting group are the Toddington marshes. These form a unique series, the soil at individual sites varying from base-poor to base-rich and from mineral (that is marsh in the strict sense) to organic (that is fen or bog). The extremes are represented by Tebworth Marsh and Fancott Bog respectively.

A particular feature of the flora of this series of marshes is the range of sedges to be found there. In his study Dr Dony recorded no less than fifteen species, of which five are county rarities (Table 4.14).

AQUATIC HABITATS

In this section attention will be concentrated on springs, streams, dykes, and rivers.

Perhaps the most conspicuous of the county's aquatic habitats are the flooded quarries: gravel-pits, clay-pits and sand-pits. These hold such a significant place among the county's aquatic habitats that they will be dealt with in a separate chapter (Chapter 8 'New Waters').

There is one clear distinction between the running waters and the still waters of the county: the former are more or less permanent water-bodies (except when water or drainage authorities deem otherwise!), the latter are transient, silting-up and evolving into first swamp, then

marsh, then carr, and finally woodland. In this chapter attention will be concentrated on the running water habitats.

Springs and Streams

The popular idea of a spring is a free spring, where a strong flow of water emerges from the ground to form an instant stream. More often though, springs are much less dramatic, often appearing as no more than a diffuse area of marshy ground from which a trickle flows. This habitat merges so inextricably with marsh that it is dealt with under that heading, earlier in this chapter.

In Bedfordshire free springs are few in number and correspondingly precious as wildlife habitats. Undoubtedly there were more in the past. Even those surviving are threatened by ever-increasing extraction of water from subterranean aquifers. Because springs are particularly simple ecological systems they have been studied around the world by ecologists unravelling the complex interactions of plants and animals. In Bedfordshire springs have not yet attracted the attention they deserve.

The best examples of free springs in the county are those associated with the junction between permeable chalk strata of the Chilterns and the underlying impermeable clay. (Figure 4.18 shows their distribution.) Of these, among the best known and most impressive are the group known as Barton Springs, which are now within a National Nature Reserve. However, their continued existence depends on the extent of future extraction of water from the south Bedfordshire Chalk by the regional water authorities.

Several local rivers arise from chalk springs. At Leagrave and East Hyde springs feed into the River Lea, as does a small tributary from springs in Cowslip Meadow beside the Bedford road in the northern suburbs of Luton. Near the Buckinghamshire county boundary a series of chalk springs feed the River Ouzel – some, beside the Tring road, recently filled in by spoil dumping. In the east, just across the boundary in Hertfordshire, the River Oughton arises dramatically from springs at Oughtonhead, the River Purwell from Ninesprings and the River Ivel from springs at Radwell. The water quality of each of these chalk streams is quickly degraded by the inflow of treated effluent from sewage works, by road drainage water, or by farm run-off rich in nutrients, all of which change the character of the water irretrievably.

At Barton Springs there are six major free springs at the head of the stream and another twenty or so downstream in the first 800 metres, before the stream turns sharply west (Figure 4.19). Over this distance the stream falls 30 m or more, varying greatly in character on the way. In some places there are rapids where the stream cuts into chalk bedrock, in others fallen trees have dammed the stream to form silty pools which allow vegetation to gain a footing. Elsewhere the stream bed comprises large pebbles and flints, or granular chalk gravel or chalky silt, depending on the current. Some feeder springs form marshy flushes on the banks, adding to the variety of wetland habitats, while others reach daylight as full-flowing streams comparable in vigour to the head springs.

At first sight the stream at Barton may seem lifeless, but closer inspection soon reveals that this is far from true. It is to be hoped that one day its freshwater biology will be afforded the careful study it deserves. Even a superficial inspection reveals that caddis, mayfly and black fly larvae, the freshwater shrimp, *Gammarus pulex*, and the Triclad flatworm *Polycelis felina* are all abundant.

There are several species of caddis here, reflecting the zoning of current and stream-bed. The most conspicuous are *Agapetus*, whose stone-covered cases are plastered onto flints where the current flows swiftly. Also common at Barton are stone-dwelling caddis which build long winding tunnels over the flints; these are *Psychomyidae*. Also in the fast-flowing reaches the flat nymphs of mayflies of the family *Ecdyonuridae* are to be seen darting over the surfaces of the larger pebbles, while other species shelter under-

Figure 4.18 *Chalk-springs are a feature of the foot of the Chiltern Hills, where chalk meets clay, there are also a few on the gentler southern slopes of the chalk.*

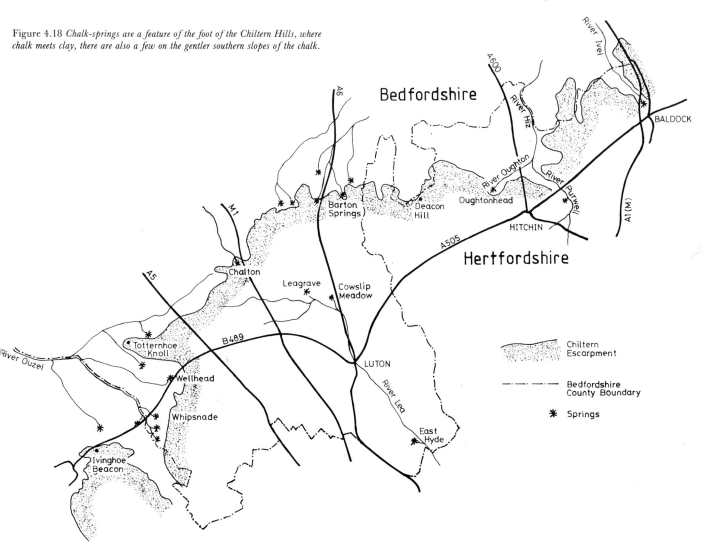

Figure 4.19 *Barton Springs is an impressive series of chalk-springs along the foot of Barton Hills, in the National Nature Reserve. Their waters form a chalk stream with a fascinating diversity of microhabitats and aquatic fauna.*

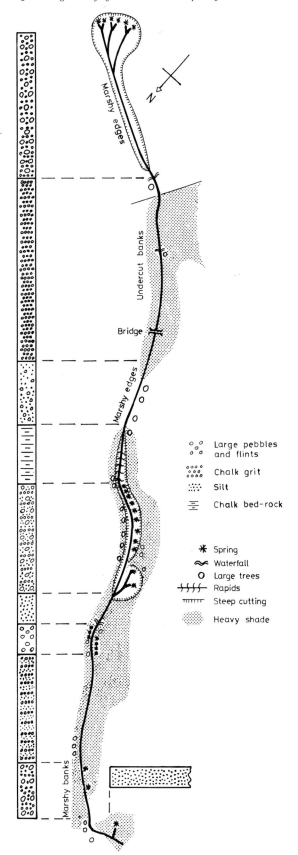

neath the same pebbles. The larvae and pupal cases of the Simulid Black Flies are confined to the fastest flowing water and can be seen attached to the chalk bed-rock of small waterfalls.

The dark brown flatworm *Poycelis felina*, a few millimetres long, is very common. In outline its shape recalls a sitting cat with large ears! This is a characteristic species of streams. At Barton it is often to be seen in great numbers near the head springs, sliding over the stones, heading upstream and apparently perpetually disappearing into the springs! One particular classic flatworm of streams and springs has not been found in Bedfordshire, although it might have been expected; *Crenobia alpina* prefers cool water so perhaps Bedfordshire springs are too warm.

The other very conspicuous animal at Barton is the freshwater shrimp, *Gammarus pulex*. One has only to turn over a stone to see a 'shower' of shrimps explode in all directions. In slower-flowing reaches it can be found in large numbers in the silt. This shrimp, widespread in the county, is one of the four Amphipods known from

Figure 4.20 *Stevington Holy Well Nature Reserve contains a series of springs flowing from the limestone of the flank of the Ouse valley. In late winter pink spikes of Butterbur are abundant, to be followed later in the year by huge umbrella leaves which dominate the Reserve.*

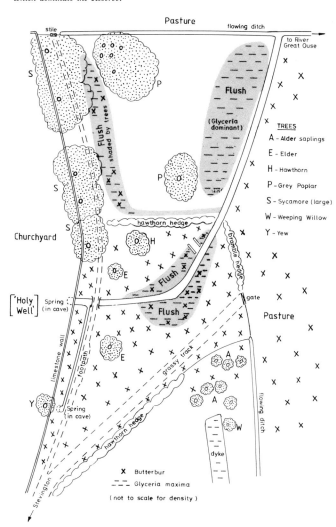

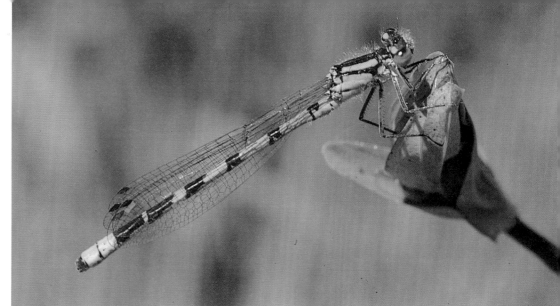

Plate 8: *The waters of former gravel workings can be rich in birdlife, plants and dragonflies.* (Bottom) *White Waterlily, Common Club-rush, and White Willows at Felmersham Nature Reserve.* © R. Revels. (Top) *The Common Blue Damselfly* (Enallagma cyathigerum) *is abundant in summer round flooded gravel-pits.*

© Mary Sheridan

Bedfordshire – the others being river species. There may be others yet to be discovered but tentative attempts to find subterranean species of the genus *Niphargus*, which can occur in wells, have not yet been rewarded.

The Barton stream is also a site for the rarely seen Water Shrew, a species which catches its insect prey in the water. There are few known sites for this animal in the county although it is secretive and easily overlooked.

There are few free springs away from the chalk, with one notable exception, the Holy Well at Stevington Church. Despite the name there is no well, it is a complex of springs (Figure 4.20). Two are free springs, each flowing from a small cave beneath the churchyard wall. The cave walls are papered with flat fronds (thalli) of the liverwort *Concephalum conicum* and the water surface is home for a few skating Water Crickets (*Velia caprai*) – actually a bug, not a cricket, and common on flowing water in the county though usually unnoticed.

Nearby there are several marshy flushes where more water emerges, and a submerged spring which feeds into a dyke. The flushes support what is perhaps the best display of Butterbur in the county. Its pink flower-spikes appear very early in spring, long before the enormous umbrella leaves which dominate the area in high summer. The Bedfordshire plants of this species are almost invariably male but in more northern counties females predominate. The Stevington site is now a nature reserve.

Dykes

Now attention will be given to the richly vegetated slow-flowing ditches and meandering streams of the river valleys. Good examples are now hard to find in the county but several still survive, just. Among the best are one that winds across Biggleswade Common, recently disrupted at one end by new gravel quarrying to the north, another that winds through a former water meadow beside the River Ivel at Langford, and a third which divides fields between Felmersham Nature Reserve and the River Ouse. Of these the Biggleswade dyke was perhaps the best example, having varied margins and a range of submerged and emergent vegetation, frogs and toads, and dragonflies; but having been dredged in the summer of 1986 it remains to be seen how well it will recover. It is sad that so little of this lowland aquatic habitat survives when it must once have been so widespread in lowland Britain.

Rivers and Canals

In Bedfordshire today it is often difficult to separate natural waterways from man-made canals. Sadly, most of the length of our few major rivers has been canalised to speed the flow of water to the sea. This has been necessitated by the more rapid run-off of rainwater from land developed for urban use and from farmland drainage activities. Farmland still makes up most of the county and

is now more thoroughly drained than ever before. Further canalisation has resulted from a desire to convert river-valley grassland for cereal growing, currently yielding better subsidies, and requiring a lowering of the water table.

A major river engineering scheme of this type has been under way during the past decade or so along the River Great Ouse, combined with a scheme to restore navigation between Bedford and the sea. The canalisation of

Figure 4.21 *Some Bedfordshire willows: long narrow leaves of Osier (top right) and Crack Willow (left), and the oval leaves of the 'sallows', Rusty Willow (lower middle) and Goat Willow (bottom).*   © P. Walton

Table 4.15 Willows of Bedfordshire

Species	Status	Form	Leaves
White Willow	VC	tall tree	Silvery, elongate
Crack Willow	VC	tall tree	Shiny light-green, long
Bay Willow	R	shrub, 7m	Dark-green and shiny above
Almond Willow	L	shrub, 7m	Shiny light-green, long
Purple Willow	LF	shrub, 3m	Dark-green, untoothed
Eared Willow	R	shrub, 2m	Dark, oval, wrinkled
Goat Willow	VC	shrub, 8m	Dark-green, broadly oval
Rusty Willow	VC	shrub, 5m	Dark-green, oval
Osier	F	shrub, 5m	Silver underside, v. long

VC = very common, F = frequent, L = local, R = rare

the River Ivel preceded this and the River Ouzel is currently under threat. These agriculture-oriented activities have resulted in the loss of much of the variety of riverine habitat – gravelly shallows, deep pools, muddy backwaters, marshy margins and flowery water meadows. New sluices have replaced old weirs, banks have been graded, and the rivers themselves have been dredged. The monotonous graded banks and uniform channel of the River Ivel, and much of the Ouse, are a poor exchange for the varied interest of a natural river.

A particular feature of our river valley landscapes are the willows. Old pollarded White Willows and Crack Willows add a special charm to the riverside scene. In Table 4.15 the species of willow found in the county are listed to show their status and some of their distinctive characters. In addition to these species there are many hybrids, which makes identification difficult.

The River Lea has suffered mainly from urbanisation. At Leagrave the river water levels are now higher than they were, but surrounding marshland has been built up by the dumping of spoil and so even here there is less wetland habitat than there used to be. Marsh-marigolds do, however, still flower around the springs at Leagrave, making a welcome splash of gold in spring in an otherwise suburban desert. In Luton's northern suburbs the Lea still retains a quite rich and varied aquatic flora. However, as the Lea traverses the centre of Luton it collects a great deal of road drainage water, polluted with oil, rubber and road dust. Then south of Luton its flow is boosted by effluent from the East Hyde sewage treatment works. All of which contribute to the degradation of what would be, if left to itself, a no less pleasant chalk stream than Hampshire's famous River Test.

Figure 4.22 (Top) Barton Springs: a chalk stream is fed by a series of springs at the foot of a chalk escarpment in the Barton Hills National Nature Reserve. (TL 089295, October 1986) (Bottom) River Great Ouse, Odell: broad shallow and swiftly flowing. The river margin here has a lush and varied growth of emergent water-plants, including Flowering-rush, Water-plantain, Yellow Flag, Greater Pond-sedge and Common Club-rush, used for basket making. (SP 966574, September 1986) © B. S. Nau

Figure 4.23 *(Top) Biggleswade Common dyke: a slow-flowing dyke on river flood-plain pasture provides breeding habitat for much aquatic-life. The leaves of Floating Sweet-grass and Broad-leaved Pondweed float on the surface in the shallows where cattle drink. (TL 189460, April 1986). (Bottom) Maulden Church Meadow pond: a rare example of a well cared for field pond, shown here two years after cleaning-out. Thread-leaved Water-crowfoot is flowering. (TL 059382, May 1977)*

© B. S. Nau

Figure 4.24 *Two rivers which rise from the Chalk in the south of the county. (Top) River Lea at East Hyde: a pleasant view but like many rivers its waters have a high proportion of road-drainage and treated sewage effluent. The small spring-fed stream in the field to the right has an abundance of Water-cress.* (TL 128172, 1983) © Beds. C.C. *(Bottom) River Ouzel at Linslade: the river winds along the foot of an outlier of the Greensand Ridge (right) separated by a small marsh of Reed Sweet-grass and Greater Tussock-sedge. The willows lining the bank have been pollarded and show several years of regrowth from the trunk.* (SP 911273, February 1978)

© B. S. Nau

Table 4.16 Emergent water-plants of Bedfordshire rivers

Species	Status
Flowing Shallows	
Common Club-rush	Locally common
River Water-crowfoot	Locally common
Flowering-rush	Thinly scattered
Arrowhead	Thinly scattered
Shallows	
Water-plantain	Widespread
Narrow-leaved Water-plantain	Occasional
Slow Reaches and Backwaters	
Yellow Water-lily	Common
Amphibious Bistort	Fairly common
Fat Duckweed	Fairly common
Common Reed	Locally common
Common Duckweed	Locally common
White Water-lily	Local
Silty Margins	
Lesser Pond-sedge	Common
Greater Pond-sedge	Common
Branched Bur-reed	Common
Sweet-flag	Fairly common
Bulrush	Local
Yellow Iris	Thinly scattered
Muddy Margins	
Water Forget-me-not	Common
Brookline	Common
Blue Water-speedwell	Local
Pink Water-speedwell	Fairly common
Marsh Woundwort	Fairly common
Yellow Loosestrife	Local, upper Ouse
Brookweed	Local, declining
Water-pepper	Common
Tasteless Water-pepper	Local, lower Ouse
Water Dock	Widespread
Orange Balsam	Locally fairly common
Water Chickweed	Common
Bog Stitchwort	Local
Marsh Yellow-cress	Common
Great Yellow-cress	Common, Ouse
Creeping Yellow-cress	Local
Water-cress	Locally common
Fool's Water-cress	Widespread
Large Bitter-cress	Rare
Celery-leaved Buttercup	Widespread
Marsh-marigold	Local
Trifid Bur-marigold	Common
Gipsywort	Widespread
Common Marsh-bedstraw	Fairly common
Skullcap	Widespread
Water Mint	Widespread
River Banks	
Hemlock	Common
Common Comfrey	Local
Indian Balsam	Increasingly common
Purple-loosestrife	Common
Hemp-agrimony	Fairly common
Great Willowherb	Common
Water Figwort	Common

The water-life most immediately conspicuous to the casual observer is emergent plantlife. This is now mostly confined to undisturbed backwaters, though sometimes quite prolific in the more extensive shallows in the upper reaches of the Great Ouse, at Pavenham, Clapham and Odell. Table 4.16 summarises the species to be found in our rivers and at their margins. The two most attractive are, perhaps, the stately Flowering-rush, with its conspicuous pink flower-heads in high summer, and the Arrowhead, with its fascinating arrow-head-shaped leaves lifted clear of the surface and its white flower spike.

The Sweet-flag has an interesting history. The leaves resemble those of the familiar Yellow Iris but the edges are crinkled and if the leaf is crushed it gives off a strong lemon fragrance. This explains why the plant was introduced to Britain for use as floor litter in times when domestic hygiene arrangements were less efficient than they are today.

In summer, the emergent plants lining the river banks are often alive with dragonflies. The most conspicuous species has wings broadly banded with Prussian blue in the male, and a metallic blue body; this is the Banded Demoiselle. It rarely strays far from flowing water, unlike some of the larger species, but is quite abundant along the upper reaches of the Ouse. Another species confined to rivers is the White-legged Damsel-fly. Particularly fond of beds of Amphibious Bistort on the upper Ouse, it is close to the northern limit of its British range in Bedfordshire. Many other species of dragonfly can be encountered along the rivers in summer but most are just as likely to be found by the still waters of gravel pits and lakes.

An insect which is totally confined to our rivers is a water-bug, *Aphelocheirus aestivalis*, unique among British insects in spending its entire life under-water. By contrast the dragonflies, mayflies, caddis, etc. emerge briefly to fly and mate when adult. This insect has adapted to its special way of life by evolving a coating of velvet-like hairs. These retain a film of oxygen from which the insect can breathe, the gas being replaced by diffusion of dissolved oxygen from the water. This process depends on a plentiful supply of oxygen in the water and so the bug is confined to well-aerated water where it lurks under the edges of stones on the river bed. It is still known from several reaches of the upper Ouse, where there are fast-flowing shallows, though sites at Kempston and Bromham have recently been destroyed by dredging.

Another group of animals which are particularly characteristic of the river-bed are mussels. The Great Ouse is noted amongst British conchologists for its richness in species. Table 4.17 summarises those known from the river. Only one other species is known from the county, the little orb-mussel *Sphaerium rivicola*, which is in the Grand Union Canal but not in the Ouse.

Shrimps are among the most common large invertebrates of our waterways. Two are met with very frequently, *Gammarus pulex* and the introduced North American species *Crangonyx pseudogracilis*. An interesting species found in the Grand Union Canal at Linslade is *Corophium curvispinum*. Most of its close relatives are brackish-water or marine species, and are a prime food source for waders on mud-flats. Our *Corophium* is to be found in the algal growths on vertical stone or concrete walls lining the canal bank. It appears to be well established in the canal, from the Chiltern summit northwards to Leicestershire at least.

An unusual shrimp which has been found in the county on occasion is a sand-hopper called *Orchestia cavimana*. This behaves just like the familiar sand-hopper on seaside beaches. It was found at Great Barford and Willington under stones on small gravel beaches at the riverside. That was before the river level was raised with the re-opening of the navigation to Bedford. It has also been found commonly on beaches in the old river channel below Cardington Mill and in the channel below Broom Lock on the Ivel Navigation – at a time when this was temporarily almost devoid of water.

Another Crustacean, allied to the shrimps, is the Crayfish. There is remarkably little information on this animal in Bedfordshire, though it is certainly common in some Hertfordshire waters, including the Grand Union Canal, and is widely distributed in England. A specimen was found in the Canal at Linslade by Beryl Rands in 1978, the only recent report. The native species is *Austropotamobius pallipes*, but a European species *Astacus astacus* has probably been introduced into Britain, and so care is necessary with identification. The shape of the 'nose' and the detail of the ridge(s) behind the eyes are diagnostic. In the *Victoria History*, it was reported that Crayfish were '... abundant in the River Lea south of Luton Hoo'. Subsequent pollution of the river with the growth of Luton may well have changed this situation.

The most characteristic animals of fresh water are, of course, fish, but such has been Man's interest in these that few if any species still have an entirely natural distribution. Species desirable to anglers are regularly replenished or moved between waters, including both coarse fish and trout. In addition some alien species have been introduced into our waterways from overseas, the Zander and Rainbow Trout for instance. Unsuccessful attempts to introduce one British species, the Barbel, were made periodically over the last 115 years but there is recent evidence that they may now be breeding in the upper Ouse.

Three migratory species have occurred naturally in the county. One is the Eel, which is common despite the hazards of a return journey from the distant breeding grounds in the Sargasso Sea, to Britain and back. Eels were common enough in historic times to warrant permanent Eel traps at various water-mills on our rivers. The other migrant is a great rarity, the Salmon. Three occurrences are on record: at Cardington Mill a six-pounder was caught in an Eel trap in 1841 and a ten-pounder twelve years later and in 1880, at Kempston Mill, a nine-pounder was similarly trapped.

Before leaving the subject of migratory fish, mention must be made of the eel-like parasitic Lampern, or River Lamprey, a very primitive jawless vertebrate and possibly semi-migratory. Only two records were known to the author of the fish section of the *Victoria History* in 1904, in the Lea at Luton and in the Great Ouse at Milton Ernest. A record from Pavenham in 1800, noted by Thomas Orlebar Marsh, was overlooked. By 1947 no further records were known to F. G. R. Soper when he reviewed the status of Bedfordshire's fish, nor, more recently, have any records been brought to the attention of the Fish Recorder of the Bedfordshire Natural History Society. The smaller relative of the Lampern, the Brook Lamprey has never yet come to notice in the county. Both of these interesting creatures could be passed over as Eels – here then is a challenge to anyone interested in fish!

The smaller species of fish, beneath notice to the angler, are of particular interest to the naturalist, because they have a more natural existence. There are six species that can be so categorised. The Three-spined Stickleback is the most abundant and ubiquitous, and the most likely to

Table 4.17   Mussels of the Great Ouse and their status

Species	English name	Status
Large species (50–150 mm)		
Anodonta anatina	Duck Mussel	Very common
Unio pictorum	Painter's Mussel	Common
Unio tumidus		Common
Anodonta cygnea	Swan Mussel	Local
Pseudanodonta complanata		Uncommon
Dreissena polymorpha	Zebra Mussel	Declining
Orb mussels (5–30 mm)		
Sphaerium corneum		Common
S. lacustre		Scattered
Pea Mussels (1.5–13.0 mm)		
Pisidium casertanum		Common
P. milium		Common
P. subtruncatum		Common
P. henslowanum		Common
P. nitidum		Common
P. moitessierianum		Common
P. amnicum		Fairly common
P. hibernicum		Fairly common
P. supinum		Fairly common
P. personatum		Local
P. obtusale		Local
P. tenuilineatum		Possibly extinct
P. pulchellum		Very rare

Figure 4.25 *River Great Ouse from the road bridge at Great Barford (top) before and (bottom) after being restored for recreational boating in the 1970s. The river was shallow and fast flowing with dense beds of Common Club-rush; the remains of a lock from an earlier period, when commercial boat traffic used the river up to Bedford, is visible in the middle distance* (TL 134516)

© Beds, C. C.

be encountered by anyone wielding a hand-net. It is a species of open water or the edges of vegetation, often netted amongst grass drooping into the water's edge. A close relative to this is the Ten-spined Stickleback. This prefers to remain in the cover provided by weed beds and is less likely to be encountered by chance. It is perhaps more common than is often thought and can usually be found when an effort is made.

The Stone Loach and the Bullhead are found where the river bed is gravelly or has stones to provide cover. Both seem quite common in our rivers but more especially in reaches with fast-flowing water and gravelly shallows. Apparently much less common is the Spined Loach, rather likely to be passed over as its relative. Finally, there is the Minnow, a species typical of swiftly flowing water and correspondingly common in shallower reaches of the upper Ouse between Bedford and Turvey.

Of the mammals of rivers, the most publicised is the Otter. Sadly this is now extinct as a resident of Bedfordshire and adjoining counties. Up to the 1940s it seems that Otters were fairly common on our rivers but as early as 1952 the decline of the Otter in the county was being noticed by local naturalists. The last holt known to be in use was one on the Ivel at Sandy, used up to 1960.

The Buckinghamshire and Courtenay Tracy Otter Hounds were hunting and occasionally killing Otters on the Great Ouse and Ivel up to 1964, and continued hunting until the mid-1970s, killing only when requested by landowners. During the 1970s and early 1980s there were a few scattered records, sometimes well substantiated. These were mostly in the upper Ouse valley and the lower Ivel. The gravel lagoons of Felmersham Nature Reserve were particularly productive. These observations probably referred to roving individuals rather than established residents, Otters are great travellers.

Reasons for the Otter's decline seem to be the increasing disturbance caused by recreational use of rivers, the clearance of bankside vegetation and the grading of river banks. But the major impact was probably the build-up of pesticide residues in the food chain. Otters being high in the chain suffered particularly severely with increasing use of persistent pesticides in the decades following the Second World War.

As the last of the Otters were being recorded so the first of the North American Mink appeared. Indeed Mink are sometimes reported as Otters. These alien members of the weasel family became established in Britain as a result of animals escaping from fur farms. They can hardly be regarded as a desirable addition to the fauna. They are efficient hunters and ruthless killers of birds, animals and fish. It is particularly ironic that some misguided 'animal lovers' have deliberately released Mink from fur farms in eastern England, adding to the ecological impact of this unwelcome alien.

First reported from the Ouse at Wyboston in 1979, it was in 1981 that the Mink really became apparent. In this year there were four reports spread over the north of the county from Cardington to Turvey. Since then it has spread rapidly and by 1983 Mink had been reported all along the Ouse from the Buckinghamshire border to Milton Ernest, and all along the river from Bedford to the Cambridgeshire border. The Mink surely must now be a permanent and major feature of our fauna!

A mammal which may suffer at the 'hands' of the Mink is the Water Vole. This has always been a widespread, familiar and common animal along our waterways but there is now concern that it may have been declining in recent years. Nevertheless, it is still present even on the headwaters of the River Lea in the northern suburbs of Luton.

The smallest of our aquatic mammals is the Water Shrew. Being a shy and inconspicuous animal it is probably often overlooked but there are reports of the species from many parts of the county and it may be more common than the intermittent records suggest.

Few of our bird species need a specifically riverine habitat although many are particularly attracted by it. Indeed, in Bedfordshire, only the Kingfisher and Grey Wagtail are truly river species in the strictest sense.

The Kingfisher population is thought to be about twenty breeding pairs, mostly to be found along the Great Ouse and the Ivel, but some along smaller waterways and flooded quarries. This population seems to be smaller than at the turn of the century when Steele Elliott considered the species 'very common'. The factor limiting the population is likely to be lack of suitable nesting cliffs, especially along the lower Ouse and lower reaches of the Ivel. Graded banks have largely eliminated suitable sites.

The Grey Wagtail is a much scarcer bird in the county, having even more restrictive breeding territory requirements. It needs fast-flowing water and a protected nest-site, on or in stonework or brickwork. This more or less confines it to the vicinity of weirs, locks, or mill-races. The recent county breeding-bird census revealed about a dozen localities over a ten-year period but only a few of these were regular sites. The closely related Yellow and Pied Wagtails have quite different requirements. The Yellow Wagtail particularly favours river-valley grassland. This is a less demanding requirement and is reflected in a breeding population estimated at about 250 pairs. The Pied Wagtail is even less demanding and has a breeding population which is probably in excess of 2000 pairs.

The Mute Swan is a bird particularly associated with rivers, although as often found on lakes and flooded quarries. A slightly misleading impression of abundance is given by the habit of non-breeding birds collecting together in a herd; they do not breed for at least two years.

A particularly notable herd was a feature of the Great Ouse in Bedford town during the 1950s. This amounted to 70–100 birds during winter and about half that number in summer. This herd appears to have reduced in number since the early sixties although there are now good numbers to be seen again in summer. During the early 1980s the winter herds have been seen on local gravel pits and have been no larger than 40–50 birds.

The county breeding-bird census in the early 1970s indicated about 45–50 pairs of swans, half of these on rivers. In 1983 there were twenty pairs on the Great Ouse, although only four of these raised young. The River Ouzel at Linslade had two pairs that were unsuccessful because of late spring flooding; the River Ivel had one successful pair. A number of pairs were reported from other waters. It seems that the adult swan population now differs little from that thirty years earlier, but the breeding success seems remarkably low. More detailed studies are needed to complete the picture but in view of reports of decline in East Anglia, attributed to lead poisoning from anglers' weights, there does seem to be cause for some concern.

The waterbirds which are frequently encountered along our rivers, in addition to those already mentioned, include the Moorhen which is numerous, and Coot and Mallard, which are both common. Less frequent are Heron, Little Grebe, Tufted Duck and Teal – in order of decreasing abundance. Teal, in fact, are rather rare along our rivers and do not breed. In the vicinity of gravel workings the Common Tern is not infrequently seen fishing along our rivers in summer.

Along the river margins the Reed Bunting is common in summer and the Sedge Warbler is frequent too. The Reed Warbler is more restricted, needing the cover of a reed bed. The 1970s breeding census indicated about thirty colonies, but often in adjacent gravel lagoons rather than on the river.

The river valleys were once rich in the damp meadows favoured by Redshank and Snipe, but now these meadows have mostly been rendered unsuitable as breeding habitats. The breeding-bird census revealed only one pair of Redshank in such habitat and Snipe were hardly more numerous, although in winter they are more common. Several hundred Snipe winter in the county, mostly in the river valleys.

Figure 4.26 *Mute Swan herd on the Ouse at Bedford, immature non-breeding birds congregate here.*   © R. Revels

Chapter 5

Changes in the Flora

The flora of the county is better documented than any other group. Records span nearly two hundred years. The work of Charles Abbot at the end of the 18th century provides an historical baseline whilst major studies in about 1950 and again twenty-five years later by the author of this chapter provide modern points of reference.

Factors for Change

The flora of Bedfordshire has shown continual change due to two main factors: one is the climate of the county, the other the impact of Man on the countryside.

There is evidence of gradual changes in the climate which must have had some influence on the plant life, but short-term extreme weather conditions can also have an effect. For example during the severe winter of 1962–3 Broom was severely cut back throughout the county. Parasitic on the Broom at Rowney Warren was the rare Greater Broomrape, known there since at least 1823. When the Broom recovered the broomrape made one feeble attempt to return but has not been seen there since. Other similar but undocumented instances may well have occurred.

Man has had a much greater effect on change in the natural vegetation of the county. Since Neolithic Man's first clearances of the primaeval forest for his settlements, agriculture and pastures for his grazing animals, Man's influence has grown ever more rapidly. Only enough of the woodland was left to satisfy his needs, all other land being cleared.

Figure 5.1 *Some of the plants lost from Bedfordshire since records began (left to right); Juniper, Grass-of-Parnassus, Common Butterwort, Fritillary, Greater Broomrape, Round-leaved Sundew, Cranberry, Bog Asphodel, Moonwort.*
© P. Walton

Changes in the face of the countryside began accelerating rapidly during the later years of the 18th century, gaining full momentum in our own time.

Through Abbot's Eyes

It is fortunate for us that Charles Abbot's *Flora Bedfordiensis* was published in 1798 at more or less the beginning of the period of increased change. This allows some investigations to be made of subsequent changes in the flora of the county (Figure 5.2).

Thanks to the work of Abbot 771 species of flowering and allied plants were known in the county at the time of his death in 1817, seventy-eight of which are no longer to be found. Since his time additional species have been found, many of which are now also presumed to be extinct in the county.

If Abbot could return he would find the vegetation of many sites that he knew still recognisable. Most of the woods he visited are still there with their wild flowers still to be found – if not always in the same abundance. He would no doubt be as pleased to be shown some plants found since his time as he would to find newcomers on the chalk downland and by the Ouse riverside.

Hedgerows and walls would still have most of the plants he knew and more have been added. In fact both these habitats have increased, the hedgerows by the enclosures and the walls (and bridges) by the coming of the railways and increased number of buildings. He would no doubt be perturbed to find so little Heather on the Lower Greensand and in the south of the county, it having been replaced by conifer plantations. Of one thing we can be certain, he would have been distressed to find the wetlands that in his day were so productive of interesting plants now mainly gone. Such was the fate of Maulden Moor, Priestley Bogs and Potton Bogs, not many years after his death.

Most of his familiar common weeds of the cornfields such as the Corncockle and Cornflower have been lost as a result of grain seed being more pure and weed killers more selective (Frontispiece).

The 20th Century

Lest it should be thought that the loss of the plant species of the heaths and wetlands all took place a long time ago a recent assessment shows that it still continues. In 1949–50 detailed studies were made by the author of the vegetation of eighty-six selected sites. A sample area with a radius of five yards was carefully analysed at each location. These studies were repeated in 1976, allowing measurement of loss or gain of species in the intervening time. The conclusions can be summarised by habitat type.

Woodlands (24 sites). In 1976 three of the sites no longer existed as woodland and two had deteriorated, one only temporarily. There was a net loss of 4.6 per cent of the woodland species compared with the total loss of these species in the county of 5.8 per cent since 1817.

Base-rich pastures (8 sites). In 1976 one site no longer existed as pasture. There was a net loss of species of calcareous pastures of 4.3 per cent compared with a total loss of these species in the county of 6.6 per cent since 1817.

Heaths and heathy pastures (11 sites). In 1976 six of the sites had deteriorated and one was inaccessible and could not be re-examined. There was a net loss of 17 per cent of the heathland species compared with a total loss of 18.6 per cent of these species in the county since 1817.

Wetlands (18 sites). In 1976 four of these sites were no longer wetlands and eight had deteriorated. There was a net loss of 22.8 per cent of the wetland species in these sites, compared with the total loss of 35.5 per cent of these species in the county since 1817.

The remaining twenty-five sites were miscellaneous in nature, allowing no useful comparisons to be made.

Sites of Special Importance

The recent loss of wetlands can be shown by examination of a list, prepared in 1949 by the Bedfordshire Natural

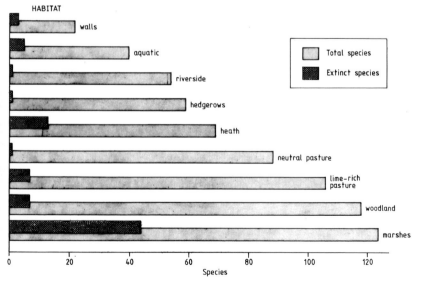

Figure 5.2 *Numbers of plant species recorded from various habitats and the numbers subsequently lost from the county. Notice the high proportion lost from marshes.*

Figure 5.3 *Rowney Warren, near Shefford, about 1950 when the heath was planted with conifers. Now this is a tall dense conifer plantation with little ground vegetation and few signs of its former heathland fauna and flora.* © H. A. S. Key

History Society, of sites in the county considered to be of importance for their natural history.

A. Sites of national importance (2). One, chalk downland (Knocking Hoe), is a National Nature Reserve and the other, wetland (Flitwick Moor) is gradually drying out and an important part has been ploughed. By the end of the century naturalists may wonder why it was considered to be so important.

B. Sites of great local importance (10). Three are chalk downland, one of which (Barton Hills) is now a National Nature Reserve, the other two (Deacon Hill and Galley Hill) have changed little. Two are mainly woodland: Kings Wood (Heath and Reach) and Bakers Wood, with adjoining heath, comprise a national Grade 2 site (*A Nature Conservation Review*). Cooper's Hill, a heath, is a Local Nature Reserve. Another woodland site (Dedmansey Wood) is diminished in size, with the wildlife interest of the remainder deteriorated. There were three wetland sites, of which Cow Common is now ploughed, Westoning Moor completely dried out and Stevington Bogs drained.

C. Sites of great local interest (12). One is chalk downland (Totternhoe Knolls), now a Local Nature Reserve. Six are woodlands (West Wood, Great Hayes Wood, Potton Wood, Judges Spinney, Marston Thrift, Cockayne Hatley Wood), all of which have changed relatively little compared with most other habitats. One, a

series of bogs (Wavendon Heath Ponds) has changed little. Two were heaths; of these, one, Rowney Warren, is now a conifer plantation and Whipsnade Heath is suffering scrub invasion. An area of incipient scrub (The Wilderness) is now a ploughed field. One site only was a wetland, Eaton Socon Water Meadows, now in Cambridgeshire. This has been covered with soil to become a recreation ground.

Twenty-two of these twenty-four sites, that is, all except Potton Wood and Cockayne Hatley Wood, were scheduled as Sites of Special Scientific Interest. To this must be added two that were later designated as National Nature Reserves, two as Local Nature Reserves and two combined to make a Grade 2 site. It is, however, sad to see that while the eight woodland sites (with only one partial exception) and the four chalk downland sites remain virtually unchanged, the five wetland sites have suffered, two disappearing completely.

Heath and Wetland

A full list of the heath and wetland species that have gone could make sorry reading. The losses in the 19th century would include Moonwort, Bell Heather, Cross-leaved Heath, Cranberry and Bog Asphodel – and there is no consolation in knowing that they also went in most adjacent counties. The present century saw the passing of Round-leaved Sundew and Fritillary – the last sites to retain Common Butterwort and Grass-of-Parnassus were on chalk downland, not their normal habitat.

The loss of these plants, with very many more, has been mainly due to the direct destruction of the sites in which they grew but this is not entirely so. There has also been a gradual lowering of the water table followed by the drying out of some wetlands. This caused the loss of Westoning Moor and the once species-rich Totternhoe Mead. It is the cause also of the drying out of Flitwick Moor. Notwithstanding this it is with regret that one must reflect that most of the wetland sites in the county that have been lost since the Second World War could have been saved with some forethought and more prompt action.

The Brighter Side

This need not, however, be read as a complete story of woe. In spite of all that has been lost there are now more wild flower species to be seen in Bedfordshire than in the time of Abbot. Some of these, the Oxlip in Potton Wood, the Moon Carrot and Spotted Cat's-ear on Knocking Hoe were no doubt there for Abbot to have found but the Man Orchid and Musk Orchid are new to Totternhoe Knolls, which leads to the speculation that their arrival could be the result of a climatic change. The Springbeauty was first recorded in Britain near Ampthill, in 1852 by T. Corder, since when it has flourished and is now common in hedgerows and on bare ground along the Greensand Ridge.

Figure 5.4 *Springbeauty was unknown in Britain until it was discovered in Bedfordshire, between Ampthill and Maulden, in 1852. It is now common and widespread in hedgerows on the Greensand Ridge.* (Cox Hill, Sandy, TL 178493, May 1986)   © B. S. Nau

Figure 5.5 *Orange Balsam is an introduced waterside flower at present confined to the valleys of the Great Ouse and Ouzel.*   © R. Revels

Introduced Species

Most of the additions to our flora are the result of improved communications, enabling plants to be more readily introduced. If they find their new surroundings conducive to their growth they remain to flourish and there are many instances of this.

The familiar Pineappleweed, very common in Bedfordshire, arrived in the county about 1906, although it was not until 1917 that a botanist bothered to record it. Oxford Ragwort, now abundant around our towns and in waste places elsewhere, originally escaped from Oxford Botanic Garden in about 1840. It spread slowly at first, but during the Second World War expanded its distribution rapidly by means of the railway network, which provided excellent habitat. By the Ouse and the Ouzel the Orange Balsam (Figure 5.5) now appears to be happily at home but it is known that it spread slowly along the canal network until it reached these Bedfordshire rivers via the Grand Union Canal. When it arrived in the county is not known.

Most of the newcomers are cosmopolitan species, making it sometimes difficult to be sure of their means of introduction but with some there is more certain evidence. During the Second World War, when labour was scarce, the permanent ways of the railways were not maintained, with the result that by the end of the war many plant species had colonised the railway tracks. These included two found normally growing on the coast, Sea Mouse-ear and Danish Scurvygrass. As it would appear unlikely that they had travelled so far inland since the beginning of the war perhaps they had been present earlier, unnoticed. The railway plants disappeared once the tracks were maintained again, leaving one to wonder if their seeds are still there dormant, waiting for favourable conditions to return.

It has recently become apparent that there is a similar, and possibly more permanent, addition to the Bedfordshire flora: Reflexed Saltmarsh-grass, as its name would suggest, is another coastal species. It can now be seen on many of our roadside verges, its introduction being no doubt due to the use of salt on the roads for de-icing in periods of cold weather. It is especially abundant on the verges of the A1 and by roads leading from it, and common also by some roads in the north of the county, but strangely absent from some in the south. How far it has spread along the verges of the M1 motorway is not yet known.

Arable land is a likely venue for introduced plants. Abbot recorded many weeds; some, apparently frequent in his time, have long since gone. It is possible that a few could have been temporary introductions even then. One of our weeds, Great Pignut, was not recognised to be a member of the British flora until 1839, soon after which it was found to be abundant in fields in the south of the county but scarce elsewhere in the British Isles. It went

from the fields thirty or more years ago but it is still abundant on disturbed land, of which there is much on the chalk. This is fortunate, as it is without doubt Bedfordshire's most distinctive wild flower.

Some mention must also be made of an unusual means of plant introduction into the county, the use of shoddy. The market-garden lands in the middle of Bedfordshire are on light well-drained soils. Any means of retaining moisture is beneficial and this can be done by the application of wool waste (shoddy), which probably also has other virtues. Much of the shoddy is the residue from the scouring of raw wool. It contains glutinous seeds that stick to the wool and fruits having burs that cling to it. By this means plants growing on sheep-runs as far afield as Australia and South America have been introduced. About 400 species, many strange and exotic, have been found in the county. Most are short-lived – it is rare to find any in fields a few years after the last application of shoddy. One species only, Green Nightshade, may have become permanently established, but in a few fields Thorn-apple (Figure 5.6) and London-rocket (so-called because it was abundant on waste ground in London after the Great Fire of 1666) have persisted for some years. Much less shoddy is used now, making it uncertain how much longer we shall continue to have these unusual plants.

While the changing pattern of the wild flowers of Bedfordshire adds much to the interest of their study, many of us would have far preferred not to have gained the Oxford Ragwort and to have kept the Round-leaved Sundew.

Figure 5.6 *Thorn-apple is one of the 'wool-aliens' accidentally imported with wool waste, formerly widely used to condition the dry fields of the Greensand Ridge for horticultural crops.* © P. Walton

Chapter 6

The Chalk Downs

Introduction

The Chalk region of the county is an extension eastwards of the Chiltern Hills. It is, perhaps, the most scenically attractive area of Bedfordshire, with the steep scarp covered by woodland and crowned in several places by beech hangers and it is an area rich in natural history. (Plate 9) We are fortunate in having two designated National Nature Reserves and one Local Nature Reserve on the Chalk. One of the former, Knocking Hoe, is ecologically delicate. It is also on private land and thus does not have public access. The other two, Barton Hills and Totternhoe Knolls, have many special plants and, having public access, may be freely visited. Sharpenhoe Clappers, with its beech hanger, is owned and managed by the National Trust, and, again, is of great natural history interest and open to the public, as are Dunstable Downs.

We have much to be thankful for in our county – that we have such chalk downland areas over which we can walk freely. But we must pause and think of the changes, some good but many bad, that are occurring in such habitats. Perhaps the worst is the invasion by hawthorn scrub, a theme to which we shall return. Large areas of former downland, in particular the southern dip slopes, have been turned over to arable farming. The areas that we have remaining to us are precious and must, at all costs, be retained if future generations of Bedfordshire people are still to see the marvellous diversity that chalk downland can produce.

What is special about chalk, for such regions often seem to contain rare and beautiful flowers, especially those of the orchid family? The answer to this would require a book to itself, and for those interested one entitled *Ecology of the English Chalk* by C. J. Smith (Academic Press, London, 1980) is recommended. But, what is chalk? It is a very pure form of limestone consisting of more than 90 per cent calcium carbonate. This substance is derived from the skeletal remains of countless minute organisms which lived in the clear seas which once covered the area many millions of years ago. Subsequent earth movements, glaciation and weathering have given us the countryside we see today, as has been described in Chapter 1.

In geological terms there are three main subdivisions of the Chalk, all of which are relevant to us in Bedfordshire. These, in order of decreasing age, are called the Lower, Middle and Upper Chalk. Because of the weathering and overlying glacial deposits, it is not always clear which parts of the region belong to which subdivision. But there are certain features which can be attributed to them as shown in Table 6.1. If further scientific information on the subdivisions of the chalk is required, the book cited above should be consulted.

Totternhoe Knolls

This is not, strictly speaking, part of the chalk downland, standing a mile or so to the north of the Chiltern escarpment, but it is such an important chalk site, especially botanically, that mention must be made of the natural history of Totternhoe Knolls. It is the site of a mediaeval castle and, as is obvious from a distance, has been extensively affected by quarrying. Indeed it is due to the quarrying that the Knolls now stands as an island, apparently surrounded by a sea of agricultural land. Some of this land has been reclaimed by drainage in recent years, with the consequent loss of several interesting plants, especially a damp area at the foot of the hill, called Totternhoe Mead.

One of the most noteworthy features of the flora of Totternhoe Knolls is the presence, within a relatively small area, of nine species of orchid, which include the

Figure 6.1 *Chiltern Hills: (left) Barton Cutting to Sharpenhoe Clappers.* (Viewed from Pulloxhill, May 1986) *(right) Dunstable Downs to Whipsnade Zoo.* (Viewed from Ivinghoe Beacon, July 1986)   © B. S. Nau

Figure 6.2 *Musk Orchid: one of the smallest orchids is a speciality of Totternhoe Knolls Nature Reserve. It arrived in the county sometime during the past hundred years.*
© R. Revels

Table 6.1 The chalk subdivisions of Bedfordshire

Subdivision	Feature	Sites
Upper Chalk	Overlay of Clay-with-Flints (to 10 m). Abundant flints	Whipsnade Downs Dunstable Downs Warden Hill
Middle Chalk	Some overlay of glacial gravels. Contains some flints	Deacon Hill Barton Hills (upper) Galley Hill
Lower Chalk	Has band of very hard chalk – Totternhoe Stone. Free of flints	Totternhoe Knolls Sharpenhoe Clappers Knocking Hoe Barton Hills (lower)

family. This species is more or less confined to the Lower Chalk and requires ground that has been disturbed. Its population fluctuates from year to year but there has been no significant overall change in its distribution over the last thirty-five years. The total distribution of this plant in the British Isles stretches from Cherry Hinton in Cambridgeshire, along the Chalk through Hertfordshire and Bedfordshire, as far as Ivinghoe in Buckinghamshire. Although it is fairly common at some sites, and is known from at least thirty localities in its main area, because of the overall restricted range it is listed in the *British Red Data Book* as an endangered species.

It is clear from studies of the natural history of Totternhoe Knolls that the ecology is characteristic of a site that has been disturbed at some time in its history, probably some hundreds of years ago. More recently there was grazing, by Sheep until about 1931, and by Rabbits until they were virtually wiped out by myxomatosis in 1953.

Table 6.2 The orchid species of Totternhoe Knolls and their frequency in Bedfordshire

Species	Tetrads
Man Orchid	2
Musk Orchid	3
Frog Orchid	4
Fragrant Orchid	15
Pyramidal Orchid	38
Early-purple Orchid	46
Bee Orchid	57
Common Twayblade	89
Common Spotted-orchid	117

('Tetrads' are 2 × 2 km National Grid squares)

nationally rare Man Orchid and Musk Orchid. A list of these orchids, along with the number of tetrads (*see* Chapter 3) in which they occur in Bedfordshire, is shown in Table 6.2. The number of plants fluctuates from year to year and these variations have been the subject of scientific studies over the years by staff of the Nature Conservancy Council.

A plant species of great interest which can be seen at Totternhoe Knolls, as well as at other sites on the chalk, is the Great Pignut, a member of the Umbellifer (Carrot)

But when grazing ceased hawthorn scrub rapidly colonised much of the site, an occurrence that has been repeated on many areas of our chalk downland. Recently, under the active management of the local Wildlife Trust, the invading scrub has been cleared from some parts of the hill and Sheep have been returned to graze during the autumn and winter. Many typical chalk downland plants are now increasing, for example, Kidney Vetch and Horseshoe Vetch, which are food plants for butterflies, and the colourful Sainfoin and Clustered Bellflower. Gradually much of the former glory is returning to larger areas.

Knocking Hoe

This is still on the Lower Chalk but, in contrast to the disturbed Totternhoe Knolls, Knocking Hoe is possibly a piece of old virgin chalk grassland; indeed it may not have been disturbed for a few thousand years. This site too has been the subject of ecological study, and, in 1953, was the first National Nature Reserve designated in Bedfordshire. It is fitting to record here that we owe the existence of this

Figure 6.3 *Marbled White: despite its name a member of the 'Brown' family; common on chalk grassland where the grass is tall.* © A. J. Martin

reserve, and the saving of its botanical treasures, to John Dony, the county recorder for flowering plants. It is designated a national Grade 1 site by the Nature Conservancy and is the smallest site (9 ha) in Britain to be so designated. The main reason for its status is the presence of several uncommon species of plant. It is not included as an example of a particular ecological type as is usually the case with Grade 1 sites.

An interesting common factor concerning some rare species of flowers is that they have a very fragmented distribution in the British Isles – the technical term for this is *disjunct*. For example the Moon Carrot, another member of the Umbellifer family, occurs locally in Hertfordshire and Cambridgeshire but its only other locality is in Sussex. A second species of this nature is the Spotted Cat's-ear, a member of the Daisy family. Its other sites are as far apart as Cornwall, Caernarvonshire and Lancashire, giving this species a classic disjunct national distribution. The reasons for these distributions are not completely understood but are possibly connected with the responses of the plants to climatic variations over recent geological times.

Knocking Hoe projects slightly to the north of the main sweep of the hills. It is likely that, like these, it was covered in scrub, possibly Juniper and Box, which was cleared in Early Bronze Age times. The small cultivated fields were bounded by earthworks, called *lynchets*, which can still be seen on the west side of nearby Deacon Hill. The scrub was fairly easy to clear with primitive tools and as Man moved down to the lower ground, the cultivated areas reverted to grassland and were kept as such by the grazing of flocks of Sheep. Thus for many hundreds of years the grassland developed and the plants and insects of chalk downland developed their special communities. It is the continuance of these communities that is one of the objectives of conservation in the late 20th century.

Barton Hills

The Barton Hills National Nature Reserve is probably the best known area of chalk downland in Bedfordshire (Figure 6.4). It has long been recognised as an area of great natural history interest and this was finally recognised in 1982 when it was designated the county's second National Nature Reserve. It had already been declared a

Figure 6.4 *Barton Hills National Nature Reserve: on the facing page (top) The steep well-grazed slopes are a classic chalk downland habitat favoured by such attractive flowers as orchids, bellflowers, the Pasqueflower, and others; some of the most attractive butterflies are confined to such habitat. (1983)* © Beds. C. C. *(centre left) Duke of Burgundy butterfly: a downland species.* © R Revels. *(bottom) Cowslips flourish despite heavy grazing, they spread by seeds which germinate with little competition in the loose soil of mole-hills. (TL 088301)* © M. Sheridan. *(centre right) Pasqueflower: this anemone flowers in April–May on the steepest downland slopes.* © R. Revels

Plate 9: *Where Hawthorn scrub has not encroached, the chalk grassland of the Chilterns is the home of many attractive plants and insects. (Centre) A profusion of Pyramidal Orchids on downland.* © *A. Ford. (Top) The Chalkhill Blue butterfly is confined to chalk grassland, and (bottom), Chiltern Gentian – a truly Chiltern plant found almost nowhere else in Britain.* © *R. Revels*

national Grade 1 site by the Nature Conservancy Council, but it is good to know that this area will be safe for the future. However, because there are large areas of developing scrub, the management will be important.

Much of Leete Wood, on the hillside to the west of the stream which issues from Barton Springs, is only some seventy years old. This is indicative of the speed with which downland can change to woodland. As with Totternhoe Knolls, the deterioration set in about 1930 when Sheep grazing ceased, but the presence of Rabbits helped to keep the scrub in check. Myxomatosis, at its height in the mid-1950s, removed the remaining defence against the spread of scrub.

Now, once more, some of the scrub has been cleared and, with the erection of suitable fencing, Sheep have been returned to the hills, and the turf is again being kept in good condition.

Barton Hills is the main site in Bedfordshire for what is arguably the county's most splendid plant, the Pasque-flower. In some years the hillside is thick with the purple trumpet flowers and well over a thousand can be present, although in other years the numbers are in the low hundreds. Over the last few years in late April or early May, the Bedfordshire Natural History Society has made a regular pilgrimage to count these flowers. It is to be hoped that this exercise will continue for many years to come so that the annual fluctuations can be recorded.

Other unusual plants of these hills are the Field Fleawort, an attractive member of the Daisy family; and a dwarf form of the Hairy Violet with a flower resembling a Maltese cross – being quite different from the normal plant. The bright yellow Common Rock-rose and Yellow-wort, Salad Burnet, Wild Thyme, Dwarf Thistle and Squinancywort, to name but a few, are common. In the spring large areas are covered with Cowslips, a species that appears to be increasing here.

As mentioned earlier, the southern dip slope of the chalk has been converted to arable farming. But even in these days of well-sprayed crops, there is still to be found a wealth of arable weeds around the crop's edge. These species, as a group, are dwindling in the country to such an extent that the Botanical Society of the British Isles is organising a national survey in an attempt to measure their status. Many cornfield weeds are confined to the chalk, and many are beautiful plants, albeit sometimes on a rather small scale. Among the most notable are Venus's-looking-glass, a few uncommon species of fumitory and Knotted Hedge-parsley. Not far away, in a small Wildlife Trust reserve, is the rare Ground-pine, a close

relative of the Bugle but with small yellow flowers. At a nearby site grows another nationally rare weed, the Broad-fruited Cornsalad, which, however, is far from spectacular! It is to be hoped that agricultural practices do not eliminate these very interesting members of our flora; certainly they do not cause the problems of grain seed contamination associated with Cornflower and Corncockle, both of which are extinct in the county.

Dunstable Downs and Whipsnade Downs

An interesting account of the natural vegetation of these two downs was reported in *The Bedfordshire Naturalist* (**35**) by John Dony. The recent history of the two sites makes for interesting comparison because, within the bounds of the zoo, Whipsnade Downs has been almost continuously grazed since 1930, in the main by Wallabies. In contrast, on Dunstable Downs Sheep grazing ceased at about this time. As happened elsewhere when Sheep grazing came to an end, scrub invasion occurred on Dunstable Downs, but it is mainly limited to the lower slopes. The upper part is subject to increasing pressure from human feet, being an amenity area for nearby Dunstable and Luton, as well as many London suburban areas; the interest of observing the gliding and, more recently unofficial hang-gliding, has maintained the pressure once exerted by Sheep.

In Dony's survey of the two areas, 166 species of plants were recorded, of which sixty-eight were present only on Dunstable Downs, sixteen only on Whipsnade Downs, and the remainder, eighty-two species, were recorded from both sites. Of these, the thirty-two listed in Table 6.3

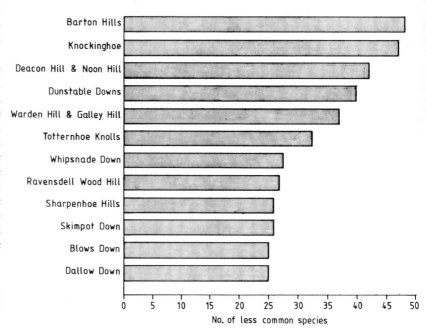

Figure 6.5 *The floral richness of twelve downland sites in the county. The species counted are those known from fewer than one third of all 'tetrad' squares in Bedfordshire.*

Figure 6.6 *The wildlife interest of chalk downland depends on a delicate balance of grazing pressure, without balance grazing deterioration rapidly sets in. (Left) The richest flora and fauna are where soil is thin; here the many special flowers of chalk thrive while coarse grasses and other plants, which swamp all competition elsewhere, cannot survive. (Bison Hill, Whipsnade SP 499188, September 1986) (Top) Dense Hawthorn scrub shades out all the fine chalk flora and with it are lost the butterflies and other insects dependent on it. (Dunstable Downs from the north, TL 006208, July 1986)* © B. S. Nau

may be considered to be species of lime-rich grassland, although they are not all necessarily confined to this type of habitat. It is interesting that these species have survived both the trampling on Dunstable Downs and the continuous grazing of Whipsnade. It is also remarkable that so many chalk downland species have survived in both sites, even if not in the profusion they formerly enjoyed. These sites are compared with others on the Chalk in Figure 6.5.

Chalk Quarries

Chalk has been quarried in the past in many places along the chalk escarpment – Barton-le-Clay, Sundon, Houghton Regis, Sewell and Totternhoe – and currently at Kensworth. These former quarries now provide some of our most attractive chalk habitats, rich in flowers and insects. The rare Chiltern Gentian, in particular, thrives in such sites. High on the list of conservation priorities must be the safeguarding of one or more of these sites, which are being lost one by one.

Table 6.3 Plants occurring on both Dunstable and Whipsnade Downs

Autumn Gentian	Dwarf Thistle	Quaking-grass
Burnet-saxifrage	Eyebright (2 species)	Salad Burnet
Carline Thistle	Fairy Flax	Sheep's-fescue
Clustered Bellflower	Hairy Violet	Small Scabious
Common Bird's-foot-trefoil	Harebell	Spring Sedge
Common Milkwort	Horseshoe Vetch	Squinancywort
Common Rockrose	Large Thyme	Upright Brome
Cowslip	Meadow Oat-grass	Wild Mignonette
Crested Hair-grass	Mouse-ear Hawkweed	Wild Thyme
Downy Oat-grass	Musk Thistle	Yellow Oat-grass
	Pyramidal Orchid	

Figure 6.7 *New chalk habitat in the making: disused chalk-quarries provide a range of chalk habitats as they are slowly colonised by typical downland flowers and insects. (Top) An early stage in colonisation of a disused quarry, at Houghton Regis. This site has the added interest of springs which provide crystal-clear 'marl pools' and marshy areas which attract wading birds. This site is at risk of building developments.* (TL 006235, 1979) © B. S. Nau. *(Right) Spoil heaps in former chalk workings at Upper Sundon have developed an attractive and diverse flora and fauna, although the conspicuous erosion caused by motorcycles has been a serious problem.* (1983) © Beds. C. C.

Insect Life

The chalk downlands are probably the most important butterfly habitat in Bedfordshire. The total number of species recorded there is thirty-one, this being the highest for any region in the county. The hawthorn scrub invasion is, as might be expected, changing the distribution patterns of species, causing a decrease in the numbers of some of those that are specific to the chalk.

Table 6.4 lists the butterflies that are virtually confined to the chalk, and also gives their larval food-plants. Several of these plants, for example the Horseshoe Vetch, Kidney Vetch and Common Rock-rose, are confined to the chalk. The occurrence of these butterflies is greatly affected by the changes in the plant populations.

The Chalk-hill Blue butterfly has decreased in recent years in line with the decrease in Rabbits, which has affected the quality of the turf. The effect on the Horseshoe Vetch is very noticeable. In contrast the Small Blue, with Kidney Vetch as its larval food plant, is still found in good numbers. This plant is better able to stand up to competition with coarse grasses and readily colonises disused chalk-quarries. A particular feature of this

Table 6.4   Butterflies of the chalk downland and their larval food plants

Species	Larval food plant
Brown Argus Blue	Common Rock-rose
Chalk-hill Blue	Horseshoe Vetch
Dark-Green Fritillary	Violet species
Dingy Skipper	Common Bird's-foot-trefoil
Duke of Burgundy	Cowslip
Green Hairstreak	Various
Small Blue	Kidney Vetch
Marbled White	Grasses

butterfly is that it lives in very small colonies extending over 100 metres or less.

The Dark-green Fritillary only just survives in Bedfordshire because it is on the eastern limit of its distribution and numbers appear to vary with the severity of the winter. The Duke of Burgundy butterfly is frequent all along the chalk, where its food plant, the Cowslip, is common, but tends to prefer the more sheltered lower slopes. One of the most striking species to be seen on the downland, although it is not, in fact, confined to the area, is the Marbled White. This species may have increased as a direct result of reduction in Rabbit grazing, because the larval food plants are various grasses. So here we have a case where the habitat changes favour one species, the Marbled White, whilst causing the decrease of a second species, the Chalk-hill Blue.

There are several species of migrant butterflies which can be seen on the chalk and one in particular, the Clouded Yellow, appears to favour areas where Lucerne grows. In recent years the number of occurrences has increased and one theory for this is that Lucerne has returned as a crop in northern France thus encouraging, once again, the spread of this beautiful butterfly nearer to the shores of Britain.

It is not only butterflies that may be seen on the wing on chalk grassland in summer, Bedfordshire also has a number of day-flying moths, which can be seen flying in the sunshine. Although nocturnal species may be disturbed from their daytime resting places there are species which are truly diurnal and may sometimes be very abundant. Most are rarely recognised: the Clearwings, for instance, look more like sawflies than moths whilst others behave rather like butterflies.

Figure 6.8 Whipsnade Green: heath on 'chalk', an area of grass heath just a few hundred metres from the chalk escarpment, once one of the county's richest sites for mining bees, solitary wasps and their relatives. (TL 002179, September 1986)
© B. S. Nau

The Narrow-bordered Five-spot Burnet, the Six-spot Burnet and The Cinnabar are among our more familiar day fliers. They are common in the county and can be seen both on the chalk downland and in flowery grassland elsewhere. Two rare Bedfordshire species are the Four-spotted Footman and the Marsh Pug, which seem to be restricted to grassland. Two other moths which favour grassy places are the Mother Shipton and the Burnet Companion. These can be found throughout the county but some species are much more restricted to downland; these include the Cistus Forester, the Wood Tiger and the very common Chimney Sweeper. The latter does occasionally occur in other habitats as well. Grassland away from the chalk, on the Greensand, also has its interest to the lepidopterist; the male Emperor moth, the Orange Underwing and the Beautiful Yellow Underwing may all be seen there flying in daytime.

In 1971 an account of the changes in the bee and wasp fauna was written by V. H. Chambers (*The Bedforshire Naturalist* **26**) and is well worth quoting:

> Moving . . . on to the chalk downs proper, the great changes in this area since Sheep grazing had to be stopped as a direct result of plebianisation of the motor-car, and the destruction of the Rabbit, are known to naturalists. Dunstable Downs carried a rich flora in a short turf, from relict Heather patches on the top down to the banks along the arable fields below: this was never a good locality for bees although some unusual species occurred e.g. *Nomada flavoptica* and *Andrena marginata*, but there were always the flowers upon which they could be found. The slopes are now little more than a hawthorn-infested coarse grass monoculture.

Perhaps John Dony's recent survey discussed above paints a more optimistic picture. Chambers continues:

> . . . The area around Totternhoe Knolls was richer – and is still of interest – more particularly the grassed-down ancient quarries which carried the entrances to the stone adits, destroyed after 1948 by extensive chalk quarrying. Here in some seasons almost every dandelion carried one of the shell-nesting bees, *Osmia bicolor*, a species only seen occasionally today. Its relative, *O. spinulosa*, flying two months later, has also nearly vanished. Restriction of nesting sites and reduction of forage plants (e.g. arable weeds, prune orchards) has reduced the solitary and bumble bee population at Totternhoe since my pollen-foraging studies of 1944–45. However, the conservation work underway at Totternhoe – and more recently the welcome start with scrub clearance by the National Trust at Sharpenhoe – should help the survival of downland species.

Only a few hundred metres south of the downland escarpment was one of Chambers' best localities for bees and wasps, Whipsnade Green (Figure 6.8). Although so close, this heathy grassland is more affected by the Clay-with-Flints and the well-drained turf provided habitat for nineteen species of *Andrena*, solitary mining bees, and eleven species of *Nomada* bees – dependent on the

Andrena. Sixty or more species of bees and wasps were known here in its heyday in 1945, but it was much deteriorated by 1971.

Bird Life of the Chalk

It was on the chalk downlands of the county that birds such as Stone Curlew, Whinchat and Red-backed Shrike bred. The Stone Curlew was a common summer visitor until about 1815, when it decreased in numbers until breeding ceased in 1894. However, a recovery took place during the first half of this century, with regular breeding until about 1960. The last record for the species was from the Pegsdon area in 1971. The present national distribution is a narrow belt from Norfolk to Wiltshire with a break, in the middle of which lies Bedfordshire. It is always possible that an intensive search in early spring, when the Stone Curlew is most vocal, could still reveal the presence of a small population.

The decline of the Whinchat and Red-backed Shrike in the county is closely correlated with their general decline in southern England. This is probably linked to a combination of human disturbance and climatic change. The last breeding of these species occurred during the early to mid-1970s and it is feared that both may be permanently lost as breeding species in Bedfordshire. Also in decline, but still present, is the Wheatear. In this case the causes are linked to the increase of coarse grasses and scrub, due to the smaller Rabbit and Sheep populations, resulting in less available breeding habitat.

There are several distinct breeding habitats on the chalk, listed in Table 6.5. Some species have taken advantage of the increasing scrub, for example the Turtle Dove, Whitethroat, Willow Warbler and Redpoll.

On Dunstable Downs, since 1980, the Skylark has shown a decline in numbers due, probably, to scrub invasion and the hard winter of 1981–82. But over the same period the Meadow Pipit has increased because it has a preference for open scrub. The resident species, such as Blackbird, Robin and Dunnock, have remained relatively stable but the Wren is badly affected by hard winters.

Summer visitors, such as Blackcap and Garden Warbler, are irregular and do not breed every year. Table 6.6 shows the fifteen most regular breeding species of Dunstable Downs over five years from 1979 to 1983.

Figure 6.9 *Some examples of the variety of animal life of the Chilterns in Bedfordshire. (Top) Wood Tiger: this strikingly marked moth is found on downland, although not confined to this habitat. (Centre) Glow-worm: common on downland, this is a female in its glowing position on a grass stem. (Bottom) The Fat Dormouse* (Glis glis), *established in the Chilterns, is an introduced relative of the similarly nocturnal Common Dormouse. It reached the eastern limit of its range at Studham and Whipsnade. The Common Dormouse itself is a rarity in the county, found only in this same locality.* © R. Revels

Table 6.5 Typical bird breeding species of the chalk downland and habitats

Habitat	Species
Grassland	Meadow Pipit
	Skylark
Open scrub	Meadow Pipit
	Linnet
	Tree Pipit
	Willow Warbler
Dense scrub	Turtle Dove
	Wren
	Blackbird
	Robin
	Garden Warbler
	Magpie
	Great Tit
	Willow Warbler
Dense, closed canopy scrub	Woodpigeon
	Mistle Thrush
	Pheasant
	Redpoll

(Based on S. Halton, unpublished data)

These are based on fieldwork by S. Halton and are detailed enough to give a relative order of abundance. Of the thirty-one species, with an average 144 breeding pairs per year, these fifteen common species accounted for approximately 90 per cent of the breeding population. The Willow Warbler was by far the most common, with the Yellowhammer less than half as frequent.

The chalk escarpment is a regular migration route for many of the regular summer visitors to Britain. Birds such as Swallows and Meadow Pipits can be seen on passage here in large numbers. One of the most interesting migratory visitors is the Ring Ouzel, a handsome bird, which can be regularly seen in spring on its way to its more northerly breeding grounds, together with Redstarts, Whinchats and Black Redstarts. Most observers' attention in recent years has been given to Blows Downs and

Table 6.6 The frequency of the fifteen most common bird breeding species of Dunstable Downs (1979–1983)

Species	Breeding %	Species	Breeding %
Willow Warbler	28.1	Great Tit	2.5
Yellowhammer	12.4	Magpie	2.5
Dunnock	8.6	Chaffinch	2.4
Robin	8.1	Linnet	2.4
Blackbird	7.0	Skylark	2.2
Woodpigeon	3.9	Song Thrush	2.0
Wren	3.2	Whitethroat	1.8
Meadow Pipit	2.5		

(Based on S. Halton, unpublished data)

Whipsnade Downs, but there is no doubt that time spent on the other chalk downlands during the spring would pay dividends.

In winter large numbers of birds roost in the comparative safety of the thick scrub, at Whipsnade and Blows Downs in particular. The former site is noted for its large gathering of members of the crow family, that spend the day feeding on offal from an adjacent pig farm. As many as 150 Magpies have been recorded flying in to roost nearby. Blows Downs is more notable for its Starling roost, with massive 'murmurations', several thousand strong, swirling in just before dusk. Winter thrushes and finches also join the throng hoping for 'safety in numbers' protection from hunting Sparrowhawks and the occasional Longeared Owl.

Of Mammals and Molluscs

Of the larger mammals of Bedfordshire the Badger is probably one of the most elusive. It is interesting that the Luton and Dunstable area, which has the largest concentrated area of human population, also has the highest density of active setts. Those in the Dunstable area are associated with the Upper Chalk and there is no doubt that Badgers prefer its well-drained soil for excavation. Chalk has the great advantage to a burrowing animal of being structurally self-supporting and the undulating countryside provides ample slopes into which the Badgers can easily dig. Yet again the increase in scrub has affected one of the county's animals; where not too dense, it has allowed setts to become established in such places as Blows Downs and Dunstable Downs, all since 1954.

There is a distinct lack of setts along the eastern part of the chalk. This includes the areas from Warden and Galley Hills, through Sundon, Sharpenhoe and the Barton Hills to the Pegsdon Hills. Even if a few unrecorded setts do exist in these areas, there would still remain a marked difference in population density. There is no immediately obvious explanation for this distribution.

The Whipsnade–Studham area is the only part of the county where the introduced Fat Dormouse is found (Figure 6.9). Like a small squirrel, it often makes a home in lofts or attics. These animals derive from some released at Tring in 1890 by Lord Rothschild. At present they show little sign of spreading beyond the well-wooded plateau bounded by Dunstable Downs.

To consider much smaller, much less mobile, animals, one of the most distinctive land snails of Bedfordshire, the rather winkle-like *Pomatias elegans*, is an inhabitant of the chalk in the south of the county. This snail can be found in open woods, hedgebanks and open screes, providing the soil is highly limy and friable, as it requires to be able to burrow easily. The county distribution reveals its presence on small outcrops of limestone in the Odell area and

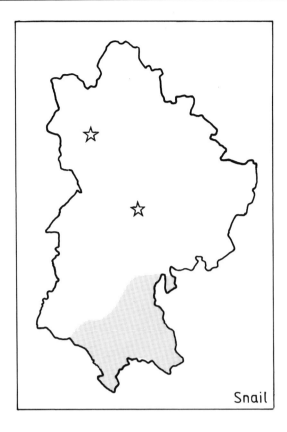

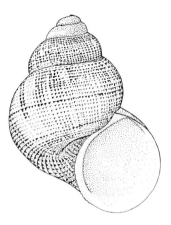

Figure 6.10 *The rough shell of the winkle-like snail* Pomatias elegans *(above) is very characteristic of shady chalk-scree.* © D. Guntrip. *This snail is scarcely found away from the Chalk, as can be seen from the map.*

high on the hill in Wilstead Wood, although the main centres of population are clearly in the south on the Chalk (Figure 6.10).

There are several distinctively banded brown and white snails which are characteristic of downland grass. They may be seen resting in full view, a thing most snails with their retiring habits would never do. In hot, dry or windy weather they cling to the stems of grasses and seal their mouths with a membrane to reduce water loss. This behaviour, called *aestivation*, is a common sight in Mediterranean countries, where clusters of snails are to be seen on the stems of grasses and other plants. The warm dry nature of our downland turf perhaps has something in common with the habitats in warmer climes. Snails most commonly seen aestivating in this way in Bedfordshire are species of the sub-family Helicellinae and *Monacha cantiana*.

One of the snails *Helicella itala* is in some danger. Few sites are known where it is thriving. The reason for its decline, as is so often the case, is not immediately apparent. Perhaps it is due to climatic changes, loss of habitat, or a combination of many factors, some

unknown. Its close relatives *Candidula intersecta* and *Cernuella virgata* are much more widespread, and often live together in dry, open, lime-rich sites such as downland, roadside verges and even deserted railway tracks. Far more local, apparently, is *Candidula gigaxii*, but it may have been overlooked because of its similarity to *C. intersecta*.

A quite unrelated species is the Blind Snail, *Cecilioides acicula*, which burrows deep underground amongst roots, but its empty shells can often be found amongst the fine soil of ant hills and mole hills on downland.

The Future of the Chalk Hills

With the National Nature Reserves (NNRs) and Local Nature Reserves (LNRs), together with the designation of Areas of Outstanding Natural Beauty (AONBs) and Sites of Special Scientific Interest (SSSIs), it would be possible to be led into a false sense of security concerning the safety of some of our most precious habitats. Many of these areas can be affected by undesirable farming practices, whilst the management of all is very important. Road improvements may have deleterious effects. Indeed as this is being written one particular site at the top of Barton Cutting has come under threat. The site is an SSSI and contains two particular plant species, the Green-flowered Helleborine and the Yellow Bird's-nest, of which are very rare in the county. The proposed path of the road would totally destroy these plants, but it is to be hoped that the outcome of the public inquiry will have regard to the needs of conservation.

Chapter 7

The Greensand Ridge

Its Landscape

On a clear day there are magnificent views northwards across the Bedfordshire countryside from such vantage points as Sharpenhoe Clappers and the new National Nature Reserve at Barton Hills. The northern skyline is fringed with woodland; with the aid of binoculars this resolves into a mosaic of woodland and fields covering the crest and flanks of a long ridge, the Greensand Ridge. A similar impression is gained from vantage points near Bedford looking south across the Marston Vale. From this direction the Greensand Ridge stands out very sharply because the Ridge falls more steeply on its northern face.

The 1:250 000 scale Ordnance Survey map of East Anglia (the old ¼-inch series) clearly reveals how the ridge extends twenty-eight miles diagonally across the county, from Leighton Buzzard and Linslade in the west to Gamlingay over the Cambridgeshire boundary. It also shows that the ridge is peppered by a mosaic of woodland and is sliced through by two north-flowing rivers, the Ouzel and the Ivel.

At Linslade the River Ouzel has cut a narrow valley of great charm and interest to the naturalist; it also marks the old county boundary between Buckinghamshire and Bedfordshire. Away to the east the River Ivel has formed a broad valley along the foot of a promontary capped by the pines of Sandy Warren. This is a major landmark in the east of the county and overlooks the town of Sandy. This part of the Ivel Valley has long been an intensively cultivated market-gardening area from which much of the wildlife habitat has been squeezed out. This renders what little remains more precious. Fortunately on the remoter parts of Biggleswade Common you can still enjoy Cowslips, Marsh-marigolds and Meadow Saxifrage in spring.

The Ridge is generally four or five miles wide. But west of the cutting carved out for the M1 motorway in the late fifties, a confusion of low hills merges with the southern edge so that it is quite difficult to pick out a ridge at all. What then distinguishes the Greensand Ridge? The Greensand Ridge is actually an outcrop of sandy geological beds which curve deep below London to re-emerge beyond the North Downs and again along the south rim of the Weald of Kent and Sussex.

Special Features

The sandy strata of the Greensand are interleaved with sandstones – hard enough to use as a building stone, as in the churches of the Ridge – and this reinforcement is the reason why the Greensand forms high ground where it outcrops. Being sandy too, it drains very freely, forming dry warm soils which are attractive to warmth-loving southern species of animals, especially insects of open sandy places. These find a niche on the Greensand in areas which would otherwise be too northerly.

Although the Chalk also has these features, it differs in a fundamental way. Chalk is soluble in ground-water and is able to replace lime leached from the soil by drainage. On the other hand, insoluble lime-free sand is unable to provide plant nutrients in this way and so it forms acid soils. The flora and fauna of the sand are therefore quite different from those of the chalk.

Heather is an *indicator species* for the Greensand, as are

Figure 7.1 *Broom: its yellow flowers are a feature of the Greensand Ridge, to whose sandy soils the shrub is confined in the county.* (Sandy, TL 179489, May 1982)

© B. S. Nau

Plate 10: *The animal life of woodlands can be great and varied in ancient woods with open rides or glades. (Top) Wood Mouse – common, but rarely seen by the casual visitor.* © D. G. Rands. (*Bottom*) *The Purple Hairstreak butterfly finds sunshine round the tops of oak trees in woodland in high summer.* © R. Revels. (*Centre*) *This longhorn beetle,* Agapanthia villosoviridescens, *is a striking sight on Hogweed in a woodland ride. It seems more common now than earlier in the century.*
© Mary Sheridan

Gorse, Broom, the creeping mats of white-flowered Heath Bedstraw, and the delicate silvery heads of the Wavy Hair-grass: reference to the plant-distribution maps in the *Bedfordshire Plant Atlas* will show how these plants, and other Greensand indicators, are distributed along a narrow diagonal band across the middle of Bedfordshire, following the sand.

An example of these fundamental differences is the way in which woodland leaf-litter and fallen branches are quickly decomposed and recycled in damp lime-rich woods, but only slowly in dry acid Greensand woods. The organisms at the base of the food pyramid responsible for this important task cannot operate, litter builds up and logs lie for years where they fall. Only a specialised flora and fauna can exploit such an environment. These characteristics of the Greensand are some of the features to be aware of when visiting the Greensand Ridge, but there are others too.

An important feature of the Ridge is the presence of a cap of chalky Boulder Clay, adding greatly to the diversity of its wildlife. This clay was deposited over the sands in glacial times but has since been completely eroded from large areas, especially on south-facing slopes. Now the wet poorly-drained soils formed from the Boulder Clay are mainly confined to the crest of the Ridge.

These Clay areas are marked by a distinctive vegetation and for this reason the vegetation on the Ridge may change very suddenly over the space of just a few feet, where clay gives way to sand. Figure 7.2 illustrates the distribution of these glacial clay-deposits.

History of Land Use

Since the clay cap was too wet and heavy to be ideal for agriculture many such areas were left as woodland, from primaeval times right through to the mid-20th century. But in the last few decades many of these ancient broadleaf woods have been irreparably damaged by clear felling and replanting with conifers. In these woods only where there are broad rides with shrubby margins has some of the previous interest survived. The planted conifers are so closely spaced that after ten to fifteen years all flowering plants and woodland shrubs are shaded out. When this happens, not only the flowers and shrubs are lost but the bird population is reduced in variety and numbers. Native woodland insects disappear too, the butterflies being a very conspicuous loss. Not until the trees approach maturity does some wildlife interest begin to return, but this hardly compensates for what is lost.

Figure 7.2 *The geology of the Greensand Ridge.*

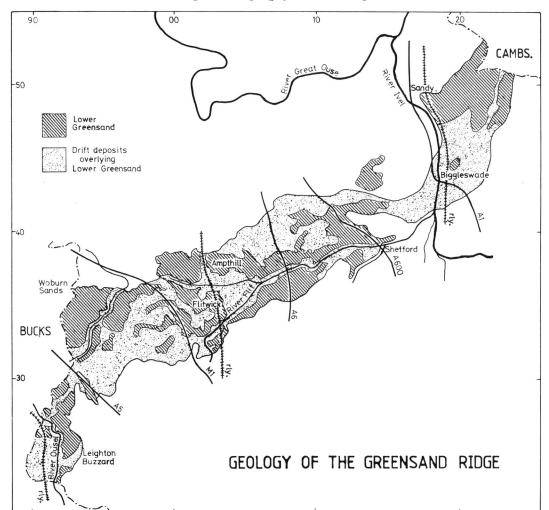

GEOLOGY OF THE GREENSAND RIDGE

Figure 7.3 *Heathland habitat. (Top) Cooper's Hill (Ampthill): extensive Heather with scattered Gorse and Birch; bare sand in the foreground with sparse Wavy Hair-grass. (TL 028375, September 1986). (Bottom) Old Scots Pines on Shire Oak Heath (Heath and Reach) (SP 917285, May 1985).* © B. S. Nau

Plate 11: *There is a vast display of springtime flowers in our woods before leaves appear on the trees and shade the plants beneath. By high summer, flowers and the insects attracted to them are to be found mainly in sunny glades and rides.* (*Top*) *May Bluebells en masse in Lowes Wood near Woburn* (May 1984). © D. G. Rands. (*Bottom*) *Primroses and Ground Ivy prefer partial shade and flower later in the season.*

© D. Tyler

The history of the sandy areas of the Ridge has been quite different from the clay. The most sandy areas were probably heath or heathy pasture until the late nineteenth century, and Sheep and Rabbits would probably have kept this close-grazed. In places there would have been purple drifts of Heather in late summer – at Heath and Reach (a significant place name!) there was Heather in quantities sufficient to be cropped as a fuel for brick-kilns. Now one must look hard to find the fragments of Heather which survive. There are a few small patches in and around Stockgrove Country Park. In other parts of the county there are remnants along the rides through plantations on Wavendon Heath (no longer an appropriate name!) and just a few plants in Maulden Wood. Only at Cooper's Hill (Ampthill) and Sandy Warren does Heather still survive in drifts – and even here not to be compared with more fortunate regions of Britain.

Heather and Heathland

In Bedfordshire the surviving heathland and its Heather is not the same habitat which covers so much of the damp upland regions of Britain – the Pennines, Dartmoor, the Welsh and Scottish moors; it is in fact the Southern English Heath that is exemplified so well in counties south of London, in Dorset, the New Forest and the Suffolk Brecklands. The Heather is usually interspersed with Wavy Hair-grass and Gorse; the latter, and Bracken, sometimes threaten the existence of the Heather – as also does the attractive but very invasive Birch tree.

Only the East Anglian Brecklands and the heaths of the North Norfolk Ridge are more northerly examples of Southern Heath than those in Bedfordshire.

The Heather forms a habitat which carries a particularly distinctive insect fauna, many of the species being found only where this plant grows. For instance there is a small green plant-bug called *Orthotylus ericetorum* which is found on its leaves and flowers in summer. Another, like the first with a Latin name indicating the family of its host plant (*Ericaceae*), is a predatory bug called *Nabis ericetorum*. It is commonly found in the thick, warm dry litter which builds up under large old Heather bushes. Here, too, is to be found a rich fauna of beetles, especially ground-beetles and hibernating ladybirds, also many harvestmen and spiders. Brushing the Heather with an entomologist's sweep net often produces the Heather Beetle in large numbers (an ochre and black insect called *Lochmaea suturalis*), and the adults and young of an attractive brown and white leaf-hopper (*Ulopa reticulata*).

Amongst the Heather of Sandy Warren an interesting, if undistinguished, spider has been found. This is *Zelotes electus*, which is more usually found on coastal dunes. Two other dune animals found in the county are a large Ground Beetle, *Broscus cephalotes*, and the Archer's Dart

moth. The beetle has been found in recent years on the sand at Clophill and the moth in the vicinity of Stockgrove Park (Heath and Reach). Both are widespread in sandy coastal localities but very local inland.

Where the vegetation thins out to expose bare sand a warm day in spring or summer provides a fascinating pageant of insect life to anyone prepared to rest a while and emulate that great French observer and naturalist, Henri Fabre, who studied the intimate lives of some of the same insects we find on the Bedfordshire Greensand. Any small holes are worth a second look to see what emerges. In level ground one frequently sees the thumb-sized holes of the nocturnal black dung beetle, *Geotrupes* – whose remains figure so often in Fox pellets, and are often mistaken for Ground Beetles. The similar holes of bumblebees are often found in a bank or low 'cliff' where the sand has been eroded. Smaller holes in such sites, often clustered in groups, are inhabited by some of the more attractive of our solitary bees, such as *Andrena*. Then there are the holes of our many smaller wasps, attractive harmless insects which few people notice, even though they are found readily enough in bare sandy banks. You may be lucky and see one of the long, slender, solitary hunting-wasps urgently backing along, heedless of all obstacles, dragging a caterpillar towards a distant nest hole. The prey are 'drugged' before storage in the hole to provide fresh food for the wasp's larvae, when they hatch in due course.

More active and difficult to stalk are the tiger beetles. Only the large metallic-green *Cicindela campestris* is usually found in the county. These fly off when approached within a few yards but with patience it is possible to creep close enough to see their large rapacious jaws.

These warm sandy spots are also good places to see grasshoppers, especially the Mottled Grasshopper which is almost restricted to these sites in the county.

There are few more rewarding pastimes on a warm day than to sit quietly by such a sandy bank or track, though it is sad to reflect on how much we have lost of this habitat and the creatures which depend upon it.

Another form of heathland is grass-heath, now almost lost from the Greensand Ridge but, probably, once very widespread. This habitat has already been described in some detail in an earlier chapter (Chapter 4, 'Wildlife habitats').

New Heathlands

By contrast with the loss of ancient heath to forestry and agriculture, sand quarries have actually been a source of new 'heath' and so too have some of the cuttings made for roads and railways through the Greensand (Figure 7.5).

One of our best railways for such habitat is the now

Figure 7.4 *Characteristic insects of sandy places. (Top) The active metallic green Tiger Beetle* (Cicindela campestris), *is common in some bare sandy places.* © R. Revels. *(Bottom) The Mottled Grasshopper is almost confined to the Greensand Ridge.* © D G. Rands.

silver hairs, so that they have the shape and feel of a mouse's ear. The Hare's-foot Clover, less well named, has an abundance of pale pink clover-like flowers and is sometimes numerous too. The dark-blue Sheep's-bit, like a small scabious, and the true Goldenrod are specialities which may need a longer search.

The blue flowers of Harebell, diminutive red flowers of Sheep's Sorrel, and yellow of Bird's-foot-trefoil, named for its seed-pods, are colourful and common. This species of trefoil and the sorrel are doubly valued since the trefoil is the foodplant of the Common Blue butterfly while the sorrel hosts the larva of the Small Copper butterfly. Not surprisingly, this habitat is often rich in butterflies in summer as these species are joined by an abundance of grass feeders, Meadow Browns as well as Large, Small and Essex Skippers.

Gorse and Broom are a conspicuous feature of this habitat, attractive for their yellow flowers but also hosting a rich variety of insects. The Gorse has a feature of particular value to insects needing a dry, sheltered place to over-winter. It accumulates masses of fallen leaves in the crotches of its branches. These build up quite remarkably over a period of years and are much favoured by ladybirds. Clusters of dozens of Seven-spot Ladybirds can sometimes be found in winter.

The severe winters of 1981–82 and 1985–86 killed off the Gorse extensively in the county, especially on the M1 embankments. It is likely that road-salt spray was a contributory factor. Broom too suffered but to a lesser extent. However these are both vigorous plants and will soon recover from such setbacks.

The importance of temporary open sandy habitats to our many small bees and wasps is overlooked by most of us, who only know the Common Wasp, the Honey Bee and the conspicuous bumblebees. These smaller species were studied by the late Dr V. H. Chambers over many years, before and after the Second World War. In 1971 he wrote about the changes he had observed in the bee and wasp fauna of the county since 1930 and one could not do better than quote at length his words on some of his favourite sites along the Greensand Ridge where he studied his beloved Hymenoptera Aculeata, the bees and wasps:

The uncultivated areas of the lower greensand are *par excellence* localities for bees and wasps. Cooper's Hill, Ampthill, the conifers having been felled in the 1914–18 war and not replanted, was largely covered by heather, a minimum of bracken, extensive bramble and gorse, some young birch, an area of sandpits and heavily rabbit-infested. A characteristic

dismantled line from Sandy to Potton. The road verges are less extensive but the best are probably those of the A6, north and south of Clophill. Shorter lengths elsewhere can be very rewarding, as at Fox Corner (Heath and Reach) for instance.

Short sparse turf with a varied flora is a feature of these sites. But often there is added variety and interest provided by mosses and lichens. The pixy-cup lichens, *Cladonia*, are a particularly attractive feature when viewed in close-up. When fruiting they are tipped with scarlet fruiting-bodies. Sometimes there may also be a quite different type of lichen with broad seaweed-like lobes (thalli) called the Dog Lichen (*Peltigera*).

The dwarf stature of many of the plants means that, like the insects, they are best appreciated when observed right down at their level. Among the typical flowering plants of these sandy verges is the yellow-flowered Mouse-ear Hawkweed, which flattens its leaves to the ground to suppress competition. The leaves are covered with long

Figure 7.5 *Disused sandpit at Clophill, with Birch trees colonising the higher levels. Such sites provide habitat for a wide range of insects which favour warm, sandy places; a large ground-beetle of coastal sand-dunes* (Broscus cephalotes) *has colonised this site.* © V. W. Arnold

sand-wasp fauna (fifty species) nested at the edges of sandy paths, the vegetation providing the variety of insect prey. Broken bramble stems gave sites for five species of *Prosopis* bees, including the rare *P. cornuta*. The bee fauna was not as rich as elsewhere, the only Mining Bees being six *Andrena* (but characteristic species) and eight *Halictus*, and the only Nomad Bee was *Nomada lineola*. But it was one of the few sites for the maritime leaf-cutter bee and its curious inquiline *Coelioxys conoidea* [an 'inquiline' is a species which shares the home of another species (ed.)]. Today, with the spread of bracken, cultivation and the elimination of brambles, the fauna is severely affected. However, recent visits show that characteristic species survive: the heather bee *Colletes succincta*, with its pretty grey, pink and white inquiline, *Epeolus variegatus*; several Andrenas; *Ammophila sabulosa*, the large red-black sandwasp can still be seen searching for large moth caterpillars, and as elsewhere on the sand, the late solitary wasp *Mellinus arvensis* is conspicuously abundant. Probably owing to reduction of small insect prey, the many species of tiny sandwasps, including the spider-hunters, are no longer numerous on the banks. Up to 25 years ago 83 species of bees and wasps were known: erosion by public access may also be a reducing factor.

The heaths within Aspley Heath parish were never first rate

Figure 7.6 *The largest concentration of sandpits in the county is around Heath and Reach, and Leighton Buzzard. These provide much new habitat for wildlife.*

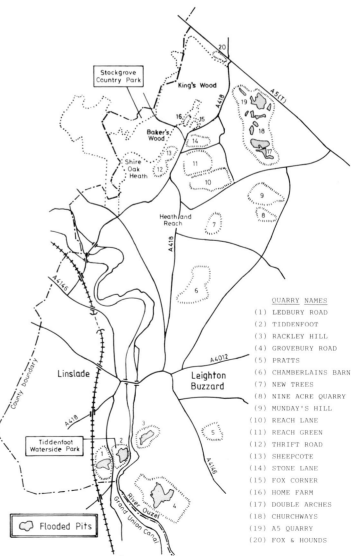

QUARRY NAMES
(1) LEDBURY ROAD
(2) TIDDENFOOT
(3) RACKLEY HILL
(4) GROVEBURY ROAD
(5) PRATTS
(6) CHAMBERLAINS BARN
(7) NEW TREES
(8) NINE ACRE QUARRY
(9) MUNDAY'S HILL
(10) REACH LANE
(11) REACH GREEN
(12) THRIFT ROAD
(13) SHEEPCOTE
(14) STONE LANE
(15) FOX CORNER
(16) HOME FARM
(17) DOUBLE ARCHES
(18) CHURCHWAYS
(19) A5 QUARRY
(20) FOX & HOUNDS

Figure 7.7 *Two species particularly associated with the Greensand Ridge: (Top) Hare's-foot Clover, a low growing plant with soft pink flowers, common on open sandy verges. (Bottom) The Hornet is not common in Bedfordshire, it is occasionally reported from sites on the Greensand Ridge.* © R. Revels

bee and wasp localities but I have records for seventy species. Planted-up in the late 18th century and last felled during the 1914–18 war, heather and huckleberry [= Bilberry (ed.)] spread rapidly: once in the mid thirties while collecting on the heath, I was told by estate constable Emerson that after the war he issued annually 200–300 permits for the locals to collect berries. The growth must have led to an increase in *Andrena lapponica*, a bee which forages only on *Vaccinium*, which I last recorded in 1949, and which is probably now extinct. Entirely as a result of the growth of the pines, planted in 1924–28, leading to elimination of heather, shading and erosion of nesting sites and disappearance of forage/prey, most of the recorded species appear to have gone or become greatly reduced in numbers. I still frequently visit the area: even *Ammophila sabulosa*, formerly numerous, I have not seen for several years; apart from *Mellinus*, only the specialised sand bee *Andrena barbilabris* flourishes, with its inquiline *Sphecodes pellucidus*. This is because, burrowing deeply in loose sand, it is not disturbed by human and horse traffic, and it has the ability to orientate foraging flights along the rides between the tall pines, enabling it to collect in distant hedgerows, as I have shown by pollen forage studies. Changes in the fauna of such habitats must be regarded as cyclic: no doubt increases in some species may follow present and future fellings.

It must be remembered that up to the 1939–45 war, farming was not prosperous: some marginal areas were not worth cultivating. Throughout the greensand were small corners of fields or woodland edges tumbled down to heath: I knew several in Clophill, Maulden, Sandy, Shefford and near Rushmere with unusual bee and wasp fauna. These have now gone and with them rare and beautiful insects such as the long-haired bee *Dasypoda hirtipes* and the largest and most striking of the Andrenas, *A. thoracica*. However I am sure that as new sandpits are opened and old exhausted in the Heath and Reach area, new habitats will be created for many of the species formerly found in the district. It would be excellent if an old pit could be managed as a special reserve but unfortunately this area is in demand for housing. Again, due I suspect to increased trampling, the paths leading to Bragenham over the heath near Bakers Wood no longer support colonies of *Cerceris* and other wasps, although colonies of the slave-making ant *Formica sanguinea* – the only locality in this part of England – still flourish. The opening by the County Council of the adjacent country park will undoubtedly lead to erosion, but it is hoped that further encroachment can be contained.

The Bedfordshire Naturalist **26,** pp. 52–54.

One can but echo Vic Chambers' hopes for a sandpit to be set aside as a nature reserve for those creatures and plants which form such a distinctive feature of open sandy places.

Marshes and Bogs of the Greensand

It might seem surprising to find wetlands on a sand ridge but where impermeable strata occur in the sand, marshes and bogs are to be found. In most cases their size is very small, making Greensand wetlands very fragile habitats (Table 7.1). Few Greensand marshes have retained the

Figure 7.8 *Flitwick Moor from the air (1969): the Moor is mainly 'woodland', some of the open water near the east side, adjacent to the light-coloured pasture, has since become overgrown by sedges and Bulrush.* © Beds, C. C.

Table 7.1 Some wetlands of the Greensand Ridge

MIRES (marshed, fens and bogs)					
Valley bottom		*Hill slope*		*Dammed stream*	
Flitwick Moor (pt)	045350 +++	Ampthill Park	025384 +	Eversholt Lakes (pt)	980324 +
Pennyfather's Moor	073370 +++	Broom	181427 ++	Southill Lake (pt)	145428 ++
Shefford Hardwicke	136393 ++	Cooper's Hill	025379 +	Wavendon Hth. Ponds	931337 ++
Sutton Fen	205475 ++	Eversholt	986317 +		
Westoning Moor	022325 ++	Haynes	070407 ++		
		Horsemoor Farm	935332 ++		
		Husborne Crawley	953353 ++		
		Lower Alders	130390 ++		
		Millbrook, village	013383 +		
		Millbrook, woods	006367 ++		
		Nares Gladley	908278 ++		
		Pulloxhill	055335 +		
		Stockgrove Country Park	919293 +		
		Washers Wood	994315 +		
		Westminster Pond	019383 +		

OPEN WATER					
Valley-bottom swamps		*Hill ponds*		*Lakes (dammed streams)*	
Flitwick Moor (pt)	045350 +++	Ampthill Park	025384 ++	Aspley Guise	946364 ++
		Aspley Heath	939347 ++	Battlesden Lake	956287 ++
		Cox Hill	177496 +	Eversholt Lakes (pt)	980324 ++
		Ireland	139412 +	Flitwick Manor Lake	031340 +++
		Maulden Church	059383 +	Shuttleworth Lakes	145445 +++
		Maulden Woods	064384 +	Southill Lake (pt)	145428 +++
		Milton Bryan	974300 +	Stockgrove/Rushmere	917290 +++
		Palmers Shrubs	983314 +	Tingrith Lakes	005328 +++
		Trilley Pond	074385 +	Woburn Park Lakes	960330 +++
		Pinfold Pond	940327 +	Woburn Park, south	970317 ++
		Segenhoe Manor	983362 +		
		Westminster Pond	020383 +		

Key: + = tiny, 0.5 Ha or less
      ++ = medium, 0.5 to 2 Ha
      +++ = large, over 2 Ha

richness of marshes elsewhere but their special interest is that they are usually fed by neutral or even acid soil water, making them suitable for plants and invertebrates which cannot survive in limy conditions. Elsewhere in the county most of our wetlands tend to be lime-rich.

A striking example is a tiny marsh at Ampthill. It straddles a trickle fed by muddy springs and is narrow enough to step across in places. Back in 1798 when Abbot published his *Flora Bedfordiensis* he referred to the Marsh Violet growing here. In the mid-1980s it is still to be seen flowering in the same spot! This is a violet which is rare in lowland Britain because it needs acid conditions.

The largest wetland site on the Greensand, with the richest fauna and flora, is Flitwick Moor (Figures 7.8 and 7.9). This important site has already been referred to in Chapter 4 ('Wildlife Habitats'). In many ways Flitwick Moor has much in common with Askham Bog near York, a site which was a Mecca for British entomologists before tree growth and drainage took their toll.

Figure 7.9 *Sphagnum moss in a boggy glade on Flitwick Moor in an area of old peat cuttings now becoming Birch woodland.* (TL 047354, September 1986)
© B. S. Nau

Sadly, despite the status of Flitwick Moor as a national Site of Special Scientific Interest, designated by the Nature Conservancy, landowners uncaring or ignorant of its value continue to destroy areas of it, raising the level by dumping spoil.

Flitwick Moor presents interesting contrasts. It owes its existence to thick peat deposits which are poorly drained. The peat is watered by springs, which are acid, and the River Flit, which is lime-rich (rising from the chalk in south Bedfordshire). This gives rise to an unusual complex of wetland habitats.

Those areas undisturbed by peat cutting are, ecologically speaking, fen, having a flora and fauna characteristic of lime-rich peat wetland. By contrast, the extensive disused peat cuttings are bog, having long since been leached of nutrients, so that they are now an acid habitat, where the flora is more typical of the moorlands of upland Britain – Common Cotton-grass, Wavy Hair-grass, Sphagnum and other mosses.

For its size this is one of the richest sites for mosses and liverworts in south-east England, with a total of 108 species recorded. It also holds some rarities: for six of the mosses and two of the liverworts this is the only site in the county, whilst many of the others are found only at a handful of places elsewhere in the county and Flitwick Moor is much the best site for these. Of particular interest is a curious white liverwort which grows underneath the *Sphagnum*, feeding on it as a saprophyte. The liverwort *Cryptothallus mirabilis* was overlooked in Britain until 1948 and was first recorded at Flitwick Moor in 1967; it seems to fluctuate in abundance.

A particular problem in trying to manage the site and preserve its special interest, is the prolific regeneration of Willow and Oak in the fen areas and Birch and Alder in the bog areas. This calls for a continuous programme of felling – which may look brutal to the uninformed visitor but is absolutely essential if the future value of the Moor is to be ensured. Already it has lost Marsh Violet, Bogbean, Bog Pimpernel, Round-leaved Sundew and Marsh Lousewort – among others.

The richness of the wildlife interest of Flitwick Moor was brought out strongly when the Bedfordshire Natural History Society analysed information from several hundred sites in the county for the County Council in 1980. The Moor rated highest of any site in the county; eleven of the Society's specialist wildlife recorders put it in their top group of sites. This was for such groups as flowering plants, mosses, fungi, moths, bugs, grasshoppers, hoverflies, Hymenoptera, birds, amphibians and water-life.

The flooded peat-workings at Flitwick Moor are now almost overgrown by emergent water plants and provide a breeding ground for Toads and Frogs which is unequalled in the county. Here too the Water Rail finds a home, its only regular breeding site in the county.

These swamps are dominated by sedges in most places but Bulrush has been an unwelcome intruder in some parts. A sedge of particular interest for its insect fauna is locally abundant in the old cuttings; this is the Bottle Sedge, which has formed a large bed in one area. Here we find our only colony of a wetland cricket called the Short-winged Conehead (Figure 7.10); also several county rarities among the plant bugs are found here as well as two rare water-surface bugs, living on the water amongst the sedge stems, *Gerris lateralis* a pond-skater, and *Hebrus ruficeps* a miniature water-cricket, only 1.5 mm long.

Where the old peat cuttings are boggy but not permanently flooded there are impressive stools formed by Greater Tussock-sedge. These grow to a metre or more in height amongst the Alder coppice near the Flitwick-Greenfield road. These boggy areas are notable too for ferns and fungi, and the drifts of Opposite-leaved Golden-saxifrage which are a feature in spring. The latter is a comparatively recent arrival.

One of these fungi is particularly associated with Alder and when first found here was only the second British record. Its name is *Russula pumila* (Figure 7.10); it has a purplish cap and the stem dries to black, resembling a stick of charcoal. There are also two milk-cap species here which are uncommon in the county, *Lactarius cyathula* and *Lactarius obscuratus*, and several small brown species of the genus *Haworia* which are all associated with Alder.

The Moor has two mosses which are quite recent additions to the British flora; both probably originate from the southern hemisphere. *Orthodontium lineare* appeared in Britain in 1920, in Bedfordshire in 1947 and Flitwick Moor in 1958. Now it is very common there, being found particularly on peaty ground and rotting wood. The other species, *Campylopus introflexus*, appeared in Britain in 1941 and in Bedfordshire, at Flitwick Moor, in 1966. This too has rapidly become established, colonising bare peat and burnt ground, among other habitats. This moss is also now established, among other sites, at Sandy Warren and Rowney Warren and in both places it has spread rapidly.

The zonation of the Moor is very nicely demonstrated by the footpath which traverses the Moor north to south, from the car-park to the meadow. At the northern end of the path old cuttings have evolved into dry Oak-Birch woodland, and it is easy to miss the signs of their history as peat-cuttings. Further south, the Oak has not yet become established and it is Birch that flourishes on the peat ridges. These ridges are separated by water-logged depressions filled by mosses and Common Cottongrass. Continuing south, water is more extensive and colonised by Common Reed, with *Sphagnum* around its roots. Then, south of the footbridge over the stream are the most recent cuttings. These are deeply flooded and still have areas of open water, now being colonised by dense swamps of

Figure 7.10 *Two specialities of Flitwick Moor: (Top) Short-winged Conehead: this wetland bush-cricket exists at a single colony in the county, in a sedge swamp on Flitwick Moor.* © D. G. Rands. *(Bottom) A rare fungus, Russula pumila.*
© A. R. Outen

Table 7.2 Characteristic vegetation zones of Flitwick Moor

'Recent' Peat-cuttings	
Flooded	Bulrush
	Bottle Sedge
	Lesser Pond-sedge
Wet	Soft Rush
	Lesser Pond-sedge
	Greater Tussock-sedge
	Opposite-leaved Golden-saxifrage
Ridges	Heath Bedstraw
	Tormentil
	Purple Moor-grass
	Alder
	Downy Birch
	Goat Willow
'Old' Peat-cuttings	
Flooded (open)	Common Reed
	Sphagnum mosses
Flooded (shaded)	Common Cottongrass
	Moss species
Ridges	Downy Birch
	Pedunculate Oak
	Wavy Hair-grass
	Broad Buckler-fern
	Narrow Buckler-fern
Undug Fen	
Ungrazed	Meadowsweet
	Butterbur
	Great Willowherb
	Wild Angelica
	Goat Willow
	Pedunculate Oak
Grazed	Tufted Hair-grass
	Reed Sweet-grass (wet depressions)

sedges (Plate 12). Table 7.2 summarises characteristic vegetation zones of the Moor.

This variety of habitats is reflected in the variety of bird life. Mallard and Teal fly in to feed, Woodcock frequent the woodland, Sedge Warblers and Willow Warblers abound in summer. In winter, Siskins and Redpolls feed on the cones of the abundant Alders. Kingfishers feed along the waterways throughout the year.

Woodland and Hedgerows of the Greensand Ridge

Historically the many woods scattered along the Ridge fall into two groups. First those which were heath or sheep walks in historic times. These have mostly been planted with pines, firs or larch during the last hundred years or so. The second and much more interesting group to the naturalist are those which have always been woodland, in some form or other. These are relics of the primaeval forest formed after the Ice Age. Because of this continuity a rich and varied fauna and flora has become established in these woods.

The Woods

One might expect that the woods perched on the Greensand Ridge would be rather alike but this is not the case. They differ in a number of ways. Some are relics of primaeval forest and some are relatively recent plantations on old heath or sheep walks. Some are on the clay cap, some on sand, and some specially interesting woods are partly on clay and partly on sand. The aspect is another variable feature: Maulden Wood and Kings Wood (Heath and Reach) face south; Wilstead Wood and Kings Wood (Houghton Conquest) face north; Potton Wood sits high on a more-or-less level plateau.

Wetness is another variable feature. The clay woods on the crest of the Ridge are often poorly drained, so that the

Plate 12: *Flitwick Moor provides habitats unique in the county and is the home of many unusual species of plants and animals. (Bottom) Well marked zoning of swamp vegetation – Bulrush in the centre, and Bottle-sedge, centre left, merging into willow and Alder carr in flooded peat workings. (May 1981)* © B. S. Nau.
(Top) A drift of Opposite-leaved Golden-saxifrage in a boggy depression shaded by Alders.
© R. Revels

Figure 7.11 *Two faces of Maulden Woods, as typical of the Greensand Ridge, old broad-leaf woodland on clay and modern conifer plantation on sand. (Top) The main east-west ride runs through the most ancient part of the wood, on the wet Boulder Clay, it is bordered by verges rich in flowers and insect life and by a varied 'hedge' of shrubs and broad-leaf trees which conceal the conifer plantations beyond.* © A. J. Martin *(Bottom) Scots Pines on the sand, planted between the wars; the presence of Elder bushes and Common Nettle under the trees are signs of the enrichment of the soil during its previous use as a poultry farm.*

© S. C. Nau

resulting flora and fauna have much in common with those of marshland – Marsh Thistle, extensive growths of Pendulous Sedge and Tufted Hair-grass, and frequent clumps of rushes. This is well shown in Maulden Wood and Potton Wood.

The woods on sand are mostly 'secondary' woodland, that is, they are on land once cleared for farming but replanted with conifers during the last century or so. The most extensive are at Aspley Heath and Rowney Warren. A rare exception to this picture is Baker's Wood (Heath and Reach) which is an old Oak wood on the sand. This wood still shows signs of coppicing in former times, clusters of trunks rising from a common base. It is also remarkable amongst old coppiced woodland in the county for the lack of shrub layer beneath the standards.

Since the Second World War, when much of the large timber was felled in our deciduous woods, replanting has been largely with conifers, even on clay soils. The tree most widely planted was Corsican Pine, which has longer needles than the Scots Pine and lacks the pink-tinged bark. Many of these woods still look superficially like Oak-Ash woods from a distance, but on closer inspection they are found to contain conifer plantations. However, where there are broad rides much of the original flora and fauna may hang on and the wood can still be surprisingly rich.

The woods on the Greensand Ridge are important for many of the county's more interesting bird species. All three woodpeckers are to be found, and our populations of Nuthatches and Tree Pipits are largely confined to Greensand woods. Here too Woodcock are more frequent than elsewhere, whilst Lady Amherst's Pheasant is more common here than anywhere else in Britain. Our very small breeding populations of Redstart and Wood Warbler are restricted to these woods, which provide the rather specialised habitats required by these birds.

A good example of a Greensand wood is Maulden Wood, which was extensively studied by the Bedfordshire Natural History Society during the 1970s (Figure 7.11). A more extreme example, not on the Ridge, is Dedmansey Wood on the Clay-with-Flints at Studham; here the narrow fringe of shrubs and deciduous trees bordering the rides is responsible for almost all its surviving wildlife interest. Maulden Wood is particularly varied since part is on a clay plateau and is very wet; part is on clay-covered slopes with a southerly aspect and is better drained but still lime-rich; and the lower slopes are on sand which is very well drained and leached of nutrients.

The clay areas of this wood have a continuous history as woodland but much of the sandy part was only planted in the 1930s. Changing planting policies for the wood have further added to the variety; almost every compartment is different. There are Scots and Corsican Pine, European Larch, Norway Spruce, Lawson's Cypress, Beech, Pedunculate Oak and, on the steeper slopes of the sand, Sweet Chestnut. The age of the plantings is also very varied, producing a wide range of tree age-groups.

The BNHS studies show how much newly replanted areas contribute to the variety – even if extensive clear felling is not a desirable feature from the long term viewpoint of the truly woodland fauna and flora.

Using live traps to study small mammals, investigators found one- to three-year-old plantations have a flourishing population of Harvest Mice as well as large numbers of Field Voles. In plantations reaching maturity, Wood Mice and Bank Voles predominated, while Pygmy Shrews and Common Shrews were less common.

Birds too benefit in the short term. A three-year-old plantation yielded thirty-four species of breeding bird in 1974. At this age a clear-felled area on clay has a lush, tall vegetation, rich in regenerating shrubs as well as grasses and herbaceous plants. It more closely resembles a field than a wood and many of the birds are actually field species; the Grasshopper Warbler finds these areas particularly attractive. In the first year or two, the Nightjar is attracted to cleared areas but as the tussocks of Tufted Hair-grass spread, a rampant grass on wet clay, the habitat quickly loses the essential bare ground and the Nightjars move on. During the mid 1970s it was a memorable experience to walk slowly along the main drive of Maulden Wood at dusk in June. Woodcock would be roding overhead as they patrolled their territories; Grasshopper Warblers and Nightjars would be churring, and in the grassy verge the occasional Glow-worm would be seen. Muntjac Deer too could be heard barking.

Among the larger mammals the Muntjac Deer, well established in the county, flourish amongst the regenerating shrubs of these replanted areas (Figure 7.12). In January 1975 a five hectare compartment yielded fifteen Muntjac, a surprisingly large population density. These deer are largely browsers and 'prune' leafy twigs of shrubs and regenerating hardwood stumps. This activity is of such an intensity that it must have a permanent impact on the regeneration of our native trees and shrubs.

In woods just across the Cambridgeshire border, Fallow Deer can be found and they have a similarly severe impact on attempts to manage woodland by coppicing. It would be an interesting study to assess the impact of the introduced Muntjac on its new home.

The clay in the upper parts of Maulden Wood permits ponds to be formed and these prove very popular with birds, and bird-watchers. Regular counts at two of these in 1974 gave forty-two species at one in the edge of Oak-Ash woodland, bordering pasture. Another in the middle of a forty-year-old Scots Pine plantation on the sand produced thirty-six – showing the attraction of water in a dry area. Goldcrests were a particular feature at this pond, whilst the other attracted more field species. In each case the Robin was the most recorded bird but the Bullfinch was not far behind.

The diversity of this wood is reflected in its flora and invertebrate life. The species lists of plants (387), butterflies (29), moths (353), bugs (192), molluscs (62) and hoverflies (71) are all exceptional. Partly this is because of the time devoted to their study here but, equally, it is a reflection of the site's intrinsic richness. For the bugs (Heteroptera), this site (including its non-woodland periphery) has probably the longest list of any in Britain, over 190 species.

Another wood which has been intensively studied is Hayley Wood, nearby in Cambridgeshire. Here the emphasis was on its historical evolution and vegetation. This wood most closely resembles our own Potton Wood, being on a boulder clay plateau. The interested naturalist will find O. Rackham's book on Hayley Wood fascinating reading. (*Hayley Wood: Its History and Ecology.* Cambridgeshire and Isle of Ely Naturalists' Trust, Cambridge, 1975.)

The subtleties of slight changes in drainage are reflected very sharply in the ground vegetation in Hayley

Figure 7.12 *A Muntjac Deer browsing in a clearing in Maulden Wood. This introduced deer is now common where scrub provides cover. Its 'bark' is a familiar sound of woodland in the county.* © D. G. Rands

Figure 7.13 *Spring flowers are a striking feature of woodland habitats: (Top) Wood Anemones are a common sight in damp open areas of Boulder Clay woodland; (Bottom) Oxlip: a species of damp Boulder Clay woodland, common in some Cambridgeshire woods but only found in Potton Wood in Bedfordshire.*

© R. Revels

Wood. Seven zones can be recognised, ranging from wettest to driest in order as follows:

Zone 1 This is very wet and is dominated by sedges, which almost completely cover the ground, except under heavy shade.

Zone 2 Dominated by Meadowsweet and Oxlip, this also contains some Wood Avens and Wood Anemone but the vegetation is more open, with bare ground visible.

Zone 3 Here Bluebell replaces Meadowsweet as the co-dominant species with Oxlip and the ground cover is almost total. This zone has many other plant species too, including Yellow Archangel and Bugle, violets, strawberries, Early-purple Orchid and Common Spotted-orchid, Lesser Celandine, and the straggling stems of Dewberry.

Zone 4 A dense mass of Bluebell takes over almost completely in this zone, producing a sheet of blue when it is in flower in late spring. Oxlip is almost squeezed out but the first signs of Dog's Mercury appear here. Some of the other Zone 3 species also occur here together with some Sanicle and Common Twayblade, an inconspicuous orchid.

Zone 5 Dog's Mercury is co-dominant with Bluebell here; together these squeeze out most other species.

Zone 5a Dog's Mercury dominates here but Bluebell still occurs here and there.

Zone 6 Dog's Mercury here achieves virtually total domination, forming a rather monotonous carpet of vegetation in this driest zone.

These zones correspond closely with the slope of the ground in Hayley Wood as this governs the dampness which is the main controlling factor. When drainage is improved by ditching, the vegetation evolves towards the later, drier zones with their more uniform and less interesting flora.

In our own clay woodlands similar zones and trends may be recognised, except that Oxlips are absent. The Oxlip is a Primula with a curiously local distribution in Britain, although it is widespread in Europe. In woods near the conjunction of Essex, Suffolk and Cambridgeshire it can be quite abundant, but we are at the edge of its range and to see it in Bedfordshire one must search very diligently in Potton Wood, where just a few survive under neglected coppice.

Maulden Wood too shows good examples of vegetation zoning. The main east-west drive through the clayey northern part of the wood follows the edge of a plateau, so that to the north of the drive there are the wetter zones,

1 and 2; and to the south of the drive, the drier zones. Bluebell and Dog's Mercury are correspondingly more abundant to the south whilst Pendulous Sedge, Soft Rush, Meadowsweet and Marsh Thistle are characteristic of areas to the north.

Except in the wettest zones Tufted Hair-grass flourishes for several years after a compartment is felled or thinned. Primroses or Wood Anemones may flourish for a season or two but the hair-grass and a few other vigorous plants soon form continuous cover and suppress these spring flowers. The Tufted Hair-grass is easily recognised by its long stiff leaves which form dense tussocks from which the delicate silver flower-heads extend.

In the southern section of Maulden Wood, on the sand, there are zone types not present in Hayley Wood. It is not easy to decide which are due to local soil features and which to historical land use, since the more level ground is also secondary woodland, only planted with trees between the wars. However, there is a striking difference between the Bracken-covered slopes, which form the older parts of the wood on the sand, and the mixture of Bramble, Broad Buckler-fern and Common Nettle found on more level ground in the newer part of the wood.

It is evident that the Brambles in the south of the wood are quite distinct from the Dewberry which is so characteristic of the clay in the northern section of the wood.

The local abundance of Nettle on the sand is an indicator of former farming activities in what is now woodland, flourishing where the soil has been enriched by nitrogen; usually it is accompanied by Elder. Even the fungi reflect the zoning in this part of the wood, the Stinkhorn being more conspicuous on the slopes than elsewhere on the sand, its evil-smelling abundance here constrasting sharply with its absence from the clay areas to the north. The Tufted Hair-grass, dominant on much of the clay, is replaced on the sand by its very distinctive relative Wavy Hair-grass, a much smaller, delicately attractive, grass.

The zoning of the vegetation in Maulden Wood is matched by that of the animal life, particularly noticeable with the butterflies. The sandy parts of the wood are almost a butterfly desert in comparison with the best zones of the clay, which attract both woodland and field species. In high summer, the main drive's verges are alive with butterflies, attracted by the sheltered warmth and a profusion of flowers, of which that noxious weed Creeping Thistle is, perversely, the most favoured. A dozen species may easily be seen in the course of a morning.

The moths of Maulden Wood have been studied quite intensively over the past ten years or so, with frequent moth-trapping sessions using mercury vapour lamps. This has been carried out at all seasons of the year; it is particularly interesting that there are still moths to be found even in the depths of winter. Thirteen species were recorded

Figure 7.14 *Two rarities of the ancient woods of the Greensand Ridge: (Top) Wood White: a scarce woodland butterfly,* © R. Revels *(Bottom) Lily-of-the-valley in King's Wood, Heath and Reach.* © E. G. Meadows

Table 7.3 Moths recorded in Maulden Wood during December–February 1975–76 and 1976–77

The Satellite	Early Moth
The Chestnut	Spring Usher
Oak Nycteoline	Dotted Border
The Herald	Mottled Umber
March Moth	Pale Brindled Beauty
Shoulder Stripe	Small Brindled Beauty
Winter Moth	

(Arnold, Martin and Rands, 1977, *The Bedfordshire Naturalist* **31**, pp 59–62)

during the period December to February over the two winters of the study. The species are listed in Table 7.3.

The damp clay areas of Maulden Wood are equally rewarding for the naturalist with an interest in other insects. The coleopterist will find a rich variety, including attractive longhorn beetles; the dipterist will find an exceptional variety of hoverflies – these are at their best early in the season; and the hemipterist will find plant-bugs in great variety, each species having its preferred host plant. The variety of plant feeding insects directly reflects the variety of plant species found in zones 1 to 4.

Amongst the other invertebrate groups the molluscs (snails and slugs) have been studied in some detail both in Bedfordshire and in the clay woods of adjoining Cambridgeshire.

As in some other groups there are 'indicator species' which are found only in ancient woodland and these turn up in the clay-cap woods of the Greensand Ridge. Maulden, for instance, has *Limax cinereoniger* – largest of British slugs, the attractive *Cochlodina laminata*, which has a glossy spindle-shaped shell and is found under damp logs, and *Phenacolimax major*, which is extremely local in Britain. The reader will find detailed accounts of the Mollusca of Boulder Clay woods in a series of papers in the *Journal of Conchology* (C. R. C. Paul 'The ecology of Mollusca in ancient woodland', Part 1 in Vol. **28**, No. 5, pp. 301–328; Parts 2 and 3 in Vol. **29**, No. 5, pp. 281–300).

Galls too have been studied in Maulden Wood (Figure 7.15); seventy kinds were found and this was certainly not a complete list. The causers of galls come from many different groups of organism; those in Maulden Wood are listed in Table 7.4. More details will be found in *The Bedfordshire Naturalist* (**34**, pp. 57–61).

Oak is the tree which has the greatest variety and abundance of galls. One of these is a recent invader of Britain which is now common in Bedfordshire; it forms the large

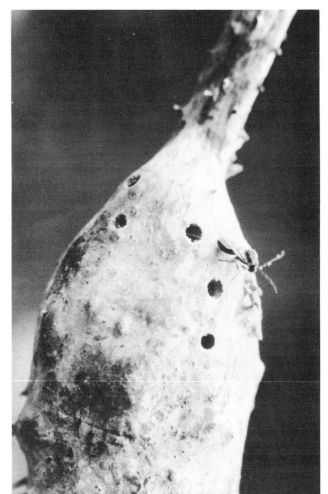

Figure 7.15 Many galls are caused by insect larvae living in the leaf or stem of a plant; the cause can be identified from the form of the gall and the species of host plant. (Top) A stem gall on bramble caused by the gall-wasp Diastrophus rubi. *(Bottom) A 'spiked pea-gall' on a rose, caused by the gall-wasp* Diplolepis nervosus.   © D. G. Rands

Table 7.4 Organisms causing galls in Maulden Wood

Gall causer	No. of species
Wasps and relatives	26
Flies	21
Mites	13
Bugs (Hemiptera)	7
Moths	1
Round-worms (Nematodes)	1
Fungi	1

irregular 'Knopper Gall' which apparently grows on the acorn, although actually attached to the inside of the cup.

We have dwelt at some length on the wildlife of Maulden Wood, not because it is unique or even the best example of the features mentioned, but because it has been studied more intensively than any other site in the county and there is easy public access. The naturalist will find equal fascination in other clay woods – on the North Bedfordshire Boulder Clay plateau or on the Clay-with-Flints of South Bedfordshire, as well as other clay-cap woods on the Greensand Ridge. Most will have some of the features mentioned here and others which are quite different. The challenge to the naturalist is to recognise these, picking out the really characteristic features and trying to explain these in terms of soil, climate, historical and other factors.

Hedgerows
In many ways the wildlife of the hedgerow resembles that of a woodland glade or the edge of a wood; a hedgerow is, as it were, an edge without a wood. True, there is more exposure to wind, and the humidity is lower and these factors account for the different habitat of the Primrose and the Bluebell in Bedfordshire; in other parts of the country Primroses and Bluebells often grow in profusion in hedgerows and open grassland, but in our county, in one of the driest parts of Britain, the low humidity drives both into the woods.

Some insects show similar behaviour and some of our most exciting butterflies are creatures of the woodland

Figure 7.16 *Some examples of the variety of wildlife on the Greensand Ridge. (Top right) Elephant Hawk-moth at Honeysuckle, this is one of the several hundred moths known from Maulden Woods.* © R. Revels. *(Bottom right) Wood Ant nest: this large ant is well established on the sand in Maulden Wood, having been introduced many years ago; this nest was on the centre reservation of the main A6 road.* (TL 076382, August 1981) © B. S. Nau. *(Top left) An earth-star, one of a group of strikingly shaped fungi only occasionally noticed in the county.* © D. G. Rands. *(Bottom left) A bright-green fungus* Chlorociboria aeruginascens. *Wood stained by this fungus was once used in the manufacture of ornamental inlaid 'Tonbridge Ware'.*
© B. S. Nau

glade including hairstreaks, most fritillaries (now lost from Bedfordshire), Wood White and Speckled Wood. Interestingly one of this group of butterflies, the Chequered Skipper, was first discovered in Britain in 1798 near Bedford at Clapham Park Wood, one of our Boulder Clay woods. This butterfly is not now found in the county, being confined to the west of Scotland.

The shrubs and trees of our county's hedgerows have been studied in some detail. 'A Hedgerow Survey', printed in *The Bedfordshire Naturalist* (**30,** pp. 39–52) in 1975, dealt with an area of the Ridge at Maulden and it was followed in 1977 by a county-wide survey. Interesting variations in the species found and in the richness of individual hedges show up in the different geological areas of the county, and even within the parish of Maulden. At Maulden it was found that hedges on the Boulder Clay cap of the Greensand Ridge are generally much richer than those on the sand itself. They may have fourteen or more species of shrubs and trees compared with only nine or so for hedges on the sand.

One reason for the richness of the clay hedges is that the Boulder Clay is lime-rich and so can support demanding 'chalk' shrubs, like Wayfaring-tree and Traveller's-joy. Then there are differences too between the history of land use on the light sandy soils and that of the wet, intractable clay. It is difficult to decide which of these effects is the more important.

Changes in land use continue to have an effect. An aerial photograph shows that an area on the clay just to the west of Maulden Wood had fourteen hedged fields in 1969; a 1976 aerial photograph shows that these have been reduced to just four large fields. This is a trend generally true of the Boulder Clay areas throughout Bedfordshire.

The Maulden fields mentioned above are interesting too for the way in which their boundaries match with those of Maulden Wood. (*See* also Chapter 4, 'Wildlife habitats'.) It seems very likely that these field hedges mark the original boundaries of ancient clearings made in a much larger wood. This must have been very early, as even the earliest maps show Maulden Wood to be very similar in size to the present wood. From the field boundaries it is easy to imagine how this ancient wood might have been progressively cleared from west to east. The resulting hedges would have been formed directly from the wood – perhaps with some extra planting to make them stock-proof.

In Conclusion

In this chapter we have described, albeit briefly, one of the most fascinating areas of the county, including heathland habitats, wetlands and woodlands. It has only been possible to hint at the riches of their natural history; much surely remains to be discovered. Nevertheless it is hoped that this will strike a chord with some readers and stimulate further field-studies of other sites.

Chapter 8

New Waters

Bedfordshire lacks natural lakes but as a result of the extraction of sand, gravel, chalk and clay over two hundred quarries have been created. The resulting pits have been flooded or partially flooded for differing lengths of time and, although in some cases valuable habitat has been destroyed, these new water areas have created new habitats which animals and plants have been able to colonise. Sewage lagoons, parkland lakes and, more recently, farm irrigation lagoons have also contributed to these man-made water areas. Finally, and not least, small ponds have become a common feature of gardens, particularly favoured by frogs, toads and dragonflies.

Although the extraction of sand and gravel has been carried out for centuries to provide materials for the building industry, the amount extracted before the end of the 19th century was small. In more recent times gravel was extracted at Felmersham, (now a nature reserve), during the Second World War to provide material for aerodrome runways at Thurleigh and Cranfield. The demand for sand and gravel depends primarily upon the level of activity in the house-building and road building sectors of the construction industry, and these are influenced by such factors as the mortgage rate and general level of public expenditure. As it is uneconomic to transport these materials for any great distance, the amount of sand and gravel extracted is very much determined by relatively local building projects, such as the construction of the M1 motorway, the creation of Milton Keynes and the building expansion taking place in Northampton. The creation of sand and gravel pits is directly related to these projects, and it is interesting that an important part of the natural history of the county is so greatly influenced by the country's economy.

Many of the disused pits have been filled with domestic and industrial refuse and a few have flooded naturally, but it is only very recently that it has become a deliberate policy on the part of the local authorities to flood disused pits to create public amenities. Thus, we have seen many new water areas created in Bedfordshire during the last fifty years, some of which were then destroyed by landfill projects whilst others have remained and grown in maturity. These changes have also been reflected by changes in flora and fauna, many of a transient nature but others more permanent.

The gravel quarries lie along the county's river systems, and it is here that many migrating wildfowl and waders pause to rest on their journey. Unfortunately, nearly all the flooded gravel and clay pits have steep sides and only a very narrow shore line, so that waders usually do not stop for long periods and are often seen passing over, sometimes circling several times before deciding to move on. Occasionally vertical faces have provided suitable places for Sand Martins to colonise.

Soon after the extraction of minerals has been completed the barren landscape almost resembles something from another planet – the word 'moonscape' is sometimes used to describe the appearance of clay pits during this stage. The extraction of minerals necessarily takes place over a number of years and so the pits, even while being worked, show a succession of plant communities.

Clay pits, chalk pits and, to a lesser extent, sand and gravel pits are slow to be colonised by aquatic and mar-

Figure 8.1 *Birdwatchers of the Bedfordshire Natural History Society studying waders at the Radwell Gravel-pits before the workings were flooded.* (TL 013580, August 1981) © B. S. Nau

ginal plants but colonisation, particularly of gravel pits, is often accelerated by the flooding of adjacent rivers, introducing aquatic fauna as well as seeds or plants. Nearby railway lines also serve to bring in new species. After the working of the pit has been completed the common weed species begin to colonise, usually plants which exist nearby. Such species as Colt's-foot, Common Orache, Great Willowherb, Common Ragwort and Silverweed appear along with Hogweed, Cut-leaved Cranesbill and White Campion, whilst Purple-loosestrife, Water Mint, Water-plantain, Trifid Bur-marigold and Common Fleabane may be seen by the side of pools or ditches. Often, when part of the pit has been used to tip domestic refuse, a

few alien garden plants have established themselves successfully for a few years.

Piles of earth and rubble left at these sites provide suitable habitat for Wheatears, Whinchats and occasionally Stonechats on passage, and all of these species have bred. Wheatears bred at Houghton Regis Chalk Pit in 1975 and a pair of Stonechats nested in the same area in 1977, the latter being only the second pair to breed in the county since Steele Elliott recorded one pair breeding in 1904. This was apparently not an uncommon breeding bird in Bedfordshire during the 19th century.

Gravel pit lakes tend to have a uniform depth, a regular outline and a lack of islands. Natural lakes evolve over

Figure 8.2 *Harrold-Odell Country Park: former gravel-pits now rich in wildlife interest, the main lagoon attracts large numbers of waterfowl and its gravel margins provide habitat for waders and Common Terns.* (SP 956571, June 1986)

© B. S. Nau

thousands of years and the accumulating organic sediment provides rich feeding conditions for chironomids (midges) and oligochaetes (aquatic annelid worms). In contrast the silty sediment of gravel pits is composed of clay particles and supports only a limited fauna. If there is a period of one or two years before the pit is flooded, this allows plants to develop which, when flooding takes place, provide an initial supply of nutrients in the water. This often results in a very large growth of Canadian Waterweed, which floats to the surface in vast rafts and can cover the whole of the water surface. After about three years the nutrients become exhausted and the weed declines to almost nothing. This has been seen at Harrold-Odell Country Park and Priory Country Park, for instance. The shore fauna tends to be minimal in the initial stages, and colonisation is made more difficult by the instability and erosion of banks, but in shallower areas Common Water-starwort, Rigid Hornwort and Amphibious Bistort are able to grow. Many of our pits are of recent origin and are still in a dynamic state, the plant communities undergoing rapid change both in population and diversity.

The most mature gravel pits are those comprising Felmersham Nature Reserve. These have a very rich aquatic flora, including an abundance of the yellow Bladderwort whose flower spikes rise in profusion from the surface in summer. This plant is notable for its hollow bladders and an ability to suck in and digest small animals and planktonic algae. Less conspicuous are the forked fronds of the floating liverwort *Riccia fluitans*, found in sheltered bays. Elsewhere in the county it is known only from Flitwick Moor.

The Early Stages

In the early stages water accumulates and is retained by the layer of clay underlying the gravel (Figure 8.1); shallow pools are also formed in clay and chalk pits. These pools attract waders on passage and areas of bare gravel or earth provide suitable breeding habitat for birds such as Little Ringed Plover, Ringed Plover, Redshank, Lapwings and Common Terns. Where the bottom of the pit is uneven partial flooding results in the formation of islands, where the inaccessibility has helped to protect these breeding sites from both animal and human predators.

This development of gravel pit lakes played an important part in establishing the Little Ringed Plover as a breeding bird in the county. A century ago the total number of records for Great Britain could be mentioned in one small paragraph, and it was unknown as a breeding bird in Britain until the first pair nested at Tring, Hertfordshire in 1938. In 1944 two pairs nested at Tring and another pair nested at a site in Middlesex. Since then it

has rapidly colonised this country and at least 467 pairs bred in 1973.

Before colonising Britain the Little Ringed Plover was an abundant breeding bird in parts of Europe, usually adopting such places as dried-up river beds, shingle islands, sandy wastelands or stony plains. A similar type of habitat was created in this country by the extraction of gravel, and the majority of breeding records in Britain have been at gravel pits. In Bedfordshire the first, but unsuccessful, breeding attempt was in 1951 when a nest containing three eggs was found at Cople Pits. Successful breeding took place in 1956 when two pairs bred. From that time onwards the species increased steadily until 1979, when eighteen pairs produced young at five sites (Figure 8.3). It will be appreciated that as no more than five sites have ever been involved during any single year, and since the habitat preferred for breeding is only present prior to and during the initial stages of colonisation by plants, the status of this species in the county is rather tenuous and liable to fluctuate. Indeed from 1981 to 1984 only one site was occupied and the number of successful breeding pairs fell to only one pair in 1982, as succession made previous breeding sites unsuitable.

A close relative of the Little Ringed Plover, the Ringed Plover normally nests on the coast but since the late fifties it has bred increasingly inland. The areas of sand and gravel temporarily exposed by the extraction of these minerals in many ways resemble its usual breeding habitat. Although it visited regularly on spring and autumn passage it was not until 1971 that the first pair of Ringed Plovers bred in Bedfordshire. The number of breeding pairs increased to eleven in 1979 – the year that the Little Ringed Plover attained its population peak (Figure 8.3). Presumably at this time the quarry conditions in the county were at their most suitable for the breeding of these two species.

As with the Little Ringed Plover the success of this bird as a breeding species rapidly declined, only one pair raising young in 1980; in subsequent years numbers varied between two and seven pairs.

Conditions suitable for Ringed and Little Ringed Plovers are also ideal for the Common Tern, but this species prefers to nest on islands in gravel or clay pits and it continues to occupy a site to a later stage of plant colonisation than the plovers. As with the two plovers, flooding of pits or the development of vegetation has been the reason for a fluctuating population (Figure 8.3). The first pair bred at Wyboston Lakes in 1963 and a small colony established itself at this site, with ten pairs breeding successfully in 1969. The flooding of this site wiped out the colony and no Common Terns bred in the county between 1975 and 1977. Breeding again took place at Wyboston in 1978, and the island created for birds at Barker's Lane (Priory Park, Bedford) provided the site for a small

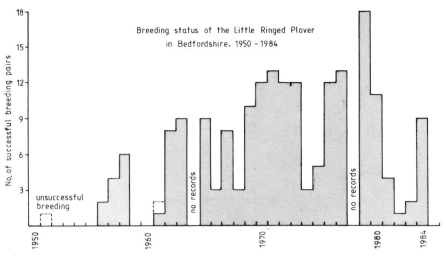

Breeding status of the Little Ringed Plover
in Bedfordshire. 1950 – 1984

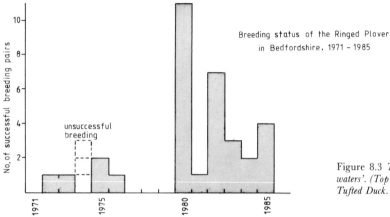

Breeding status of the Ringed Plover
in Bedfordshire. 1971 – 1985

Figure 8.3 *The history of the nesting in Bedfordshire of some birds of 'new waters'. (Top to bottom) Little Ringed Plover, Ringed Plover, Common Tern and Tufted Duck.*

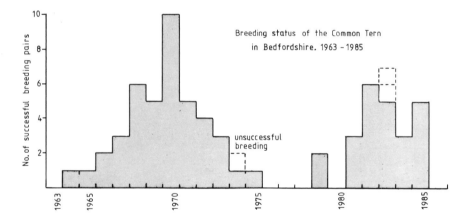

Breeding status of the Common Tern
in Bedfordshire. 1963 – 1985

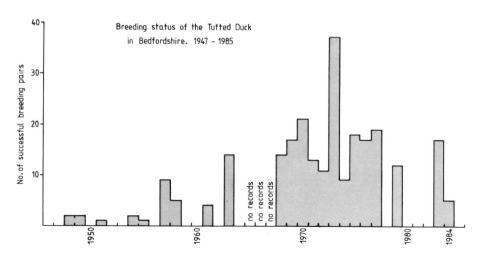

Breeding status of the Tufted Duck
in Bedfordshire. 1947 – 1985

colony, with one pair in 1980 increasing to three successful pairs in 1982. Natural growth of vegetation and planting of willows and Alder prevented breeding from 1983 onwards. Single pairs bred at three other sites in 1983. Unless islands are kept free from vegetation, or rafts are specially provided on which terns can nest, it is unlikely that this species will be other than an opportunist breeder taking advantage of the gravel pit sites during the initial stage of their development and departing for new areas when they are flooded or when plant growth becomes too dense.

When the flooding of a pit begins, the shallow pools which usually exist in the very early stages join to form larger water-bodies and it is not long before Coot, Great Crested Grebes and Mute Swans take up residence. Tufted Duck and a few Pochard may move in to breed. Cormorants have also found flooded pits to their liking and are now present during nearly every month of the year. They are often seen perched on the buoys used for sailing activities.

Gravel pits usually fill relatively rapidly from nearby rivers or from ground water but clay pits, filled by rain water, may take several years. They are usually very deep and steep-sided, so that any vegetation is submerged and islands often completely disappear. As a result there is less cover for breeding birds and numbers of breeding warblers, Great Crested Grebes, Mute Swans and Coot often decline. Most clay-pit lakes are too deep to allow the growth of aquatic vegetation; water animals thus decrease and this further discourages the breeding of diving ducks.

Plants such as Broad-leaved Dock, Teasel, Common Nettle, Great Willowherb, Colt's-foot, thistles and coarse grasses eventually take a hold in the disturbed ground surrounding the newly formed lake and also on any remaining islands. These are followed by brambles, willows and Hawthorn. This results in a gradual decline in breeding waders and terns but the additional nest cover is suitable for ducks. Pochard, Tufted Duck, Mallard, Shoveler and, more recently, Shelduck have all bred successfully.

The Great Grey Shrike, although not specific to the Hawthorn scrub and hedges around the lakes, certainly finds them attractive and many of the county recordings have been made there. Sometimes it only stays for a short time but occasionally it spends much of the winter with us. The county's only Woodchat Shrike was recorded along a Hawthorn hedge at what is now Priory Park in July and August 1972.

Dragonflies, Molluscs and Leeches

As the vegetation becomes established in and around the water, dragonflies colonise the site. The Broad-bodied Chaser is one of the earliest colonisers, with its less common relative, the Four-spotted Chaser, occurring later in the evolution of the habitat. As the site matures the abundant species through the summer are two damselflies, the colourful Common Blue and the Blue-tailed Damselfly. The Black-tailed Skimmer and nomadic Emperor Dragonfly are also to be seen occasionally in the earlier part of the summer. Later in the season three large hawkers are quite common and these are joined in high summer by the Common Darter. The commonest hawkers are the Migrant and the Southern Hawker, although the Brown Hawker is also conspicuous through summer and into autumn. The Azure Damselfly is widespread, although less numerous than the two blue damselflies mentioned above. Also widespread, but in rather modest numbers, is the Large Red Damselfly.

The Banded Demoiselle is a river species but does stray to flooded gravel pits. The same applies to the White-legged Damselfly, although this is much more local.

Among the less common species to be found on new waters are the Ruddy Darter, Emerald Damselfly and Red-eyed Damselfly, which have established colonies in some flooded quarries. It is interesting that the Scarce Chaser is not established in the county even though it is not infrequent a little further down the Ouse valley in Cambridgeshire.

As with the dragonflies, the colonisation of new waters by molluscs follows rapidly after the first plants become established. The speed of this process depends very much on the nature of the substrate; with sand or gravel the plants colonise very quickly, usually within the first year, and the molluscs arrive soon after; on clay or chalk the colonisation is much slower, taking, perhaps, several years. The first mollusc to arrive is almost always the wandering water-snail (*Lymnaea peregra*), either by crawling from a nearby colony or, more likely, by inadvertent transport by birds or mammals. Only in the most overgrown ponds is it likely to be absent, its place being taken by a tiny ramshorn snail *Armiger crista*, which may be present in countless thousands (Figure 8.4).

Figure 8.4 *This prettily sculpted water-snail* Armiger crista *is a pond species which flourishes late in the life-cycle of ponds, when leaves from trees accumulate and deoxygenate the water.* © D. Guntrip

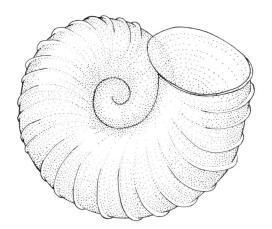

The large river mussels become established as the new water becomes more mature. Some species (e.g. *Unio pictorum* and *U. tumidus*) depend on the presence of fish, since in their early stages they attach themselves to the gills of fish. After several months they drop off to take up residence in the silty substrate.

A ramshorn snail, *Gyraulus laevis*, is normally uncommon but, in the early years of a new water, it may become established and build up very large populations for a short time. In subsequent years the population may undergo further cycles. This behaviour was noted at Wyboston Lakes, where the snail was common in the 1970s.

A different class of new water is provided by garden ponds (Figure 8.5). Snails are nearly always present, often being introduced on water plants. Two large and conspicuous species found in garden ponds are the Giant Ramshorn (*Planorbarius corneus*) – which has the flat spiral shell characteristic of ramshorns – and the Large Pond Snail (*Lymnaea stagnalis*) – which has a more conventionally shaped shell and is quite sharply pointed at its apex.

Leeches are, by general consent, one of the least attractive forms of water life. They colonise new waters as quickly as molluscs and so are often common in flooded quarries and garden ponds. Eight species are known from the county (Table 8.1), the commonest being *Erpobdella octoculata*, which, as its name implies, has eight eyes

(Figure 8.6). It is a voracious predator of small invertebrates, especially water-snails. Leeches lay their eggs in a small oval egg-case which is brown in colour and may be stuck to almost any solid object. The egg-cases are resistant to drought and the eggs may remain dormant for several years before hatching. Leeches are true segmented worms, belonging to the phylum Annelida.

Triclad flatworms resemble small flat leeches but are

Table 8.1   Leeches and Triclad flatworms of Bedfordshire

Leeches (Hirudinea)	Flatworms (Tricladida)
Piscicola geometra	*Dugesia polychroa*
Theromyzon tessulatum	*Planaria torva*
Hemiclepsis marginata	*Polycelis nigra*
Glossiphonia heteroclita	*P. tenuis*
G. complanata	*P. felina*
Helobdella stagnalis	*Dendrocoelum lacteum*
Haemopis sanguisuga	
Erpobdella octoculata	

not at all closely related to them, being members of the phylum Platyhelminthes. Although only a few millimetres long they are sometimes present in vast numbers in new waters, including garden ponds. In colour they vary from black, through shades of brown, to white depending on species. Six species are known from the county (Table 8.1).

Figure 8.5 *New waters on a different scale are provided by garden ponds, valuable habitat for Frogs, Toads and Smooth Newts. This one at Ickwell Green is a good example with a good range of water-plants and plenty of cover nearby for when Amphibians leave the water.*   © J. Dawson

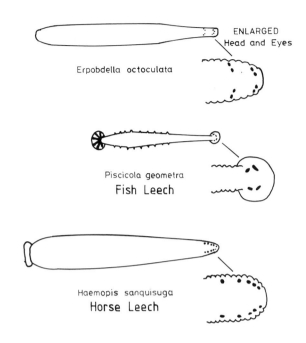

Erpobdella octoculata

ENLARGED
Head and Eyes

Piscicola geometra
Fish Leech

Haemopis sanquisuga
Horse Leech

Figure 8.6 *Leeches, showing the variety in number and arrangement of eyes.*

Gulls and Quarries

It must seem almost unbelievable to present-day bird-watchers in Bedfordshire that before 1950 gulls occurred in the county only as winter visitors and, apart from the Black-headed Gull, were quite rare.

By 1952 small parties of Black-headed Gulls were commonly reported during the winter months and it was thought that these were commuting to the roost which had become established at Tring Reservoirs. Although breeding had been suspected, the first proved breeding occurred at Dunstable Sewage Works in 1955 when eleven nests containing eggs were found. During the 1960s between one hundred and two hundred pairs nested annually, although about five hundred pairs nested in 1968 and 1973. After a decline in the early '70s breeding pairs were back up to five hundred pairs by 1978, mainly concentrated in the Stewartby and Brogborough area. This change in the population reflects the ever-changing nature of the habitat as new suitable areas arise and established sites are flooded or filled. In fact, because of lack of habitat few gulls are breeding in the county at the present time.

Rubbish used to fill disused gravel pits was also an attraction to other gulls, and apart from Black-headed Gulls there was an associated increase in Herring and Common Gulls. From being a very uncommon species in 1952 numbers of Common Gulls increased and about four

hundred were seen at Streatley in 1954. By 1955 Henry Key noted in the annual report of the Bedfordshire Natural History Society that 'The Common Gull is a regular winter visitor and passage migrant to Bedfordshire and Hertfordshire, and in spring large numbers pass through on migration'.

Immediately after the extraction of clay the small islands which remained provided suitable conditions for both the Lesser Black-backed and the Herring Gull to breed. When this happened at Brogborough in 1968 three pairs of Lesser Black-backed Gulls nested. There was a gap of three years before the next pair nested, this time at Chimney Corner Clay Pit (Kempston Hardwick), and during the same year the first successful breeding of the Herring Gull took place at Brogborough. Two other pairs of Lesser Black-backed Gulls have nested, one at Vicarage Farm Pit (Stewartby) and the other at Brogborough in 1973. In 1976 the pit at Brogborough was flooded, submerging the islands and thus eliminating these possible nesting sites. It is unlikely that any of these potential sites will remain for any length of time as the steep sides of these deep pits are dangerous and there is an obligation on the part of the owners to fill them with refuse or flood them and make use of them as public amenities.

Perhaps the event with the greatest influence on the number of gulls in the county during winter was the flooding of Stewartby Lake which commenced in 1955 and soon afterwards had attracted large numbers of roosting gulls. In 1958 about three thousand Black-headed Gulls roosted there. Nine years later, in 1964, the total number of gulls had increased to 22 200. This total included about three thousand Great Black-backed Gulls, Lesser Black-backed Gulls and Herring Gulls; most of the rest were Black-headed Gulls. The count in 1983, showed that the number of Black-headed Gulls had further increased to about 27 000.

Waders on Passage

The river systems with associated water areas provide resting places for waders as they make their way north-wards to their summer breeding grounds and again as they move south later in summer and autumn. The gravel, clay and chalk pits during their early stages of development are ideal stopping places for these birds, but this has not always been so. The most rapid development of these sites took place during the 1950s and early 1960s but before this time the old-style sewage farms of Bedford (Figure 8.9) and Dunstable were a veritable Mecca for migrating waders.

The sludge lagoons provided rich feeding grounds and Bedford Sewage Works were also bordered by the flood meadows of the River Ouse which were an added attrac-tion. These were unfortunately drained in 1953 and more

Figure 8.7 *The excavation of clay in the Marston Vale has provided new aquatic habitats for birds especially for gulls to nest and for waterfowl to feed and rest. (Top) The Marston Vale from Brogborough Picnic Site; with Brogborough Lake, a former clay-pit, in the foreground and the chimneys of Stewartby brickworks in the distance. (SP 967390, June 1986)* © B. S. Nau. *(Centre) Stewartby Lake in the early 1950s before it was fully flooded. Islands in this and other nearby clay-pits provided safe nest-sites for gulls from the late 1950s until the mid-1970s. (Bottom left) Black-headed Gull on its nest in a clay-pit at Stewartby.*

© H. A. S. Key

advanced methods of treating sewage have resulted in a decline in the number and extent of sewage lagoons. Some sewage lagoons still exist but have fallen into disuse and the subsequent colonisation by plants has also made these areas less attractive to waders. Nevertheless suitable areas do exist at some sewage works, gravel, clay and chalk pits, and a wide variety of waders are still attracted to them. In particular, effluent lagoons at Dunstable sewage purification works have attracted many interesting species over the years.

Spring passage begins with Redshanks passing through in February and early March, with the main passage of Ringed Plover, Little Ringed Plover and Dunlin taking place soon afterwards (Figure 8.10). Green Sandpipers arrive commonly during the first half of April along with more Dunlin; by the second half of the month Curlew and a few Spotted Redshanks are seen; and in early May Whimbrel usually pass through, with more Spotted Redshank and the main passage of Common Sandpiper and a few Turnstones. Less regular species which have been recorded in spring include Oystercatcher, Grey Plover, Sanderling, Black-tailed Godwit, Bar-tailed Godwit, Wood Sandpiper and Knot.

The return passage begins as early as July with Redshank, Green and Common Sandpipers. These birds continue to pass through during August and are joined by Ruff, Greenshank, Wood Sandpiper, Whimbrel and Spotted Redshank, and even the occasional Little Stint. Passage continues through into September but by the end of the month has faded to a trickle, only Dunlin, Ruff and a few Green Sandpipers being seen fairly regularly to the end of the year.

With the flooding or filling of quarries and the modernisation of sewage works the county now lacks a large area suitable for attracting waders. The potential for such a site was clearly illustrated in 1981 when a flooded gravel pit at Radwell was temporarily drained during the autumn, providing ideal conditions at a time which co incided with the peak migration of waders. During a six-week period no less than twenty-two species of waders were recorded. These included

Oystercatcher	one on 9 August
Ringed Plover	maximum twenty on 15 August
Grey Plover	one on 8 August
Sanderling	one on 1 August and one on 20 September
Little Stint	five on 13 September, three on 14 September, one on 15 September
Curlew Sandpiper	one on 4 September
Dunlin	maximum of nine on 23 August
Ruff	maximum of twenty on 9 August

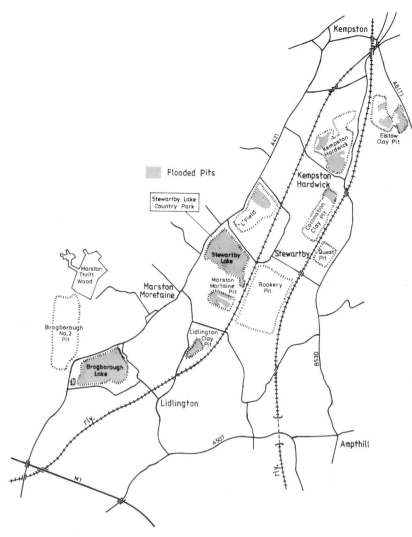

Figure 8.8 *The clay-pits of the Marston Vale as they are today.*

Whimbrel	one on 10 August
Curlew	maximum of sixteen on 23 August
Spotted Redshank	one on 15 and 23 August
Greenshank	eleven plus on 23 August
Green Sandpiper	maximum of seven on 12 August
Wood Sandpiper	maximum of four on 15 August
Common Sandpiper	maximum of sixteen on 11 August
Turnstone	one on 29 July and 9 August

This episode not only gives an indication of the number and variety of waders that pass over the county during autumn migration but also what might happen if a suitable site were set aside in the county and managed for the purpose of providing a stopping place for waders on passage.

Figure 8.9 *Typical habitat provided by traditional sewage farms, so attractive to waders. These were modernised during the 1950s and 1960s. This is Bedford Sewage Farm in the 1950s.*
© H. A. S. Key

Figure 8.10 *The seasonal occurrence of waders which may be seen in Bedfordshire more or less regularly. (Based on data of B. Nightingale and P. Smith in* The Bedfordshire Naturalist, **36**.)

	Jan	Feb	Mar	Apr	May	Jun	Jul	Aug	Sep	Oct	Nov	Dec
OYSTERCATCHER												
Lt. RINGED PLOVER												
RINGED PLOVER												
GOLDEN PLOVER												
GREY PLOVER												
LAPWING												
KNOT												
SANDERLING												
LITTLE STINT												
CURLEW SANDPIPER												
DUNLIN												
RUFF												
JACK SNIPE												
SNIPE												
WOODCOCK												
BLACK-TAILED GODWIT												
BAR-TAILED GODWIT												
WHIMBREL												
CURLEW												
SPOTTED REDSHANK												
REDSHANK												
GREENSHANK												
GREEN SANDPIPER												
WOOD SANDPIPER												
COMMON SANDPIPER												
TURNSTONE												

Legend: ▦ Breeding · ▭ Main passage or Peak numbers · —— Light passage or Normal numbers · - - - - very irregular

Along with the more regular waders several rarities have been seen. One of the delights of birdwatching is to be at a favourite site, after several months or even years of recording the common species there, when a real rarity turns up. What must it have been like to arrive at Houghton Regis Chalk Pit in the first week of July 1978 and find a Black-winged Stilt standing there? Only the person who actually saw it will ever know. Before 1983 only two Avocets had been recorded in the county, one at Harrold Gravel Pits in May 1963 and a second at Dunstable Sewage Works in March 1971. Since then a party of nineteen has been seen flying north east over Barker's Lane (Priory Park) in March 1983, two have been seen at South Mills Pit (Blunham) in April 1984, eight at Vicarage Farm Pit (Stewartby) in November 1984 and singles over Barkers Lane and at Stewartby Lake in January 1985. A Collared Pratincole spent six days at South Mills Pit in May 1983, attracting several hundred observers from all over the country who were able to watch it as it hawked insects over the shallow pool. The first county record of Temminck's Stint was of a single at Bedford Sewage Works in August 1952. Then, in 1978 one was seen at Harrold Gravel Pits in June and one turned up at Dunstable Sewage Works in August 1979. The fourth county record was of one at South Mills in May 1982.

American waders have been seen in increasing numbers since the mid-1950s, one of the earliest being a fine adult female Wilson's Phalarope at Stanford Pit for four days in May 1958 (Figure 8.12). This was not only the first county record but the second for Europe. The second occurrence of this species in the county was at Bedford Sewage Works in September 1972, where an individual remained for five days. In September 1961 two new birds, both from America, were found in the county, a Baird's Sandpiper spent twelve days at Wyboston Lakes and a Sharp-tailed Sandpiper found Bedford Sewage Works the nearest thing to paradise for just over a week. All five records of another American bird, the Pectoral Sandpiper, have been at sewage works in September and October. The first occurred at Dunstable Sewage Works in October 1956; the second found the same area to its liking between September and October 1973. One at Bedford Sewage Works which arrived in September 1978

Figure 8.12 *Wilson's Phalarope: a rare visitor from North America, one at a gravel-pit at Stanford in 1958 was only the second seen in Europe.*

© A. Harris

was joined by a second two weeks later, both remaining for a few days. The fifth record was of one bird which was present at Dunstable Sewage Works in October 1981.

The only county records of Purple Sandpiper and of Great Snipe were in May 1954 at Barker's Lane and at Stanford Pit in March 1967 respectively. There are several factors which have contributed to the increase in the number of records of some of these rare and difficult species in the county. Firstly, better field guides and equipment (for example, telescopes) have meant that observers are generally able to make correct identifications, and secondly, an enormous increase in interest in birdwatching has increased the number of observers.

Birds Through the Year

Springtime in Bedfordshire is eagerly awaited by all naturalists and for birdwatchers is perhaps the favourite time of the year. This is particularly so at the gravel, clay and chalk pits in the county for the increase in the level of activity is never so great. The catkins are beginning to form on the willows, Colt's-foot burst into flower, green buds are breaking on the Hawthorn and the air is full of bird song.

From mid-March the Meadow Pipits arrive, feeding actively amongst the short grass and bare areas surround-

Figure 8.11 *Some wading birds frequently seen in the county: Redshank, Little Ringed Plover, Dunlin and Ringed Plover.* © A. Harris

Plate 13: *The sewage purification works at Dunstable provides habitat for migrant waders. (Top left) Pectoral Sandpiper – a rare visitor to the county from North America. (Top right) Ringed Plover – formerly only a passage migrant, it began breeding in gravel-pits in the county in the 1970s, and (bottom) Common Sandpiper – a very regular spring and autumn visitor.*

© W. J. Drayton

ing the lakes. Sometimes over two hundred are seen together and a careful search may reveal the much rarer Water Pipit from the Continent and the British race known as the Rock Pipit. A few days later, the rather uncertain first attempts at song are heard from a migrant Chiffchaff. By the end of the month a few Sand Martins are seen and the first Wheatears pass through.

At the beginning of April a soft descending fluty song announces the first Willow Warbler and the Yellow Wagtails begin to arrive. Passage gathers pace towards the middle of April, with small parties of Swallows passing overhead whilst yet more Yellow Wagtails, Pied Wagtails and Meadow Pipits feed in the areas around the lakes. This is often a most spectacular sight and it is not uncommon to see fifty to eighty Yellow Wagtails with perhaps the occasional Yellow Wagtail of the blue-headed race or a White Wagtail amongst them. Nowhere was this better illustrated than at Barker's Lane (Priory Park) during the spring of 1983. In mid-April of that year eighty-five Yellow Wagtails, four Blue-headed Wagtails, thirty Pied Wagtails, three White Wagtails, over a hundred Meadow Pipits and a Water Pipit could be seen around the lake. The Yellow Wagtail has many races; in May 1966 a bird showing characteristics of the race called the Ashy-headed was seen and in the spring of 1984 the first of the Grey-headed race was recorded at Barker's Lane.

By the middle of April the first Sedge Warblers are singing from the willows and reeds, whilst over the waters newly arrived Common Terns give a dramatic display as they feed by plunge-diving into the water. In April 1980 as many as fifty-eight terns were feeding over Stewartby Lake with many Arctic Terns amongst them.

The Little Gull is a rare visitor to the county but this small blunt-winged gull with a jet-black head and dark underwing is most likely to be seen during the second half of April and the first week of May. Occasionally as many as ten have been seen together on spring passage and fifteen on the return passage, during August and September. Reed Warblers arrive towards the end of April and favour the shallow areas of lakes where Common Reed has established itself, although they will also breed in willows where these are close to the water. Both Battlesden Lake and Harrold-Odell Country Park have colonies which number around twenty breeding pairs whilst smaller colonies, of less than eight pairs, occur at some other sites. Garden Warblers which also arrive at this time take up residence in the lower close-growing willows and scrub whilst Blackcaps tend to favour the taller ones.

A bird which is not always associated with the spring,

Figure 8.13 The Sedge Warbler's song is a familiar sound beside flooded quarries in spring. © D. Kramer

the Common Scoter, may also turn up at this time. Over half of the records of this species in the county have been in April.

Passage continues into the first half of May and amongst the Common Terns a few Black Terns may be seen as they pause to feed before continuing their journey to the Low Countries of Europe. Normally no more than five are seen together but occasionally parties of more than ten can be observed flying low over the lakes, repeatedly dipping their bills into the water to pick up aquatic insects. The largest flocks have all occurred at Stewartby in May – with thirty-six birds in 1958, forty-plus in 1961, and about forty in 1966 all at Stewartby Lake, and twenty-four birds at Vicarage Farm Pit in 1970. May is also the best time of the year to keep an eye open for the Little Tern. Smaller and more vivacious than the other terns, it can hardly fail to be noticed as it plunges into the water to catch a small fish or perhaps take an insect in flight. The Arctic Tern is difficult to distinguish from the Common Tern unless very good views are obtained but this too can sometimes be seen on spring passage during late April or the first half of May, occasionally in quite large numbers. A very large passage took place at Blunham Lake at the end of April 1974 with seventeen and twenty-nine birds respectively on consecutive days; whilst in 1980 parties of forty at Dunstable Sewage Works in May and thirty-plus at Radwell Gravel Pit on the same day were quite exceptional. The most remarkable passage of this species, however, occurred in the spring of 1985. One or two birds appeared towards the end of April and then about 140 arrived at Stewartby Lake. This was followed by 126 at Priory Park with smaller numbers during the first half of May. Sandwich Terns have been seen during this period and in May 1961 the first White-winged Black Tern for the county spent two days at Stewartby Lake.

The Garganey is sometimes seen during this period, showing a preference in spring for the shallower waters of

sewage lagoons or those gravel pit lakes such as Girtford Pit which have marginal vegetation. When returning in autumn it may turn up at the larger more open waters.

During May and June these sites are busy with the breeding activities of many different birds but the amount of song gradually decreases as the adults spend more of their time searching for food to feed their hungry young. By July the young birds are very susceptible to predation and remain silent, hidden deep amongst the vegetation, making them very difficult to see. However, the ducklings of Mallard and Tufted Duck seem oblivious to the dangers which lurk below. The relatively warm water and the resulting abundance of food in these lakes have provided excellent conditions for fish such as Pike, Common Bream, Chub, Tench, Roach and Rudd to flourish, and it is not unusual to see one of the larger specimens of Pike rise up and take one of the unsuspecting chicks.

Swifts, Swallows, House Martins and Sand Martins gather over the waters in fairly large numbers to feed on the emerging insects. The vertical faces which are formed by the extraction of sand and gravel provide attractive breeding sites for the Sand Martin. About eight hundred pairs nested at Double Arches Quarry (Heath and Reach) in 1965, over 260 at Harrold Gravel Pit in 1977, 350-plus at Radwell in 1982 and 120 pairs at Grovebury Farm Pit (Leighton Buzzard) in 1983. Smaller colonies have also occurred at Tingrith, Blunham, Clifton and Girtford. The number of breeding sites of this species in the county has varied due to some habitats being destroyed or disturbed whilst others have been created. Another important factor which has affected their numbers has been the Sahelian drought in Africa, in the region bordering the southern edge of the Sahara Desert. This caused a reduction of numbers in the spring of 1969 and an even greater population crash in 1984, the numbers being only 25 per cent of the previous year. A further reduction of 80 per cent occurred in 1985. During the late summer Sand Martins, Swallows and Yellow Wagtails form roosts in the reed beds and in September 1982 about two hundred Yellow Wagtails roosted at Harrold Gravel Pit.

By the end of May the downy cygnets of the Mute Swan take to the water and Tufted Duck chicks scurry behind their mothers. Cuckoos become very active during the first two weeks of June as the females seek the nests of the Sedge and Reed Warblers in which to lay their eggs.

The Little Tern may pass through on its return journey during the second half of June or July and the county's only Caspian Tern was seen at Harrold Gravel Pit in July 1976.

The many young frogs and toads about at this time attract post-breeding parties of the Grey Heron. These parties may contain ten or more birds, mainly immatures, but in 1983 a group of eighteen were feeding in a field bordering Barker's Lane. In June 1970 the county's only Night Heron was observed at former gravel pits, now the Felmersham Nature Reserve.

Migrants in Autumn

The return passage of waders commences and is well underway by August. Young Mallard, Tufted Duck and Shoveler find their wings and disperse to other lakes whilst the earliest Pochard and Wigeon arrive. Towards the end of the month the occasional Sandwich Tern may pass through on its return journey and it is worth keeping an eye open for the unusual. The second and third White-winged Black Terns for the county were both seen at Stewartby in August, one in 1967 and another in 1983. Another rarity, the Purple Heron, tends to favour the end of August and the first half of September in which to put in an appearance. One was seen at Felmersham in 1955, another at Wyboston in 1966 and a third at Luton Hoo Park in 1977.

Thistles, docks, Teasel, Fat-hen and many other plants colonizing the disturbed ground associated with quarries provide an abundance of seeds on which such species as Goldfinch, Greenfinch and Linnet feed, often in flocks of well over a hundred. Depending on when the seeds ripen these large flocks are most frequent from early August onwards and remain until the end of October.

Ospreys may appear in either spring or autumn. The first records since 1946 were in 1952, when two were present at Woburn Abbey and one in May at Southill Lake. Between 1953 and 1970 Ospreys were only recorded twice, (May 1960 and September 1967). Since then they have been seen more regularly on both spring (April/May) and autumn (September/October) passage. This increase in recent years reflects the success of the expanding population in Scotland.

Parties of Redwings and Fieldfares begin to arrive from Scandinavia during September and many are attracted to the harvest of haws on the Hawthorns around quarry lakes, which provide them with welcome food for the winter. On the water, the appearance of flocks of Pochard, Tufted Duck and Mallard tell us that winter is about to arrive. Winter is, above all, the season of the wildfowl – a subject which will be dealt with in detail later.

Shallow reedy margins which exist at some lakes provide suitable habitat for the secretive Water Rail. These spend the winter with us, being frequently seen during the first period of freezing conditions when they are forced into the open in their search for food. The Bearded Tit has turned up at Bedford Sewage Works, Stewartby Lake, Houghton Regis Chalk Pit and Brogborough Lake. A party of up to ten roosted at the latter in March 1983.

Almost any season may see gales and, in the train of these, exotic maritime species may appear in the county. The larger expanses of water in quarries are particularly attractive to these refugees. Storm Petrel, Leach's Petrel, Shag, Long-tailed Duck, Common Scoter, Eider, Great Skua, Gannet, Kittiwake, Guillemot and Razorbill have all turned up at lakes in the county, much to the surprise and delight of birdwatchers. In November 1983 a female Velvet Scoter was present at Chimney Corner Clay Pit and what was presumably the same bird was relocated at Brogborough in December. This was only the second county record, the first being as long ago as the winter of 1890/91. A Fulmar, which arrived at Houghton Regis Chalk Pit in May 1977, was the third record for the county, being previously recorded in October 1888 and November 1890.

Wildfowl

As a result of the increase in open water in Bedfordshire Mallard, Gadwall, Tufted Duck, Shoveler, Teal, Pochard and Shelduck have all bred in recent years. This new habitat has, however, not been equally suitable for all these species. Both Teal and Shoveler require shallow marshy areas, but these are not provided to any great extent by the flooding of quarries. The lack of gently sloping sides and the associated emergent water plants, which Pochard require, is the probable reason why only one or two pairs breed annually. The best year for Pochard was in 1967 when five pairs bred. The growth of dense vegetation around the lakes and on the islands has provided ideal habitat for Mallard and Tufted Duck. The Tufted Duck in particular has found these recent changes in habitat particularly favourable and as a result the breeding population has increased dramatically. Before 1955 only one or two pairs bred each year but by 1958 this had increased to nine and by 1973 thirty-seven pairs produced young. It is noticeable that of this total twenty pairs bred at Felmersham Gravel Pit – one of our most mature gravel pit lakes, excavated during the 1939–45 war and by 1973 having acquired a rich vegetation, providing cover for this species.

The increase in man-made water areas have also been an important factor contributing to the recovery of the Great Crested Grebe in the county. Little is known of its early history except that it was very rare. In the breeding season of 1965 adults were present on sixteen groups of waters and in 1975 a British Trust for Ornithology survey showed that this number had increased to twenty-four groups of waters – all of which were man-made.

Every winter large numbers of wildfowl such as Mallard, Teal, Pochard, Tufted Duck and Wigeon, with

Figure 8.14 *Gales at almost any time of year may strand sea-birds in the county; some which have appeared in the past are (top to bottom) Gannet, Kittiwake, Leach's Petrel, Storm Petrel, Guillemot and Razorbill.* © A. Harris

smaller numbers of Gadwall and Goldeneye, arrive from the continent to spend the winter with us. Usually the largest numbers coincide with the most severe winters. A few birds begin to arrive in September, but the main arrival does not normally take place until mid-October or early November.

Before 1955 there were very few habitats in the county capable of holding large numbers of wildfowl, and wintering flocks were mainly concentrated at Bedford Sewage Works, the parkland lake at Southill, Felmersham Gravel Pit and the clay pit at Kempston Hardwick. During the first winter period of 1946 Bedford Sewage Works alone held three hundred Mallard, five hundred Teal, one hundred and fifty Pochard, a hundred Wigeon and thirty Tufted Duck, but these were unusually high numbers for the county and doubtless were influenced by the attraction of the neighbouring flooded meadows which existed at that time. The increase in flooded pits which occurred during the late 1950s attracted more wintering wildfowl, and by 1961 1500 Mallard were estimated at Stewartby. Numbers of Pochard, Tufted Duck and Coot also increased during this period and both Pochard and Coot are now very common in winter. The flooded clay pit at Brogborough has been a particularly favoured site for these two species in recent years; during 1983 totals of 842 Pochard and 950 Coot were present and this further increased the following year when the wintering Coot population exceeded 1500.

It might be expected that changing agriculture would have an adverse effect on some of the grazing ducks such as Wigeon but there has not been any significant decline in this species. Many of the newly created water areas are bordered by fields which provide suitable feeding grounds.

One species which does appear to have declined to some extent is the Teal. This bird prefers flooded meadows and marshland during the early winter period, only moving to the larger open waters during the coldest months. Land drainage, which has been such a significant feature of modern agriculture, has removed most of this valuable habitat in the county and in consequence there has been some reduction in the Teal population. Most significant for Teal was the drainage of the flooded meadows around Bedford Sewage Works. Before this area was drained it held the main wintering population of Teal sometimes numbering about five hundred birds.

Prior to 1977 the Gadwall was a regular but fairly scarce winter visitor, with usually fewer than ten birds recorded annually in the whole county. Then in 1978 eighteen were recorded at Blunham, since when this has been the main stronghold of the species. Numbers rose steadily during the following years to 133 in November 1981. Other lakes in the county recorded increases but on a smaller scale. This increase has corresponded with an increase throughout Western Europe.

The status of the Shoveler was fairly stable up to the early 1970s, the annual total rarely exceeding ten. Since 1972 the number has increased, with parties of over seventy being seen fairly regularly since 1976, and the largest number being ninety-two at Dunstable Sewage Works in September 1981. Again, a similar increase has taken place in Western Europe but, as for Gadwall, the reason for this is unclear. It has been suggested that it is linked with climatic amelioration.

The occasional hard winter also has its effect on the wintering wildfowl. Birds normally associated with more northerly areas are forced further south and some of our common visitors arrive in larger numbers. During these periods such species as Red-throated, Black-throated and Great Northern Divers, Red-necked, Slavonian and Black-necked Grebes, Smew, Goosander and Red-breasted Merganser have been seen. The gravel pit lakes are susceptible to freezing over, being relatively shallow, as the gravel beds in the county are only about three to four metres deep. The clay pit lakes are much deeper, sometimes as much as twenty-five to thirty metres and are thus the last to be frozen. In severe winters they provide the only areas of open water in the county, apart from the rivers, and at such times waterbirds are forced to move from the ice-bound gravel pits and congregate in large numbers at the clay pits of Stewartby, Brogborough and Millbrook. The effects are more noticeable when hard weather in the north of Britain is associated with similar conditions in Western Europe. An easterly wind also helps the birds fleeing these conditions to reach Britain. Such conditions occurred together during January and February 1985, when it was possible to see at Stewartby Lake a Black-throated Diver, two Red-necked Grebes, a Black-necked Grebe, three Bewick's Swans, a Scaup, ten Pintail, six Smew, thirty-six Goosander, four Red-breasted Mergansers, ten Ruddy Ducks and two Glaucous Gulls, whilst a Slavonian Grebe was at nearby Elstow Clay Pit.

Introduced Birds

Over the years several species of wildfowl have established themselves in the wild after escaping from ornamental collections. In this way Bedfordshire has gained the Canada Goose, Greylag Goose, Ruddy Duck and Mandarin (Figures 8.15 and 8.16). The man-made lakes formed by mineral extraction have provided habitats where these species have been able to establish themselves either as breeding birds or as regular visitors.

In the case of the Canada Goose, the first record of this species in Bedfordshire was of a party of ten flying over Elstow in 1949. There were only occasional records during the next twenty-two years. In 1967 a party of

Figure 8.15 *Two species of geese have become established breeding species in the county, the populations having built up from birds which escaped from wildfowl collections. (Top) A family party of Canada Geese on a lake at Wrest Park, Silsoe.* © Mary Sheridan. *(Bottom) Greylag Geese grazing on the banks of the former gravel-pits at Harrold-Odell Country Park.* © B. S. Nau

eighteen at Wyboston Lakes was considered to be large. In 1971 the first pair bred, at Luton Hoo Park. By 1975 five pairs bred at five separate sites and the species was considered to be 'well established' in the county. Numbers continued to increase rapidly, so much so that in 1979 the *Bedfordshire Bird Atlas* reported that

> By 1977 it was obvious that Canada Geese were becoming a pest in the north-east of the county causing concern to farmers and it may be necessary to impose some form of control on the rising population before the situation becomes out of hand.

During 1982 several large flocks were seen, the largest being ones of 234 at Barker's Lane in January, 357 at Brogborough Lake in September and 365 at Luton Hoo in October. The county population at this time was estimated to be up to a thousand birds and during the 1982 winter a cull of about two hundred took place. Thus in just twelve years we have seen this species increase from an occasional visitor to being considered by some to be a pest in the northern part of the county.

The Greylag Goose followed a similar pattern. Before

1966 it was recorded irregularly, only one or two at a time. Then in 1967 a party of about sixty was observed on the meadows near Bedford Sewage Works, and the first breeding in the county occurred in 1971 when two pairs reared young at South Mills Pit. After this the bird began to breed regularly and flocks increased rapidly. In 1980 124 young were reared successfully, mainly at gravel pits at Blunham, Harrold and Roxton, and the winter flock at Harrold rose to 150-plus. At least twenty pairs bred in 1982 producing 118 young and the flock in the Harrold/ Radwell area increased to a maximum of 201. By 1983 between 250 and 300 were present at Harrold, 187 at Radwell and 205 at Turvey.

The Ruddy Duck is a more recent introduction to Britain's avifauna, the first individuals being brought to Slimbridge in 1948. Since that time many have escaped, particularly between 1956 and 1963, and it has established itself as a British breeding bird. It was accepted onto the British list in 1971.

It reached Bedfordshire in December 1980 when a female was seen at Barker's Lane (Priory Park). Eight were released at Blunham during 1981 and during that and subsequent years one or two have been seen at gravel or clay pit lakes in most months of the year. The first breeding activity took place in 1983, when two pairs remained throughout the breeding season and display took place. Numbers of this species, however, have

remained low, the highest number recorded being ten at Stewartby Lake during the early cold spell in January 1985. The Ruddy Duck may increase as a breeding species within the county when more marginal vegetation is established around some of the gravel or clay pit lakes, most being in an early stage of development in this respect.

Little is known about the early history of the Mandarin in the county. It was introduced into Britain as an ornamental wildfowl in the early 18th century, and about three hundred were at Woburn around 1900. This population had decreased by half by the end of the First World War, and was reduced by half again by the end of the Second World War. As it was an introduced species little interest was shown in the Mandarin's decline by ornithologists in the county until 1971, when it was accepted onto the British List. Self-supporting feral populations were established by this time.

The first published county record in recent years was in September 1967 at Battlesden Lake. One or two pairs have bred fairly regularly since the first pair bred on the canal at Linslade in 1973. A wintering population of about twenty has been observed at Woburn during recent years.

As this species prefers to nest in holes in trees, particularly oak, the most likely sites are where well-established broad-leaved trees occur near shallow lakes. This habitat

Figure 8.16 *Ruddy Duck (left) and Mandarin Duck (right) are two exotic species of duck which now breed in the county, the original stock escaped from captivity.*
© A. Harris

occurs to a small extent around some parkland lakes but it is unlikely that Mandarin will breed around most of the gravel or clay pit lakes for some years unless suitable nest boxes are provided. However, it has been known to breed well away from water, and as the British population is increasing steadily it is possible that it may also increase in Bedfordshire. This would not be as harmful as some other introduced species have been, since, nesting in holes, it would not compete with any other British ducks. (Though it could perhaps affect the small breeding population of Goldeneye in Scotland.) Not only is it a most attractive bird but it is becoming very rare in Eastern Asia and China – so much so that the present British population, established by the introduction of this species as an ornamental wildfowl, is now thought to rival the rest of the world's declining population. Perhaps the best measure of the Bedfordshire population is the small flock which collects at Woburn in the winter months. In January 1984 this flock numbered twenty, increasing to thirty-five in 1985.

Other species such as Bean Goose, Brent Goose, Barnacle Goose, Snow Goose, Egyptian Goose, Ruddy Shelduck, Ferruginous Duck, Ring-necked Duck, Red-crested Pochard and Wood Duck have all been seen in the county, but as all are regularly kept in wildfowl collections it is difficult to know whether individuals are escapes or true wild birds. The problem is even more difficult to resolve when larger numbers than usual are recorded elsewhere in the country.

Recreation Competing with Wildlife

The creation of new waters has provided habitats suitable for colonisation by plants and animals and amongst the latter, the human species has not been slow to react.

The increase in the number of these lakes has occurred at a time when the demand for water space has risen rapidly because of the increase in popularity and number of water-based recreational activities. The larger lakes provide suitable sites for sailing, sail-boarding, canoeing, power-boat racing, water skiing, swimming, shooting, sub-aqua, rowing, fishing and natural history, as well as more informal activities such as dog-walking, picnicking or just going for a stroll. The owners of water areas are under great pressure to allow these activities, particularly when the participants are willing to pay for them.

When water-based activities are allowed over the whole of the water area, any of them has a harmful effect. On extremely large waters in other parts of the country, such as Rutland Water, it has been found that by zoning these activities it is possible to create a reserve of undisturbed water where water birds can breed and flocks of wildfowl can spend the winter, a critical time for their survival.

The situation in Bedfordshire is less easy to resolve. None of the lakes fall into the same category as Rutland Water. Most are only of medium size and zoning is less effective. Even when zoned, in winter activities such as water skiing and power-boat racing have a severe effect on bird life. Quieter activities, such as sailing and sail-boarding, have less effect but it has been found that wintering wildfowl need a learning period of three weeks to a month before most species will use the refuge zone. More work needs to be carried out on the effects of sailing both in the summer and winter periods. Fortunately, during extremely cold weather little sailing or sail-boarding takes place at present.

Whilst fishing from boats also has a deleterious effect, fishing from the shore and other lakeside activities have been found to cause little disturbance. At Priory Park (Bedford) it has been found that diverting the public away from a section of the shore during the winter period resulted in waterfowl seeking its shelter from cold winds.

The effect of all these activities on breeding birds is even more severe. Not only does the presence of boats disturb breeding birds but the wash created by them may cause flooding of nests and add to the erosion of banks.

Nearly all of the major waters in Bedfordshire such as Stewartby, Chimney Corner Lake, Arlesey Blue Lagoon, Brogborough Lake, Wyboston Lakes and Priory Park Clay Pit, support one or more forms of water-based recreational activity, whilst shooting is permitted at several others. It is surely time that at least one of these pits should be set aside solely for the purpose of observing and studying Natural History in an undisturbed environment.

Figure 8.17 *The Lapwing finds nesting and feeding habitat in quarries for a few years before vegetation covers the disturbed ground.* © A. J. Martin

Chapter 9

Graveyards and Dark Places

In this chapter attention will be given to some habitats which are often overlooked.

Churches, Churchyards and Wildlife

Churchyards and churches provide a stable refuge for many kinds of wildlife. Often they form an oasis among inhospitable surroundings, especially in areas of Bedfordshire where intensive arable farming has over-whelmed more natural habitats. Mature trees and shrubs are a particular feature and provide food, shelter and breeding sites for many birds, mammals and invertebrates. Walls and memorials are particularly important to a variety of forms of plant life, but especially to lichens.

Even the church building itself can be home to a variety of wildlife including bats, which have breeding roosts in summer or hibernate in winter. Happily these innocuous mammals are now protected by law. Pipistrelles are the commonest of church bats in the county, but other species do sometimes occur, such as Daubenton's Bat and the Common Long-eared Bat. At Northill, the village pond beside the churchyard is a favourite haunt for Daubenton's Bat and Pipistrelle Bats.

Bats are seen less often in and around churches in winter, when hibernating, than at other times of year, when they are to be seen on the wing hawking for food or emerging from the church at dusk. Churchyards, with their mature trees and rough grassland, provide them with a rich variety of insect food. The different species of bat feed at different levels. The smallest British bat, the Pipistrelle, feeds quite low, at bush level; the slightly larger Common Long-eared Bat feeds around the leafy branches of trees, whilst the Noctule, largest of British bats, flies above the tree tops in search of larger insects. It is ironic that although bats are beneficial to Man, feeding on insects, they are still frequently driven out of their ancestral roost-sites because of people's irrational fear of these harmless creatures. Worse still, timbers in buildings are treated with insecticides or preservatives which remain poisonous to bats coming into contact with them for ten years or more.

The maps in Figure 9.2 summarise the known distribution of Bedfordshire bats.

Birds which normally nest or roost in holes or crevices can find suitable sites in and around Bedfordshire churches. Some are species whose ancestors were cliff dwellers, the Swift and the Feral Pigeon are examples. In May or June the screaming Swifts circling the church tower at Barton-le-Clay are an evocative part of the summer scene. Jackdaws and even Kestrels are also known to breed in some of our church towers. Spotted Flycatchers find the shade of churchyard trees and the convenient perches provided by headstones much to their liking. At Kensworth they have found a nest site in torn netting fitted to protect the windows. Churchyard walls and crevices in ageing churches provide many nest sites for Robins and tits, whilst the Ivy cladding of many a churchyard wall provides cover for the nests of Blackbirds, Song Thrushes, Wrens and others. It is sad to see that over-tidy minds sometimes find it necessary to remove such valuable cover.

Mature trees in churchyards sometimes provide a last vestige of rural atmosphere in an urban setting, especially when, as until the last few years in Luton, Rooks still return to nest. The berries of Yew trees in churchyards are a favourite food of the Mistle Thrush and even in winter the Mistle Thrush singing high in a churchyard tree is still a feature of many Bedfordshire churchyards, adding natural charm and a reminder that spring is ahead. At St Paul's in Bedford, the street lights may keep the Mistle

Figure 9.1 *Northill Church and village pond, favoured habitat for bats.*

© B. West

Plate 14: *Flooded quarries sometimes produce the unexpected. Here is an exceptional show of Greater Spearwort flowering in a small, old, flooded quarry in Harlington. This had not been seen in the county for nearly a hundred years until it was found at two sites in 1982.* © R. Revels

Thrush awake, as it has been heard singing there late into a winter's evening.

Common Nettles are often to be found around the rubbish heap, a regular feature of churchyards necessitated by the need for a repository for dead flowers from graves. The Red Admiral and its close relatives, the Peacock and Small Tortoiseshell, lay their eggs on Nettles in neglected corners of the churchyard. Slugs and snails are denizens of these damp corners, but often the only clue is a Song Thrush's anvil on a gravestone or path. Among the churchyard slugs, *Limax flavus*, a yellowish animal with steel-blue tentacles, is only ever found in association with Man, while the two brownish-black slugs, *Milax*

budapestensis and *Milax sowerbyi*, are almost as dependent. All, no doubt, provide food for Toads, Hedgehogs and shrews.

The Holly and the Ivy

Evergreens are a particular feature of churchyards. The four species native to Britain are Holly, Ivy, Box and Yew. These have been associated with churchyards for centuries. In more recent times alien evergreen trees and shrubs have also been planted. Black Pine is one such tree which is now quite common in our churchyards; Laurel is perhaps the commonest of the shrubs. At Maulden, Giant Redwoods have been planted and these trees already form a conspicuous landmark, though still far short of the mature stature reached in the humid Sierra Nevada mountains of their native California, where they can reach a height of a hundred metres. Another exotic tree is the Indian Bean Tree at St Mary's, Luton.

The Ivy prefers the shadier, damper aspect of north or east facing walls. Here it can form dense accumulations of dry dead leaves, much favoured by hibernating insects such as the Comma butterfly, and by one of the most common of Bedfordshire woodlice, *Porcellio scaber*, which is typical of dry places in the county. The flower buds of Ivy provide food for caterpillars of one of the blue butterflies, the Holly Blue, whilst in October the massed

Figure 9.2 *The distribution of bat species in Bedfordshire.*

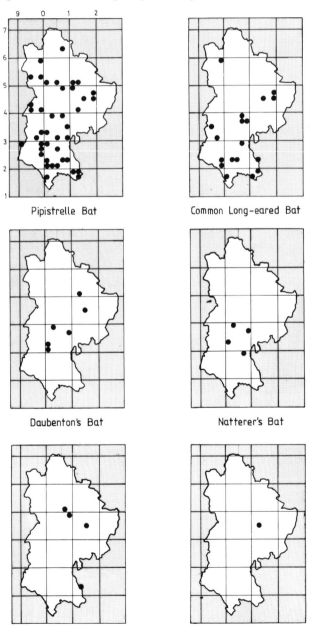

Figure 9.3 *Comma and Red Admiral butterflies feeding on Ivy nectar in autumn.*   © R. Revels

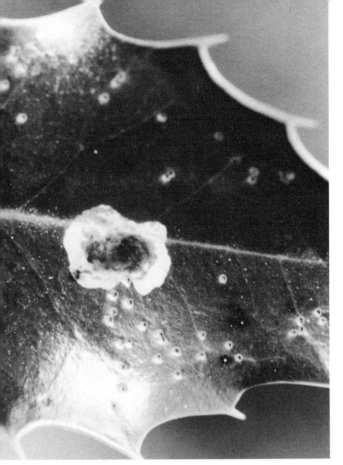

Figure 9.4 *Holly leaf gall caused by a fly larva which is often eaten by tits.*   © D. G. Rands

flowers of the Ivy attract the last of the summer butterflies, especially Red Admirals which are sometimes to be seen in abundance on the flowers in the waning warmth of the autumn sun (Figure 9.3). As one might guess, the Holly Blue butterfly feeds upon Holly as a larva, but it is only the spring brood which does so, the second brood of the year turn to Ivy. It is fortunate that in churchyards both plants grow in close proximity.

Holly must be one of the best loved of trees and it is found in most of the churchyards of Bedfordshire. However, few people are aware of an insect which lives on Holly, and is found almost wherever there is Holly in the county. This insect is an Agromyzid fly called *Phytomyza ilicis*, whose larvae live within the Holly leaves. The plant reacts to the intrusion of the fly's egg by forming pale green blister-galls, which eventually turn brown. These galls are easily found by inspection of almost any Holly (Figure 9.4). Many of the insects must be distributed around the country by Man's seasonal habit of collecting Holly for festive decorations at Christmas and then throwing it away in the New Year, often miles from where it originated. This fly is a very successful insect but it doesn't have things all its own way. Blue Tits have discovered that food is hidden within the gall and despite the slippery and prickly nature of the leaves, they are able to extract the larvae from within. Sometimes a sur-

prisingly large proportion of the galls have been attacked in this way, leaving a triangular tear in the gall.

Lichens, Algae and Mosses in Churchyards

Smooth hard surfaces provide little scope for plant growth but even here green powdery algae can thrive; *Pleurococcus viridis* is invariably found where there is a trace of dampness. Sometimes powdery lichens, not unlike the algae, give colour to drab church walls (Plate 15). In fact it is to the lichens that credit must be given for the mellow ageing of stone, brick, concrete and timber not only in churchyards but throughout the countryside (Figure 9.6). In the shadier places the lichens and algae may also be accompanied by mosses. Sadly, in Bedfordshire the dry climate and the, albeit generally modest, degree of pollution in the air limit the vigour and variety of species of lichens to be found, compared with the great richness to be found in the moist unpolluted air of the West Country for instance. In Britain, over fourteen-hundred species of lichen are known; in Bedfordshire there are about 140, of which those listed in Table 9.1 may be found commonly in Bedfordshire churchyards.

In churchyards it is the gravestones and the churchyard walls that provide the best habitats for lichens and mosses, and of these it is those built of limestone which are most favoured. Limestone is more soluble than most stone and so can provide more cracks and crevices, and more nutrients for pioneering lichens. It also has a neutralising effect on acidic sulphur dioxide from atmospheric pollution, allowing some lichen species to grow in relatively polluted areas. Since these plants grow in such a difficult habitat, they must make efficient use of any nutrients in the atmosphere or dissolved in rainwater. This specialised behaviour is also their downfall, since they are equally efficient at extracting and absorbing noxious pollutants from the rainwater.

In fact, the species of lichens in an area can be used as indicators of atmospheric pollution by sulphur dioxide and other substances emitted when fossil fuels are burnt. In Table 9.2 the effects of atmospheric pollution are

Figure 9.5 *Holly Blue butterfly: its second brood each year feeds on Ivy.*
© A. J. Martin

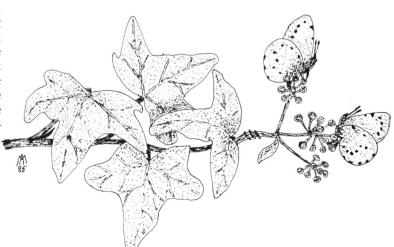

Plate 15: *Churchyards and stone walls have a characteristic flora and fauna adapted to the varied habitats they provide. The walls reflect the geology of the area, limestone in the north and sandstone in mid-Bedfordshire. The limestone wall round Sharnbrook's churchyard has a rich growth of mosses and lichens where sunshine and rain help provide the essentials of life.*

© R. Revels

Table 9.1 Common lichens of Bedfordshire churchyards

Buellia canescens	*Lecanora conizaeoides*	*Physcia adscendens*
Caloplaca aurantia	*Lecanora dispersa*	*Physcia caesia*
Caloplaca citrina	*Lecanora expallens*	*Physcia grisea*
Caloplaca heppiana	*Lecanora muralis*	*Xanthoria aureola*
Caloplaca teicholyta	*Ochrolechia parella*	*Xanthoria parietina*
Candelariella vitellina	*Placynthium nigrum*	*Lecidea lucida*
Lecanora atra	*Verrucaria nigrescens*	*Lepraria incana*
Lecanora campestris	*Parmelia physodes*	*Cladonia coniocraea*
		Cladonia fimbriata

Table 9.2 Variation in numbers of churchyard lichen species due to atmospheric pollution, and comparison with moss species

Environment	Church	Parish	Lichen species	Moss species
Rural	St Mary	Kensworth	41	22
	St Mary	Maulden	38	24
	St Mary	Potton	35	25
	St Nicholas	Barton-le-Clay	40	22
Near brickworks	St Mary	Marston Mortaine	16	14
	St Mary	Wootton	15	33
Urban	St Paul	Bedford	17	18
	St Mary	Luton	14	17

indicated by the differences in the number of lichen species at different sites around the county. Only the most tolerant species are able to survive in the most polluted areas, such as town centres. In fact, often the only species to be found is *Lecanora conizaeoides*, a powdery green species superficially resembling the algae *Pleurococcus viridis*.

Many mosses on the other hand are rather more tolerant of such pollution and their distribution in the county does not correspond to the concentration of pollutants (Table 9.2). The churchyards richest in number of species of mosses and liverworts are Flitwick, with forty species, Turvey with thirty-eight, and Wilden with thirty-seven.

It is interesting that gravestones dated before the industrial revolution are richer in lichens than those erected later. It seems that once slow-growing lichens have a foothold they can survive in adverse conditions, although they may not be able to colonise afresh. Close observation of the distribution of lichens in churchyards, on monuments and walls, reveals that the tops, edges and ridges are often particularly rich. Certain mosses, too, occur in these favoured sites. The good illumination is a factor but, more important is the nutrient enrichment from bird droppings, which are remarkably abundant in such sites. The lichens characteristic of these sites are listed in Table 9.3.

Slope and aspect of a stone also affect the lichens, cool, shady north-facing surfaces being much the richest; an old wall running east-west may support a quite different lichen (and fern and moss) flora from one running north-south; (a particularly good example is to be seen at Potton Church). The steeper faces of stones tend to be the more favoured; *Lecidea lucida*, a conspicuous powdery lime-green lichen, particularly favours the shaded, moist incisions of the inscriptions of headstones. It is to be hoped

that enthusiasm to 'tidy-up' will not lead to the destruction of the many lichen treasures surviving in churchyards.

Lichens and mosses are not only found on stone; the close-mown turf of graveyards has its own flora. Some of the most interesting churchyard lawns are found on the sandy soils across the middle of the county, as at Clophill; here one may find the flat leaf-like Dog Lichen (*Peltigera canina*), with its large grey leafy lobes. This is also to be found in coastal sand dunes.

Sandy lawns and stones bordering paths and graves are good places to look for pixy-cup lichens, in particular *Cladonia chlorophaea*, *C. coniocraea*, and *C. fimbriata*. The lichens of the county are described in more detail in *The Common Lichens of Bedfordshire* (The Bedfordshire Natural History Society, 1981).

Throughout the county churchyard lawns are rich in mosses. The most common species is *Brachythecium rutabulum*, which also occurs widely in gardens, woods and other habitats. The plant is bright glossy-green, or may be yellowish, and the leaves are widely spreading, oval in shape and have a pointed tip. Two somewhat smaller species are *Eurhynchium praelongum*, with stems regularly branched and broad-spreading stem leaves and much

Table 9.3 Some lichens associated with bird droppings on stone in churchyards

Species	Description
Xanthoria parietina	Orange-yellow rosette
Xanthoria aureola	As above
Caloplaca species	Orange-yellow encrustation
Physcia caesia	Blue-grey rosette
Physcia grisea	Grey-brown rosette

Figure 9.6 *Churchyard walls and gravestones provide excellent habitat for mosses and lichen. (Top) The cap of the brick wall round Stotfold cemetery attractively decorated with orange and grey lichens* (Xanthoria aureola, Caloplaca citrina, Physcia grisea) *and dark green mosses,* (TL224371, May 1977) © B. S. Nau. *(Centre) The liverwort* Lunularia cruciata *favours damp drainage runnels at the base of walls.* © A. R. Outen. *(Bottom) A very old gravestone at Potton completely covered by lichens of several species.* © B. S. Nau

smaller, narrow, pointed branch leaves, and *Eurhynchium swartzii* which has irregular branching and rather similar leaves on stem and branches. Other common species are *Calliergon cuspidatum*, with spear-like ends to its branches, *Pseudoscleropodium purum*, a robust-looking plant with crowded concave oval leaves and rounded shoot tips, and *Rhytidiadelphus squarrosus*, with reddish stems and leaves bent back almost at right-angles. Many other species occur less frequently and often depend on soil type.

Fungi, too, are a feature of long established churchyard lawns, in particular the brightly coloured wax cap fungi of the genus *Hygrophorus*.

Walls

The walls around churchyards may be the oldest walls in the county. This is due in no small part to the fact that the churchyard is a habitat less subject to modern development than most. For the naturalist, the best are those made of natural stone, limestone in the north of the county, where that of Swineshead is particularly attractive, and sandstone across the middle, where Potton has much the best example. But even old brick walls acquire interest as the mortar crumbles and plants gain a foothold. The best walls for flowering plants and animals, as well as lichens and mosses, are those made from limestone. This is due to the ready availability of calcium carbonate dissolved from the rock by rainwater. Snails are particularly dependent on this for the manufacture of their shells. Other things being equal, far fewer species of snails will be found around a sandstone wall than a limestone wall, although there may be large numbers of some species.

As for lichens and mosses, the cooler damper parts of walls have the richest communities of flowering plants and animals. Frogs and Toads are surprisingly frequent under fallen stones beside such walls, being very dependent on humid habitats during that part of their life cycle spent away from ponds. In churchyards, too, they find plenty of snails and slugs on which to feed. Newts are also found not infrequently.

By contrast, the warmth-loving Common Lizard and Slow Worm are sometimes found on or under fallen stones or logs in the sunnier parts of churchyards.

The age of church and churchyard walls and the fact that they are often of natural stone, rather than brick, provide a habitat rich in mosses. Limestone walls are of particular interest for mosses and here too is found a liverwort *Porella platyphylla*. Another liverwort *Lunularia cruciata* (Figure 9.6) prefers damp drainage runnels around the base of a wall; this flat liverwort bears little half-moon shaped 'cups' which contain spores. This is also the habitat for *Tortula virescens* which was thought to be an uncommon moss of trees until it was found in a runnel in Clifton churchyard, then it was found to be quite common in such sites in the county.

The four commonest mosses of walls in the county are:

Tortula muralis – this has long silvery hair-points to the leaves and erect cylindrical spore capsules.
Grimmia pulvinata – which also has silvery hairs, but the capsule is buried among the leaves, it also forms tighter 'cushions' than the above.
Bryum capillare – has long hairs, but not silvery and the capsule is on a long stalk, resembling a swan's neck; the leaves spiral round the stem in corkscrew fashion when dry.
Hypnum cupressiforme – forms dense mats of creeping shoots, its leaves strongly curved.
Homalothecium sericeum – has straight leaves but the branches appear curved, especially when dry, when they have a silky golden sheen.

Other species are found on walls but less commonly, and several mosses of the genus *Barbula* are found nowhere else.

The commonest wall ferns in Bedfordshire are three of the genus *Asplenium*; Wall-rue, which hardly looks like a fern, and the Black and Maidenhair Spleenworts. Intermediate Polypody is another wall fern found fairly often on old limestone walls in the north-west, around Turvey and Felmersham. This is the main area, too, for the Hart's-tongue fern which is so familiar in the more humid parts of Britain, such as Devon.

Early colonisers among the flowering plants are the Ivy-leaved Toadflax, with its small purple snapdragon flowers, and Procumbent Pearlwort. Later arrivals are Herb-Robert, common elsewhere in hedgerows, and Pellitory-of-the-wall, which is a close relative of the Common Nettle and grows only on walls in Bedfordshire. It is interesting to contemplate how this latter finds its way to new sites. Odell churchyard wall and the bridge over the Ouse at Turvey are places where this plant can be seen in some quantity. Among the most colourful flowers of walls are the stonecrops; the White Stonecrop and the yellow Biting Stonecrop are both a feature of the older limestone walls in the north-west of the county. The Thick-leaved Stonecrop is a rarity in Bedfordshire, known from only two sites, neither a churchyard wall, however. Wallflowers and House-leeks are often seen on walls, but are garden escapes.

Snails frequent the multitude of nooks and crannies in old walls. Three conspicuous and familiar species are the Garden Snail (*Helix aspersa*) and two familiar brown-striped yellow snails, the White-lipped Snail

(*Cepaea hortensis*), which has a white lip round the mouth of the shell, and the Brown-lipped Snail (*Cepaea nemoralis*), which has a brown lip. These will be familiar to many children; the two *Cepaeas* have also attracted much attention from genetics researchers studying natural selection. The Garden Snail is a close relation of the snail eaten in France, the Roman Snail (*Helix pomatia*), which occurs in the wild in Britain too, and reaches the limit of its range with isolated colonies in south Bedfordshire.

Two tiny cylindrical-shelled snails occur on many of our old walls; *Lauria cylindracea* is almost always present; on sandstone walls it may be the only snail but on limestone walls it is often joined by *Vertigo pygmaea* and *Pupilla muscorum*.

Of the snails of walls, some of the more exciting to the conchologist are rather insignificant in size, and two of these appeared to have died out in the county during the twentieth century – *Pyramidula rupestris* and *Balea perversa* (Figure 9.8). A much larger snail is in danger of the same fate; *Helicigona lapicida* is now only known from a rapidly disappearing roadside wall near Sharnbrook, although dead shells are to be found widely in the county, suggesting that it was once quite well established. *Balea* was known from old walls south of the river in Bedford back in 1912 but searches in suitable places in the county over the

Figure 9.7 *Ferns are less abundant in Bedfordshire than in more humid parts of Britain, but there are ferns to be found on shady walls and among the most common are: Wall-rue (top), Black Spleenwort (lower left), and Hart's-tongue.*   © T. Barker

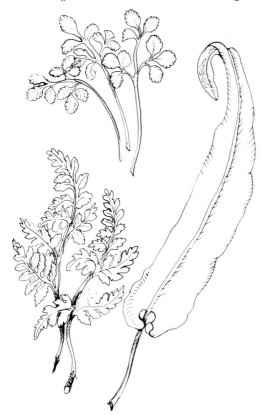

Figure 9.8 *The attractively varied shells of three snail species of walls, all three are nearly or actually extinct in the county:* Balea perversa *(top left),* Pyramidula rupestris *(top right), and* Helicigona lapicida.

© T. Barker

past twenty years have been unsuccessful in rediscovering this snail. It is probably extinct in the county now. However, *Pyramidula* seemed to have suffered the same fate until, during the past year, a small colony was discovered on a fragment of limestone wall near Odell. The snail survives but could still be lost if the site is 'tidied up'.

Things Under Things

The 'litter' deposited by Man or Nature provides a rewarding series of micro-habitats for the naturalist. Under this loose description one can include leaves and fallen timber, debris stranded in bushes and fences during river floods, rocks arranged to ornament a garden and materials left for storage as well as the real litter left around the countryside by Man. All have in common the ability to provide shelter and humidity to the animals under or within. The importance of humidity is not always appreciated, but the naturalist who has looked in vain for life amongst dry litter, and with rich rewards under damp

Figure 9.9 *The underside of a damp log bearing a multitude of the spindle-like snail* Clausilia bidentata. (Tingrith, TL 008315, May 1978)   © B. S. Nau

litter, will quickly come to realise that dampness is perhaps the most important reason why most small invertebrate animals are found 'under things'.

In talking about these habitats it is difficult to avoid using scientific names for the species since, being mostly hidden from casual gaze, few species have common English names. However, this should not be allowed to discourage anyone from exploring a fascinating hidden world.

LOGS AND LEAVES

A typical wood in Bedfordshire may yield about twenty species of snails and slugs, most of these being found under logs or fallen leaves. In this micro-habitat the humidity is usually high, which makes it suitable for these molluscs, not to mention a great variety of beetles, woodlice, centipedes, millipedes and other small creatures.

Among the snails in such places our three spire-snails are particularly attractive. *Clausilia bidentata* is very common in the county, and may be found in most hedgerows (Figure 9.9), but the slightly larger, shiny, mahogany-coloured *Cochlodina laminata* is more restricted, being found particularly in ancient woodland. Third of this trio is *Macrogastra rolphii* (Plate 3), which is quite a rarity in the county and is known only from the Chiltern plateau from Luton to Studham; we are at the northern extremity of its European range.

Under almost any damp log one can expect to find the Garlic Snail, *Oxychilus alliarius*. This snail, which smells strongly of garlic when handled, is a shiny brown colour and about five millimetres in diameter. More difficult to spot amongst dead leaves is a tiny spiny snail called *Acanthinula aculeata*. Although small it is most attractive when viewed with a hand-lens.

When a log or dead leaves are turned over the snails remain conveniently in place for study but the beetles and other small animals mostly endeavour to escape very rapidly. Of the beetle species, the Ground Beetles are perhaps the most obvious, in size and numbers. This is a large family but our commonest species in such habitats are *Pterostichus madidas* and *Pterostichus strenuus*. The really large ground beetles, which are commonly labelled as 'violet ground beetle', are actually several different species of the genus *Carabus* and five of the ten British species are known from the county. Of these, the Violet Ground Beetle, *Carabus violaceus* is probably marginally the commonest in the county. *Carabus nemoralis* is almost as common and *C. granulatus* and *C. problematicus* are both met with not infrequently.

Whilst much of interest is to be found on or under logs, one should not ignore the crannies under the rotting bark and even within the wood itself as this decays. The latter is the place to look for the Lesser Stag Beetle *Dorcus paral-* *lelopipedus* and its large grub-like larvae. This large beetle is quite common in the county, though less impressive than the true Stag Beetle (Figure 9.10). This latter has not been found in the county for many years, though it is not uncommon in parts of Hertfordshire and Essex.

By way of illustrating the richness of animal life under logs, we can give as an example the number and variety of species found under a length of plank on the bank of the Ouse at Odell in May 1981. There were over sixty animals of 'reasonable size' and this number was made up as follows:

Forty-one molluscs of eight species. One of the 'hairy' snails was very numerous, there being eighteen specimens of *Trichia plebeia*; a marsh snail, *Oxylomma pfeifferi* was also numerous, ten specimens; and a glass-snail, *Zonitoides nitidus* was only slightly less so. There was a single grassland snail *Vallonia pulchella*. There were also four slugs of three species.
Four insects comprising three beetles and one caddis-fly. The beetles were a twenty-two-spot ladybird and two metallic-blue flea-beetles, *Haltica lythri*, hibernating near their host-plant, the Great Willowherb.
More than twenty other invertebrates, including six Polydesmid Millipedes, and three woodlice, *Philoscia muscorum*, an abundant species in damp grassland. In addition there were various spiders, spring-tails (*Collembola*), worms, mites and other tiny forms.

This variety of animals is in no way unusual, although the numbers and species involved may vary.

A different micro-habitat is provided by thick tussocks of grass. These are especially popular in winter for hibernation. Spring-tails (*Collembola*), a group not studied yet in the county, are invariably abundant but tussocks are also much favoured by various beetles. Among the latter,

Figure 9.10 *The Lesser Stag-beetle* Dorcus parallelopipedus *is common in rotting logs – the true Stag-beetle* Lucanus cervus *appears to be absent from the county.* © R. Revels

ladybirds and some of the non-black ground beetles are usually common.

Three of the less familiar ladybirds are characteristic of this habitat. Two are reddish, unspotted and somewhat smaller than most, *Rhyzobius litura*, an ochre-ish insect, and *Coccidula rufa*, which is orange-red. The third species in such places is sometimes present by the dozen; it is a small ivory-coloured ladybird with sixteen black spots, whose name is *Tytthaspis sedecimpunctata* (Figure 9.11).

These ladybirds are usually accompanied by numbers of golden-coloured Ground Beetles. Of these, one with a black head is usually common, *Demetrias atricapillus*. A smaller beetle of the same general colouration is also frequent, *Dromius linearis*. The former, *Demetrias atricapillus*, has a close relative which is not uncommon in The Fens and surely must occur in Bedfordshire but remains a prize to be found in the future perhaps.

In similar sites in the marshy places another little-known ladybird is found commonly in the county, the pinkish-yellow nineteen-spotted (as its Latin name indicates) *Anisosticta novemdecimpunctata*. This ladybird is also to be found by peeling back the dead leaves from the stems of Bulrush. Whilst looking for this it is worth inspecting the seed heads of the Bulrush for a bug which

lives within their cosy warmth, *Chilacis typhae*. On sunny days they come out and sit on the surface, diving back into the seed-head when alarmed.

JETSAM AND DREDGINGS

When rivers and streams are in flood the high water washes away large quantities of plant debris, branches and Man's rubbish which has accumulated on the banks since the last flood. This flotsam is carried downstream until it is ensnared on some obstacle such as the lower branches of an overhanging tree or a fence across a field. Here it accumulates when the flood recedes (Figure 9.12). This jetsam provides a rich harvest for the observant field-worker interested in beetles, molluscs and other animals.

A particularly good site is beside the Great North Road at Tempsford, where a fence occasionally traps vast quantities of flotsam when the Great Ouse overtops its bank. Table 9.4 shows the numbers of species of molluscs noted here after floods in March 1977 and April 1979.

The effects of a river spate on beetles can be illustrated by an observation made further up the Ouse, at Radwell, on 4th February 1979. The river had spread a little beyond its banks, over an adjoining pasture, and was carrying much flotsam. On closer inspection a steady flow of beetles was noticed, swept along by the spate. In the space of a quarter of an hour, a collection of rove beetles and ground beetles rescued from the water yielded at least five species of the former and nine of the latter. More details of the species have been published in *The Bedfordshire Naturalist* No. **34.**

ROCKS, ROCKERIES AND SOIL

The Bedfordshire countryside has little natural rock, but gardeners find rockeries irresistible and this is some compensation. The moisture and shelter provided by the rocks themselves, and by overhanging mats of plants, make garden rockeries a rich site for many small creatures. The variety is added to further by the unintentional import of species from other parts of Britain, or even from abroad.

Garden rockeries are now one of the best places to look for our amphibians, the Common Frog, the Common Toad, and even the Smooth Newt. It is in gardens with pools and rockeries in Bedford that the strange Midwife Toad became established.

Figure 9.11 *The 16-spotted ladybird* Tytthaspis sedecimpunctata *is sometimes found in dozens, hibernating in dry grass-tussocks.* © B. S. Nau

Table 9.4 The variety of mussels and snails in flood-jetsam, by River Great Ouse at Tempsford (Figure 9.12a)

Species	No. of species	
	1977	1979
Large mussels (*Unio, Dreissena,* etc)	0	1
Pea-mussels (*Sphaerium/Pisidium*)	1	10
Water-snails: spire-shell (*Lymnaea* etc)	9	13
Water-snails: flat shell (*Planorbis* etc)	6	9
Marsh snails	5	3
Land snails	12	25
Slugs	0	2
Total numbers of species	*33*	*63*

The snails and slugs, having been intensively studied in the county, provide several examples of such alien species. One is the 'worm-slug' *Boettgerilla pallens*. This was discovered in Britain as recently as 1972, when it was found in the Lake District. It is believed it may have been brought from Holland with plants imported by a nursery. In 1981 it was found in Bedfordshire in a marshy site near Flitwick, since when it has been found under stones in Houghton Conquest, at Lidlington, and elsewhere. In the same year an investigation of local garden centres yielded two more aliens. One was the slug *Limax valentianus* and the other a small glass-snail called *Zonitoides arboreus*. Both are known from hot-houses in botanic gardens. A further species was added the following year from Stockwood Park nurseries in Luton; this was a West African snail which finds hot-houses to its liking; it too only has a scientific name, *Subulina striatella*. Then, most recently, in 1985 at the same place a colony was found of another small snail called *Toltecia pusilla*. This normally lives amongst mountain scree in the Mediterranean region and was the first British record. In Bedfordshire it finds a similar niche down amongst the gravel spread on the ground in garden centres. It was later found at another garden centre in Luton, and in others at Sandy and Willington.

It is not only alien molluscs which find a foothold in our gardens and nurseries. In February 1982 an alien wood-louse was found under a rock by a pool at a garden centre in Willington. This was a species called *Cordioniscus stebbingi*, a rare species in this country which has previously been found only in one or two botanic gardens in glass-houses. The same visit to this site also produced an alien millipede, called *Oxidus gracilis*. This was later found in similar habitats at Flitwick and Luton.

By contrast with these aliens, there is one small native snail which lives underground, especially in the friable soil of our downland, the Blind Snail *Cecilioides acicula*. The small spindle-shaped shells can be found by diligent searching of the soil turned-up in mole-hills, but these shells are nearly always empty – the real challenge is to find a living snail! There are also two species of subter-

ranean slug of rather unusual appearance; they are rarely seen but are most likely to be encountered in well-matured gardens. They are called *Testacella scutulum* and *Testacella haliotidea* and are distinguished in that they carry a small shell (Figure 9.13). They have been reported from gardens in Bedford, Bromham, Clapham, once in Luton, and, many years ago in Ampthill. When gardening it is worth looking out for strange-looking slugs which could be *Testacella* as they may be more widespread than the few records suggest.

The average gardener in the county is unlikely to encounter many of the animals mentioned above; the more typical species of our garden rockeries are the reddish Strawberry Snail (*Trichia striolata*); the large mottled Garden Snail (*Helix aspersa*) (which is familiar to everyone), the creamy-coloured Field Slug (*Deroceras reticulatum*) and the large Black Slug (*Arion ater*). Among the woodlice, the smooth *Oniscus asellus* and the rough *Porcellio*

Figure 9.12 *River jetsam can be a rich source of beetles and snails when flood-waters recede. (Top) Flood litter trapped by a field fence near the Great Ouse at Tempsford, January 1982.* © B. S. Nau. *(Bottom) The shells of mussels and water-snails stranded on a sand-bank in Begwary Brook, near Wyboston.*
© D. G. Rands

Table 9.5   The commonest spiders and harvestmen of grassland-scrub, caught in pitfall traps at Old Warden Tunnel Nature Reserve
Species are listed in order of decreasing abundance

Spiders	*Trochosa terricola*
	Lepthyphantes tenuis
	Agroeca inopina
	Pardosa nigriceps
	Alopecosa pulveruleuta
	Bathyphantes gracilis
Harvestmen	*Oligolophus tridens*
	Rilaena triangularis
	Paroligolophus agrestis

(Based on T. J. Thomas, *The Bedfordshire Naturalist* (**38, 39**))

scaber are both very abundant, the latter preferring drier places. The woodlice, centipedes and millipedes have been intensively studied in the county and detailed maps have been made of their distribution.

Spiders and their relatives are another group of animals which have been studied intensively in Bedfordshire by T. J. Thomas. Many spiders are associated with 'dark places' or may be found down in the vegetation at ground level. Some idea of the richness of variety of these is given by the results of pitfall trapping, a pitfall trap being a jar set flush with the ground. Over a period from 1977 to 1984 traps on the Old Warden Tunnel Nature Reserve revealed no less than 101 species of spider and thirteen species of the long-legged harvestmen. This site is an area of grassland and scrub along a cutting and tunnel-top of the former Hitchin-Bedford railway.

Six species of spider accounted for half of those caught, they are listed in Table 9.5 in order of abundance. Just three species of harvestmen accounted for the vast majority of these long-legged relatives of the spiders: these too are listed in Table 9.5. Further details can be found in *The Bedfordshire Naturalist* No. **38.**

In Conclusion

This chapter has covered many of the less salubrious habitats to be found in the countryside and in our gardens. Many of us have a natural aversion to such places and the creatures – whether slimy, damp or hairy – which live there. To those naturalists who can overcome these irrational instincts a whole new world of fascination opens up. It is to be hoped that some readers may be stimulated to explore these rich pastures, where so much remains to be discovered.

Figure 9.13 *Some of the less popular groups of animal life. (Top left) The spider* Pisaura mirabilis *carrying its egg 'sac', this is one of our larger spiders and is common in grassland.* © R. Revels. *(Bottom left) One of the few slugs* (Testacella haliotidea) *which bears a shell like other molluscs, small and flat near the tip of the tail. Rarely recorded in the county, this specimen was found in a Bromham garden.* © D. G. Rands. *(Right) One of the most abundant woodlouse of grassland,* Philoscia muscorum.   © B. S. Nau

APPENDICES

Bedfordshire Species Checklists

The checklists in the following pages cover the most 'popular' species groups. The lists relate to the last forty years; species recorded many years ago and not seen in recent times are therefore not included.

The lists include information on the current status of species in the county; for the smaller groups this is in the form of brief notes; for larger groups the species have been grouped under main headings according to status. The flowering plants and ferns comprise a very large number of species and have therefore been treated a little differently, the status being indicated by a two-letter code after the species name.

The groups listed mostly have acceptable English names for species; therefore in general only English names are given but the source of these is indicated to permit cross-referencing to scientific names. Dragonflies are an exception, various English names having been used for these over recent decades; hence scientific names are included to avoid uncertainty.

Checklists for the following groups of species are presented:

A	Birds	*B. J. Nightingale*
B	Mammals	*D. Anderson*
C	Fish	*T. Peterkin*
D	Amphibians and reptiles	*H. M. Muir-Howie*
E	Butterflies	*A. J. Martin*
F	Moths	*V. W. Arnold*
G	Grasshoppers and crickets	*D. G. Rands*
H	Dragonflies	*N. Dawson*
I	Flowering plants, ferns and fern allies	*C. R. Boon*

Birds

This list comprises those species seen in the county in the forty-year period 1946–85. The names used are from 'List of Recent Holarctic Bird Species', K. H. Voous, *Ibis* **115:** 612–638 and **119:** 223–250 (1977). The sequence within each main category follows Voous.

Resident species – population may be supplemented by immigrant or passage birds at some seasons

Little Grebe	Woodpigeon	Coal Tit
Great Crested Grebe	Collared Dove	Blue Tit
Grey Heron	Barn Owl	Great Tit
Mute Swan	Little Owl	Nuthatch
Greylag Goose	Tawny Owl	Treecreeper
Canada Goose	Long-eared Owl	Jay
Mandarin	Kingfisher	Magpie
Mallard	Green Woodpecker	Jackdaw
Tufted Duck	Great Spotted Woodpecker	Rook
Sparrowhawk	Lesser Spotted Woodpecker	Carrion Crow
Kestrel	Skylark	Starling
Red-legged Partridge	Meadow Pipit	House Sparrow
Grey Partridge	Grey Wagtail	Tree Sparrow
Pheasant	Pied Wagtail	Chaffinch
Lady Amherst's Pheasant	Wren	Greenfinch
Water Rail	Dunnock	Goldfinch
Moorhen	Robin	Linnet
Coot	Blackbird	Redpoll
Lapwing	Song Thrush	Bullfinch
Snipe	Mistle Thrush	Hawfinch
Woodcock	Goldcrest	Yellowhammer
Black-headed Gull	Long-tailed Tit	Reed Bunting
Rock Dove (= Feral Pigeon)	Marsh Tit	Corn Bunting
Stock Dove	Willow Tit	

Species which are predominantly summer visitors, breeding most years

Hobby	Sand Martin	Reed Warbler
Quail	Swallow	Lesser Whitethroat
Little Ringed Plover	House Martin	Whitethroat
Ringed Plover (*occasional in winter*)	Tree Pipit	Garden Warbler
Redshank (*also passage migrant*)	Yellow Wagtail	Blackcap
Common Tern	Nightingale	Wood Warbler (*also passage migrant*)
Turtle Dove	Redstart (*also passage migrant*)	Chiffchaff
Cuckoo	Grasshopper Warbler	Willow Warbler
Nightjar	Sedge Warbler	Spotted Flycatcher
Swift		

Species which are predominantly winter visitors

Bewick's Swan
Whooper Swan
White-fronted Goose
Brent Goose
Wigeon
Gadwall (*has bred*)
Teal (*has bred*)
Pintail
Shoveler (*has bred*)
Red-creasted Pochard

Pochard (*has bred*)
Goldeneye
Smew
Red-breasted Merganser
Goosander
Ruddy Duck (*has bred*)
Hen Harrier
Merlin
Golden Plover
Jack Snipe

Common Gull
Herring Gull
Great Black-backed Gull
Short-eared Owl
Fieldfare
Redwing
Bearded Tit
Great Grey Shrike
Brambling
Siskin

Passage migrants, occurring most years but erratic in timing and length of stay

Slavonian Grebe
Black-necked Grebe
Cormorant (*almost resident but has not bred*)
Shelduck (*has bred*)
Garganey
Common Scoter
Honey Buzzard
Buzzard (*also winter visitor*)
Osprey
Oystercatcher
Grey Plover
Knot
Sanderling
Little Stint
Dunlin

Ruff
Black-tailed Godwit
Bar-tailed Godwit
Whimbrel
Curlew
Spotted Redshank
Greenshank
Green Sandpiper
Wood Sandpiper
Common Sandpiper
Turnstone
Little Gull
Lesser Black-backed Gull
Kittiwake
Sandwich Tern

Arctic Tern
Little Tern
Black Tern
Hoopoe
Wryneck
Rock Pipit
Water Pipit
Black Redstart (*has bred*)
Whinchat (*has bred*)
Stonechat (*has bred*)
Wheatear (*has bred*)
Ring Ouzel
Firecrest (*has bred*)
Pied Flycatcher
Crossbill (*has bred*)

Vagrants, seen in fewer than five years out of the last ten

Red-throated Diver
Black-throated Diver
Great Northern Diver
Red-necked Grebe
Fulmar
Manx Shearwater
Storm Petrel
Leach's Petrel
Gannet
Shag
Bittern
Night Heron
Little Egret
Purple Heron
White Stork
Bean Goose
Pink-footed Goose
Barnacle Goose
Egyptian Goose
Ring-necked Duck
Ferruginous Duck
Scaup
Eider
Long-tailed Duck
Velvet Scoter

Red Kite
White-tailed Eagle
Marsh Harrier
Montagu's Harrier
Goshawk
Rough-legged Buzzard
Peregrine
Golden Pheasant (*introduced*)
Spotted Crake
Corncrake
Black-winged Stilt
Avocet
Stone-curlew
Collared Pratincole
Kentish Plover
Dotterel
Temmink's Stint
Baird's Sandpiper
Pectoral Sandpiper
Sharp-tailed Sandpiper
Curlew Sandpiper
Purple Sandpiper
Great Snipe
Wilson's Phalarope
Pomarine Skua

Great Skua
Mediterranean Gull
Iceland Gull
Glaucous Gull
Caspian Tern
White-winged Black Tern
Guillemot
Razorbill
Little Auk
Puffin
Ring-necked Parakeet (*feral*)
Woodlark
Shorelark
Waxwing
Golden Oriole
Red-backed Shrike
Woodchat Shrike
Raven
Rose-coloured Starling
Serin
Twite
Lapland Bunting
Snow Bunting
Cirl Bunting

Mammals

The forty species listed below are those which have been recorded in Bedfordshire in the period 1945–1985. The names are those used in *The Handbook of British Mammals* by Corbet and Southern, published by The Mammal Society in 1977.

Widespread and common

Hedgehog
Mole
Rabbit
Brown Hare
Grey Squirrel
Common Rat
Fox

Widespread and frequent

Common Shrew
Bank Vole
Field Vole
Wood Mouse
Harvest Mouse
Stoat
Weasel
Badger
Muntjac Deer

Widespread but uncommon

Pygmy Shrew
Water Shrew
Pipistrelle Bat
Water Vole
House Mouse

Local, uncommon

Chinese Water Deer
– *SW. Bedfordshire*
Mink
– *first record 1979, now established and increasing along Ouse and tributaries*

Local and rare

Natterer's Bat
– *four sites in mid-Bedfordshire*
Daubenton's Bat
– *near rivers or lakes*
Noctule Bat
– *scattered in small numbers*
Common Long-eared Bat
– *scattered in small numbers*
Yellow-necked Mouse
– *three sites in E./N., regular at these*
Fat Dormouse
– *SW. Bedfordshire, only one regular site*
Common Dormouse
– *three records from SW. Beds*

Vagrants

Barbastelle Bat
– *corpse at Old Warden in 1976*

Extinct species, formerly established

Ship Rat
– *last reported 1949 at Whipsnade*
Otter
– *last recorded 1972, in N. Beds. Was fairly numerous in 1946 near Leighton Buzzard and Turvey*
Red Squirrel
– *a few in N. and S. during 1945–47, not recorded since*

Introduced or escaped

Red-necked Wallaby
– *rare escapes from Whipsnade Zoo*
Ferret
– *occasional escapes, not established*
Red Deer
– *six records in last fifteen years, escapes from Woburn and Knebworth (Herts)*
Sika Deer
– *a small herd near Woburn Park, whence they escaped in 1983*
Fallow Deer
– *occasional strays from herds in Ashridge (Herts) and Hayley Wood (Cambs)*
Siberian Roe Deer
– *three near Woburn Park in 1950, now extinct*

Fish

The names are those used in *The Freshwater Fishes of Britain and Europe* by B. J. Muus and P. Dahlstrom, published by Collins in 1971.

Widespread and common

Gudgeon
Roach
Rudd
Perch

Widespread and frequent

Pike
Carp
Tench
Common Bream
Chub
Eel
Three-spined Stickleback

Widespread but uncommon

Ruffe

Locally frequent

Rainbow Trout
Crucian Carp
Bleak
Dace
Minnow
Stone Loach
Bullhead
Ten-spined Stickleback

Local, uncommon

Brown Trout
Silver Bream

Rare

Spined Loach

Introduced, local

Grass Carp
– *introduced to control water plants*
Barbel
– *periodically reintroduced*
European Catfish
Zander

Amphibians and Reptiles

Amphibians

Smooth Newt
– *Locally frequent, often with Common Frog, sometimes with Common Toad*

Great Crested Newt
– *a few sizeable colonies*

Common Frog
– *widespread and fairly common, breeds in many garden ponds*

Common Toad
– *widespread and common, some large breeding colonies where several hundred may be seen in spring*

Natterjack Toad
– *reintroduced to the county at The Lodge, Sandy, in 1980*

Midwife Toad
– *an introduced species in Britain, several stable colonies in and near Bedford, all traceable to an original Bedford site*

Reptiles

Common Lizard
– *uncommon but widespread*

Slow-worm
– *uncommon and local, rare in the north, most common in Dunstable/Whipsnade area*

Grass Snake
– *found along the Great Ouse, one Toddington record, unknown elsewhere*

Adder
– *local and rare, Rowney Warren has most records, also known at Kings Wood (Heath and Reach), and in the Everton/Potton area*

Butterflies

Widespread and common

Large White
Small White
Green-veined White
Orange-tip
Brimstone
Meadow Brown
Gatekeeper
Peacock
Small Tortoiseshell
Common Blue
Small Skipper
Large Skipper

Widespread and frequent

Wall Brown
Small Heath
Ringlet
Red Admiral
– breeds but does not overwinter
Comma
Small Copper
Holly Blue
Essex Skipper

Locally frequent

Speckled Wood
Marbled White
Purple Hairstreak
Brown Argus Blue
Chalk-hill Blue

Widespread but uncommon

Grizzled Skipper

Local in small numbers

Wood White
White Admiral
Duke of Burgundy
Green Hairstreak
Small Blue
Dingy Skipper

Local and rare

Dark-green Fritillary
Black Hairstreak
White-letter Hairstreak
Silver-spotted Skipper

Migrants only

Clouded Yellow
– frequent some years
Painted Lady
– annual in modest numbers
Camberwell Beauty
– rare

Moths

This list includes all Bedfordshire species recorded during the past forty years except the small moths known as 'micros' which, for the most part, do not have English names. The English names are those used in *Colour Identification Guide to Moths of the British Isles* B. Skinner, Viking, 1984. Within categories the species are in taxonomic order, the same order as in the above book. Where a year is given this indicates the year of the most recent record. The symbol (†) indicates that the species is under-recorded and is probably more common than available records suggest.

Widespread and common

Common Swift
Six-spot Burnet
Narrow-bordered Five-spot Burnet
The Drinker
Yellow-tail
Heart and Dart
Large Yellow Underwing
Ingrailed Clay

Small Square-spot
Setaceous Hebrew Character
Double Square-spot
Common Quaker
Clouded Drab
Hebrew Character
The Clay

Common Wainscot
Mouse Moth
Dark Arches
Large Nutmeg
Common Rustic
Mottled Rustic
Silver Y

Widespread and frequent

Ghost Moth
Orange Swift
Leopard Moth
December Moth
Pale Eggar
The Lackey
The Lappet
Emperor Moth
Oak Hook-tip
Pebble Hook-tip
Chinese Character
Peach Blossom
Buff Arches
Figure of Eighty
March Moth
Common Emerald
Small Emerald
Blood-vein
Small Blood-vein
Small Fan-footed Wave
Dwarf Cream Wave
Small Dusty Wave
Single-dotted Wave
Small Scallop
Riband Wave
Red Twin-spot Carpet
Dark-barred Twin-spot Carpet
Large Twin-spot Carpet
Silver-ground Carpet
Shaded Broad-bar
Common Carpet
Yellow Shell
Shoulder Stripe
Purple Bar

Barred Straw
Small Phoenix
Dark Marbled Carpet
Common Marbled Carpet
Barred Yellow
Grey Pine Carpet
Green Carpet
July Highflyer
The Fern
November Moth
Winter Moth
Small Rivulet
Twin-spot Carpet
Toadflax Pug
Mottled Pug
Lime-speck Pug
Common Pug
Grey Pug
Tawny Speckled Pug
Brindled Pug
Bordered Pug
The V-Pug
Green Pug
Double-striped Pug
Treble-bar
Small Yellow Wave
Magpie
Clouded Border
Tawny-barred Angle
Latticed Heath
Brown Silver-line
Scorched Wing
Brimstone Moth
August Thorn

Canary-shouldered Thorn
Dusky Thorn
Early Thorn
Purple Thorn
Scalloped Hazel
Scalloped Oak
Swallow-tailed Moth
Feathered Thorn
Pale Brindled Beauty
Brindled Beauty
Oak Beauty
Peppered Moth
Dotted Border
Mottled Umber
Waved Umber
Willow Beauty
Mottled Beauty
The Engrailed
Bordered White (*sometimes abundant*)
Common White Wave
Common Wave
White-pinion Spotted
Clouded Silver
Early Moth
Light Emerald
Poplar Hawk-moth
Elephant Hawk-moth
Buff-tip
Iron Prominent
Pebble Prominent
Lesser Swallow Prominent
Swallow Prominent
Coxcomb Prominent
Pale Prominent

Widespread and frequent (continued)

Figure of Eight
The Vapourer
Pale Tussock
White Satin Moth
Scarce Footman
Common Footman
White Ermine
Buff Ermine
Ruby Tiger
The Cinnabar
Garden Dart
Turnip Moth
Dark Sword-grass
Shuttle-shaped Dart
The Flame
Flame Shoulder
Lesser Yellow Underwing
Lesser Broad-bordered Yellow
   Underwing
Double Dart
Purple Clay
Six-striped Rustic
Square-spot Rustic
Red Chestnut
The Nutmeg
Cabbage Moth
Dot Moth
Pale-shouldered Brocade
Bright-line Brown-eye
Broom Moth

Broad-barred White
The Campion
Varied Coronet
The Lychnis
Feathered Gothic
Small Quaker
Powdered Quaker
Twin-spotted Quaker
Brown-line Bright-eye
Smoky Wainscot
Shoulder-striped Wainscot
Deep-brown Dart
Early Grey
Green-brindled Crescent
The Satellite
The Chestnut
The Brick
Brown-spot Pinion
Beaded Chestnut
Centre-barred Sallow
Lunar Underwing
The Sallow
Poplar Grey
The Sycamore
Grey Dagger
Knot Grass
Marbled Beauty
Copper Underwing
Brown Rustic
Straw Underwing

Small Angle Shades
Angle Shades
The Dun-bar
Light Arches
Dusky Brocade
Rustic Shoulder-knot
Marbled Minor
Tawny Marbled Minor
Middle-barred Minor
Cloaked Minor
Small Dotted Buff
Dusky Sallow
Flounced Rustic
Rosy Rustic
The Uncertain
The Rustic
Green Silver-lines
Burnished Brass
Beautiful Golden Y
Plain Golden Y
The Spectacle
Red Underwing
Mother Shipton
Burnet Companion
The Herald
Beautiful Hook-tip
Straw Dot
The Snout
The Fan-foot
Small Fan-foot

Locally frequent

Gold Swift
Little Emerald
The Streamer
The Spinach
Broken-barred Carpet
Small Waved Umber

Foxglove Pug
Chimney Sweeper
Pale Oak Beauty
Small Engrailed
Barred Red
Pine Hawk-moth

Pine Beauty
The Sprawler
Brindled Green
Bird's Wing
Rufous Minor
Pale Mottled Willow

Widespread but uncommon

Scalloped Hook-tip
Frosted Green
Large Emerald
Pretty Chalk Carpet
Sandy Carpet
White-spotted Pug
Scorched Carpet
The V-Moth
Lilac Beauty
September Thorn
Lunar Thorn
Privet Hawk-moth
Lime Hawk-moth

Eyed Hawk-moth
Puss Moth
Sallow Kitten
Maple Prominent
Lunar Marbled Brown
Muslin Moth
Short-cloaked Moth
Broad-bordered Yellow Underwing
Least Yellow Underwing
Pearly Underwing
The Gothic
Pale Shining Brown
The Shark

Large Ranunculus
Dark Chestnut
Red-line Quaker
Yellow-line Quaker
Barred Sallow
Alder Moth
Lunar-spotted Pinion
Clouded-bordered Brindle
Clouded Brindle
Small Wainscot
Frosted Orange
Scarce Silver-lines

Local, uncommon

Map-winged Swift
Cistus Forester – *on chalk downs*
Hornet Moth†
Lunar Hornet Moth†
Yellow-legged Clearwing
Orange-tailed Clearwing
Red-belted Clearwing
Six-belted Clearwing
Oak Eggar
Barred Hook-tip
Popular Lutestring
Common Lutestring
Oak Lutestring
Yellow Horned
Orange Underwing
Light Orange Underwing
Grass Emerald
Blotched Emerald
False Mocha
Clay Triple-lines
Light Cream Wave
Cream Wave
Plain Wave
Flame Carpet
Chalk Carpet
Wood Carpet
The Mallow
Beautiful Carpet
Dark Spinach
Water Carpet
The Phoenix
The Chevron
Blue-bordered Carpet
Spruce Carpet
May Highflyer
Scarce Tissue
The Tissue
Brown Scallop
Dark Umber
Sharp-angled Carpet

Pale November Moth†
Autumnal Moth†
Northern Winter Moth
The Rivulet
Barred Rivulet
Grass Rivulet
Slender Pug
Maple Pug
Haworth's Pug
Pinion-spotted Pug
Netted Pug
Freyer's Pug
Wormwood Pug
Currant Pug
Shaded Pug
Plain Pug
Ochreous Pug
Pimpinel Pug
Narrow-winged Pug
Ash Pug
Oak-tree Pug
Juniper Pug
Larch Pug
Dwarf Pug
Sloe Pug
The Streak
Broom-tip
Lesser Treble-bar
Dingy Shell
Small White Wave
The Seraphim
Small Seraphim
Yellow-barred Brindle
Bordered Beauty
Large Thorn
Spring Usher
Scarce Umber
Brindled White-spot
Grey Birch
Common Heath

Small Elephant Hawk-moth
Poplar Kitten
Lobster Moth
Great Prominent
Scarce Prominent
Marbled Brown
Chocolate-tip
Round-winged Muslin
Rosy Footman
Muslin Footman
Dingy Footman
Least Black Arches
White-line Dart
Heart and Club
Dotted Rustic
Stout Dart
Autumnal Rustic
True Lovers' Knot
Triple-spotted Clay
Dotted Clay
Green Arches
Grey Arches
Light Brocade
Tawny Shears
Marbled Coronet
Antler Moth
Hedge Rustic
Northern Drab
Lead-coloured Drab
The Wormwood
Chamomile Shark
The Mullein
Minor Shoulder-knot
Black Rustic
Tawny Pinion
Grey Shoulder-knot
Merveille du Jour
Dark Brocade
Flounced Chestnut
The Suspected

Local, uncommon (continued)

Orange Sallow
Pink-barred Sallow
Dusky-lemon Sallow
Pale-lemon Sallow
The Miller
Dark Dagger
Svensson's Copper Underwing
Old Lady
The Olive
Dingy Shears
Lesser-spotted Pinion

White-spotted Pinion
Reddish Light Arches
Small Clouded Brindle
Slender Brindle
Double Lobed
Rosy Minor
Mere Wainscot
Ear Moth
The Crescent
Bulrush Wainscot
Large Wainscot

Treble Lines
Vine's Rustic
Small Yellow Underwing
Bordered Sallow
Cream-bordered Green Pea
Nut-tree Tussock
Golden Plusia
The Blackneck
Small Purple-barred
Common Fan-foot

Local and rare

Goat Moth
Small Eggar
Fox Moth
Mocha
Birch Mocha
Maiden's Blush
Least Carpet
Satin Wave
Treble Brown Spot
Oblique Carpet
July Belle
Royal Mantle
Northern Spinach
Autumn Green Carpet
Pine Carpet
Juniper Carpet
Scallop Shell
Marsh Pug
Satyr Pug
Ling Pug

Campanula Pug
Golden-rod Pug
Early Tooth-striped
Peacock Moth
Little Thorn
Horse Chestnut
Orange Moth
Small Brindled Beauty
Satin Beauty
Great Oak Beauty
Brown-tail
Black Arches
Four-dotted Footman
Buff Footman
Wood Tiger
Light Feathered Rustic
Archer's Dart
Lunar Yellow Underwing
Beautiful Yellow Underwing

Bordered Gothic
Dog's Tooth
Southern Wainscot
Blair's Shoulder Knot
Grey Chi
The Butterbur
Twin-spotted Wainscot
Brown-veined Wainscot
Fen Wainscot
Small Rufous
Silky Wainscot
Marbled White-spot
Silver Hook
Oak Nycteoline
Gold Spot
Dark Spectacle
The Four-spotted
Beautiful Snout
Buttoned Snout

Irregular migrants

The Vestal
The Gem
Convolvulus Hawk-moth

Death's-head Hawk-moth
Humming-bird Hawk-moth
Sword-grass

Scarce Bordered Straw
Bordered Straw
Slender Burnished Brass

No recent records

The Forester, *1950*
Large Red-belted Clearwing, *1956*
Clouded Magpie, *1965*
Speckled Yellow, *1950*
Brussel's Lace, *1962*

The Annulet, *1964*
Silver-striped Hawk-moth, *1948, migrant*
Broad-bordered Bee Hawk-moth, *1945*
Cream-spot Tiger, *1960*
Water Ermine, *1950*

Small Black Arches, *1945*
Barred Chestnut, *1974*
Neglected Rustic, *1958*
Striped Wainscot, *1965*
Small Mottled Willow, *1968*

Doubtful records requiring confirmation

Red-green Carpet
Small Autumnal Moth

Cloaked Pug
Marbled Pug

Grasshoppers and Crickets

The names used are taken from *Grasshoppers, Crickets and Cockroaches of the British Isles*, by D. R. Ragge, published by Warne, London, 1965.

Bush Crickets

Oak Bush-cricket
– *widespread and frequent, particularly in hedgerows, not confined to oak*

Dark Bush-cricket
– *widespread and frequent, particularly road verges. Absent S. of Chiltern escarpment except a few in Luton Airport and Studham/ Whipsnade areas*

Short-winged Conehead
– *rare, one breeding colony, at Flitwick Moor*

Speckled Bush-cricket
– *widespread and frequent, absent from Luton/ Dunstable/Whipsnade area*

True Cricket

House Cricket
– *occurs in heated buildings, no permanent out-door colonies*

Grasshoppers

Stripe-winged Grasshopper
– *not recorded since 1950s, much apparently suitable downland habitat now covered with coarse grasses or scrub*

Woodland Grasshopper
– *not recorded since late 1940s*

Common Green Grasshopper
– *confined to the S. apart from a few scattered records across mid-Bedfordshire*

Common Field Grasshopper
– *widespread and frequent but absent from NE.; the commonest grasshopper, most records from road verges*

Meadow Grasshopper
– *widespread and frequent but absent from NE. and sparse in the E., most records from road verges*

Lesser Marsh Grasshopper
– *first recorded 1976, locally frequent across mid-Bedfordshire*

Mottled Grasshopper
– *local and uncommon; its seven localities characterised by Heather or downland*

Ground-hoppers

Common Ground-hopper
– *scattered in small numbers; ten localities known but probably under-recorded*

Slender Ground-hopper
– *scattered in small numbers, in damp marshy places*

Dragonflies

Except where there is an indication otherwise, this list relates to species recorded at breeding sites in recent years, 1973–86. Dragonflies are often seen away from their breeding sites and this must be taken into account in defining their status. Many past records did not relate to proven breeding sites, making it difficult to define accurately the breeding status of some species. English names are given but, as these are not in well-established general use, scientific names are also included. The names are from *The Dragonflies of Great Britain and Ireland* by C. O. Hammond 2nd edn, Harley Books, 1983.

White-legged Damselfly (*Platycnemis pennipes*)
– *a river species well-established along the Great Ouse. It was known from the Ouzel in the 1940s but there are no recent records*

Large Red Damselfly (*Pyrrhosoma nymphula*)
– *widely scattered in small colonies, in ponds, quarries and marshes*

Blue-tailed Damselfly (*Ischnura elegans*)
– *widespread and common in all freshwater habitats, even if slightly polluted*

Common Blue Damselfly (*Enallagma cyathigerum*)
– *widespread and common in rivers and quarries, usually the most numerous species*

Azure Damselfly (*Coenagrion puella*)
– *widely scattered records from small water-bodies, under-recorded but probably quite common*

Variable Damselfly (*Coenagrion pulchellum*)
– *no recent records. Recorded in the 1940s from Biddenham, Stevington and Sharnbrook, and from Grovebury Farm Pit at Leighton Buzzard*

Red-eyed Damselfly (*Erythromma najas*)
– *a small number of scattered localities, where there are floating leaves on the open water of gravel pits, lakes and Great Ouse*

Scarce Emerald Damselfly (*Lestes dryas*)
– *no recent records. Known from Heath and Reach area in 1940s, last recorded there in 1950*

Emerald Damselfly (*Lestes sponsa*)
– *widely scattered records from flooded quarries and ponds, probably under-recorded*

Banded Demoiselle (*Calopteryx splendens*)
– *a species of slow-flowing water, abundant along the Great Ouse, also found on the Ivel, the Ouzel and some smaller streams.*

Golden-ringed Dragonfly (*Cordulegaster boltonii*)
– *not established in the county. A migratory swarm appeared at Felmersham in 1975.*

Downy Emerald (*Cordulia aenea*)
– *A record from Heath and Reach in 1951 but no recent records*

Southern Hawker (*Aeshna cyanea*)
– *widespread and frequent, mainly ponds and gravel pits, often seen away from water*

Brown Hawker (*Aeshna grandis*)
– *widespread and common in a wide range of waters*

Common Hawker (*Aeshna juncea*)
– *no recent records, several in 1940s. Easily confused with Southern and Migrant Hawkers*

Migrant Hawker (*Aeshna mixta*)
– *widespread and common in a wide range of waters, often seen away from water*

Emperor Dragonfly (*Anax imperator*)
– *scattered records from small lakes, gravel-pits, and large ponds*

Black-tailed Skimmer (*Orthetrum cancellatum*)
– *widely scattered, associated with bare mud and gravel in new gravel pits and dredged rivers, much more common than in the 1940s*

Broad-bodied Chaser (*Libellula depressa*)
– *widespread in small ponds (including garden ponds) and quarries*

Scarce Chaser (*Libellula fulva*)
– *no recent records but is now established nearby in Huntingdonshire so might occur in the future*

Four-spotted Chaser (*Libellula quadrimaculata*)
– *widespread in ponds and gravel pits where there is well developed marginal vegetation*

Ruddy Darter (*Sympetrum sanguineum*)
– *recorded from a few scattered sites: ponds, gravel pits, and Great Ouse; under-recorded on account of confusion with Common Darter*

Black Darter (*Sympetrum danae*)
– *no recent records; recorded from Wavendon Heath in the 1940s*

Common Darter (*Sympetrum striolatum*)
– *widespread and very common; sites include flooded quarries, garden ponds and rivers*

Flowering Plants, Ferns and Fern Allies

This list comprises those species found in the county since 1945. All regular members of the flora are included whether native or adventive. Species which have (apparently) become extinct in the county during the last forty years are also included. Species which have been recorded on one or two occasions only, casual species, wool-shoddy adventives and bird-seed aliens are excluded.

Families are listed in the standard scientific order, as are species within families. Species names are from the second edition of *English Names of Wild Flowers* by Dony, Jury and Perring, published by The Botanical Society of the British Isles in 1986.

The status of each species is indicated by a two-letter code indicating its abundance and the nature of its distribution in the county, as follows:

First letter denotes abundance:
C = common
F = frequent
U = uncommon
R = rare

Second letter denotes distribution:
W = widespread
L = localised (<50% of the county)

As an example, the code 'UW' indicates a plant which occurs only in small numbers in those places where it is found but is known from many parts of the county. Detailed distribution maps are given in the *Bedfordshire Plant Atlas* by J. G. Dony, published by Luton Museum in 1976.

The code is in *italics* if the species is not considered to be native in Bedfordshire.

An asterisk (*) indicates species which have become extinct in the county during the past forty years.

Lycopodiaceae – **Clubmoss Family**		Male-fern	CW
Marsh Clubmoss	*RL	Scaly Male-fern	RW
		Narrow Buckler-fern	RW
Equisetaceae – **Horsetail Family**		Broad Buckler-fern	FW
Water Horsetail	UW	Oak Fern	*RL
Marsh Horsetail	UW		
Field Horsetail	CW	*Blechnaceae* – **Hard Fern Family**	
Great Horsetail	UW	Hard Fern	RW
Ophioglossaceae – **Adder's-tongue Family**		*Polypodiaceae* – **Polypody Family**	
Adder's-tongue	UW	Intermediate Polypody	UW
Osmundaceae – **Royal Fern Family**		*Azollaceae* – **Water Fern Family**	
Royal Fern	*RL*	Water Fern	*RW*
Hypolepidaceae – **Bracken Family**		*Pinaceae* – **Pine Family**	
Bracken	FW	Scots Pine	*FL*
Aspleniaceae – **Spleenwort Family**		*Taxaceae* – **Yew Family**	
Maidenhair Spleenwort	UW	Yew	*FW*
Black Spleenwort	UW		
Wall-rue	UW	*Salicaceae* – **Willow Family**	
Rustyback	RW	Bay Willow	RL
Hart's-tongue	UW	Crack Willow	CW
		White Willow	CW
Athyriaceae – **Lady Fern Family**		Almond Willow	UW
Lady Fern	UW	Rusty Willow	CW
Brittle Bladder-fern	*RL*	Eared Willow	RL
		Goat Willow	CW
Aspidaceae – **Buckler-fern Family**		Osier	CW
Hard Shield-fern	RW	Purple Willow	UL
Soft Shield-fern	RL	White Poplar	*UW*

Grey Poplar	*UW*
Aspen	FW
Black Poplar	RW
Italian Poplar	*FW*

Juglandaceae – **Walnut Family**

Walnut	*RL*

Betulaceae – **Birch Family**

Silver Birch	CW
Downy Birch	FL
Alder	CL

Corylaceae – **Hazel Family**

Hornbeam	FW
Hazel	CW

Fagaceae – **Beech Family**

Beech	FW
Sweet Chestnut	*CL*
Turkey Oak	*FW*
Sessile Oak	UL
Pedunculate Oak	CW

Ulmaceae – **Elm Family**

Wych Elm	CW
English Elm	CW
Small-leaved Elm	FL

Cannabaceae – **Hemp Family**

Hop	CW

Urticaceae – **Nettle Family**

Common Nettle	CW
Small Nettle	CW
Pellitory-of-the-wall	UW

Loranthaceae – **Mistletoe Family**

Mistletoe	UL

Polygonaceae – **Dock Family**

Knotgrass	CW
Equal-leaved Knotgrass	FW
Tasteless Water-pepper	UL
Water-pepper	FL
Redshank	CW
Pale Persicaria	CW
Amphibious Bistort	FW
Common Bistort	RL
Black-bindweed	CW
Japanese Knotweed	*UW*
Buckwheat	*RW*
Sheep's Sorrel	CL
Common Sorrel	CW
Water Dock	UL
Curled Dock	CW
Clustered Dock	CW
Red-veined Dock	CW
Fiddle Dock	UL
Broad-leaved Dock	CW
Marsh Dock	RL
Golden Dock	RW

Chenopodiaceae – **Goosefoot Family**

Good-King-Henry	RW
Oak-leaved Goosefoot	RL
Red Goosefoot	FW
Maple-leaved Goosefoot	RW
Many-seeded Goosefoot	FW
Nettle-leaved Goosefoot	RW
Fig-leaved Goosefoot	UW
Fat-hen	CW
Garden Orache	*RL*
Common Orache	CW
Spear-leaved Orache	CW

Portulacaceae – **Purslane Family**

Blinks	RW
Springbeauty	*FL*
Pink Purslane	*RL*

Caryophyllaceae – **Pink Family**

Thyme-leaved Sandwort	FW
Slender Sandwort	FW
Three-nerved Sandwort	CW
Fine-leaved Sandwort	RL
Common Chickweed	CW
Greater Chickweed	RL
Greater Stitchwort	FW
Bog Stitchwort	FL
Lesser Stitchwort	FW
Snow-in-summer	*RW*
Field Mouse-ear	UL
Common Mouse-ear	CW
Grey Mouse-ear	RL
Sticky Mouse-ear	CW
Little Mouse-ear	UL
Dwarf Mouse-ear	RL
Sea Mouse-ear	UL
Water Chickweed	FL
Procumbent Pearlwort	CW
Annual Pearlwort	FW
Annual Knawel	RW
Corn Spurrey	FL
Sand Spurrey	UL
Ragged-Robin	FW
Corncockle	*RL
Bladder Campion	CW
Night-flowering Catchfly	RW
White Campion	CW
Red Campion	FL
Soapwort	*UW*
Proliferous Pink	*RL*
Deptford Pink	*RL

Nymphaeaceae – **Water-lily Family**

White Water-lily	RW
Yellow Water-lily	FL

Ceratophyllaceae – **Hornwort Family**

Rigid Hornwort	UW

Ranunculaceae – **Buttercup Family**	
Stinking Hellebore	*RW*
Green Hellebore	RW
Winter Aconite	*RW*
Marsh-marigold	UW
Wood Anemone	FW
Pasqueflower	RL
Traveller's-joy	CW
Pheasant's-eye	*RL
Creeping Buttercup	CW
Meadow Buttercup	CW
Bulbous Buttercup	CW
Hairy Buttercup	RL
Corn Buttercup	UW
Small-flowered Buttercup	RL
Goldilocks Buttercup	FW
Celery-leaved Buttercup	CW
Lesser Celandine	CW
Lesser Spearwort	UL
Greater Spearwort	RL
Ivy-leaved Crowfoot	UL
Pond Water-crowfoot	RW
Stream Water-crowfoot	RW
Common Water-crowfoot	UW
Thread-leaved Water-crowfoot	UW
Fan-leaved Water-crowfoot	UW
River Water-crowfoot	UL
Mousetail	RL
Common Meadow-rue	UL
Berberidaceae – **Barberry Family**	
Barberry	*UL*
Oregon-grape	*UW*
Papaveraceae – **Poppy Family**	
Opium Poppy	*FW*
Common Poppy	CW
Long-headed Poppy	CW
Yellow-juiced Poppy	FW
Prickly Poppy	FW
Rough Poppy	RL
Greater Celandine	FW
Climbing Corydalis	UL
Yellow Corydalis	*UW*
Red Corydalis	*RW*
Dense-flowered Fumitory	UL
Common Fumitory	FW
Few-flowered Fumitory	UL
Fine-leaved Fumitory	*RL
Cruciferae – **Cabbage Family**	
London-rocket	*RL*
Tall Rocket	*UW*
Eastern Rocket	*UW*
Hedge Mustard	CW
Flixweed	UL
Garlic Mustard	CW
Thale Cress	FW
Treacle Mustard	FW
Warty-cabbage	*RL

Dame's-violet	*UW*
Winter-cress	CW
American Winter-cress	*RL*
Medium-flowered Winter-cress	*RW*
Great Yellow-cress	UL
Creeping Yellow-cress	UW
Northern Yellow-cress	UW
Horse-radish	*CW*
Water-cress	FW
Narrow-fruited Water-cress	FW
Large Bitter-cress	RL
Cuckooflower	FW
Wavy Bitter-cress	FL
Hairy Bitter-cress	FW
Hairy Rock-cress	RL
Garden arabie	*RL*
Honesty	*UW*
Small Alison	*RL
Wall Whitlowgrass	RL
Common Whitlowgrass	FW
Danish Scurvygrass	*RL
Shepherd's-purse	CW
Shepherd's Cress	RL
Field Penny-cress	FW
Wild Candytuft	RL
Field Pepperwort	UL
Smith's Pepperwort	RW
Narrow-leaved Pepperwort	RW
Dittander	*RW*
Hoary Cress	*FW*
Swine-cress	CW
Lesser Swine-cress	*UL*
Perennial Wall-rocket	*RW*
Annual Wall-rocket	*FW*
Wild Turnip	*RL*
Black Mustard	UW
Charlock	CW
White Mustard	*FL*
Hairy Rocket	*RL*
Bastard Cabbage	*UW*
Wild Radish	RW
Resedaceae – **Mignonette Family**	
Weld	FW
Wild Mignonette	FL
Crassulaceae – **Stonecrop Family**	
Orpine	RW
Caucasian Stonecrop	*RL*
Reflexed Stonecrop	*RL*
Biting Stonecrop	FW
White Stonecrop	*UL*
Thick-leaved Stonecrop	*RL*
Saxifragaceae – **Saxifrage Family**	
Rue-leaved Saxifrage	UL
Meadow Saxifrage	UL
Opposite-leaved Golden-saxifrage	UL
Grossulariaceae – **Currant Family**	
Red Currant	*UW*

BlackCurrant	UW	Wood Vetch	RL
Gooseberry	UW	Hairy Tare	FW
		Slender Tare	RL
		Smooth Tare	FW
Rosaceae – **Rose Family**		Bush Vetch	CW
Dropwort	UL	Common Vetch	CW
Meadowsweet	CW	Spring Vetch	RL
Raspberry	UW	Bitter-vetch	RL
Dewberry	FW	Meadow Vetchling	CW
Bramble	CW	Tuberous Pea	*RL*
Field-rose	FW	Narrow-leaved Everlasting-pea	UL
Japanese Rose	*UW*	Broad-leaved Everlasting-pea	*UW*
Short-styled Field-rose	UW	Grass Vetchling	UW
Dog-rose	CW	Spiny Restharrow	UW
Harsh Downy-rose	UW	Common Restharrow	UW
Sweet-briar	RL	Tall Melilot	FW
Small-flowered Sweet-briar	RL	White Melilot	*UW*
Agrimony	CW	Ribbed Melilot	*FW*
Fragrant Agrimony	RL	Black Medick	CW
Great Burnet	UW	Lucerne	*FW*
Salad Burnet	FW	Spotted Medick	FL
Fodder Burnet	*RL*	Toothed Medick	*RL*
Water Avens	*RL	White Clover	CW
Wood Avens	CW	Alsike Clover	*FW*
Marsh Cinquefoil	*RL	Strawberry Clover	UW
Silverweed	CW	Hop Trefoil	FW
Hoary Cinquefoil	RL	Lesser Trefoil	CW
Tormentil	FL	Slender Trefoil	UL
Creeping Cinquefoil	CW	Knotted Clover	RL
Barren Strawberry	FW	Hare's-foot Clover	UL
Wild Strawberry	FW	Red Clover	CW
Garden Strawberry	*UL*	Zigzag Clover	UL
Hairy Lady's-mantle	RL	Sulphur Clover	RL
Parsley-piert	FW	Subterranean Clover	RL
Slender Parsley-piert	FL	Narrow-leaved Bird's-foot-trefoil	RL
Wild Pear	*UL*	Common Bird's-foot-trefoil	CW
Crab Apple	FW	Greater Bird's-foot-trefoil	UW
Rowan	UW	Kidney Vetch	UL
Wild Service-tree	RL	Bird's-foot	UL
Common Whitebeam	RL	Crown Vetch	*RL*
Midland Hawthorn	UL	Horseshoe Vetch	UL
Hawthorn	CW	Sainfoin	*FL*
Cherry Plum	*UW*		
Blackthorn	CW	*Oxalidaceae* – **Wood-sorrel Family**	
Wild Plum	*UW*	Wood-sorrel	UL
Wild Cherry	UW		
Dwarf Cherry	*RL*	*Geraniaceae* – **Geranium Family**	
		Meadow Crane's-bill	UL
Leguminosae – **Pea Family**		French Crane's-bill	*RL*
Hairy-fruited Broom	*RL*	Dusky Crane's-bill	*RL*
Broom	FL	Hedgerow Crane's-bill	FL
Dyer's Greenweed	RL	Round-leaved Crane's-bill	UL
Gorse	CL	Dovesfoot Crane's-bill	CW
Dwarf Gorse	RL	Small-flowered Crane's-bill	UW
Goat's-rue	*UW*	Long-stalked Crane's-bill	RL
Bladder-senna	*UW*	Cut-leaved Crane's-bill	CW
Purple Milk-vetch	RL	Shining Crane's-bill	RW
Wild Liquorice	UL	Herb Robert	CW
Tufted Vetch	CW	Common Stork's-bill	UW
Fine-leaved Vetch	*RL*		

Linaceae – **Flax Family**

Fairy Flax	UW

Euphorbiaceae – **Spurge Family**

Annual Mercury	RW
Dog's Mercury	CW
Broad-leaved Spurge	RL
Sun Spurge	CW
Caper Spurge	*RW*
Dwarf Spurge	FW
Petty Spurge	CW
Leafy Spurge	*RW*
Cypress Spurge	*RW*
Wood Spurge	UL

Polygalaceae – **Milkwort Family**

Common Milkwort	FL
Heath Milkwort	RL

Aceraceae – **Maple Family**

Norway Maple	*RW*
Field Maple	CW
Sycamore	*CW*

Hippocastanaceae – **Horse Chestnut Family**

Horse-chestnut	*FW*

Balsaminaceae – **Balsam Family**

Orange Balsam	*FL*
Small Balsam	*RW*
Indian Balsam	*RW*

Aquifoliaceae – **Holly Family**

Holly	FW

Celastraceae – **Spindle Family**

Spindle	FW

Rhamnaceae – **Buckthorn Family**

Buckthorn	FW
Alder Buckthorn	RL

Tiliaceae – **Lime Family**

Small-leaved Lime	UW
Lime	*FW*

Malvaceae – **Mallow Family**

Musk Mallow	FL
Common Mallow	CW
Dwarf Mallow	FW

Thymelaeaceae – **Daphne Family**

Spurge-laurel	UW

Guttiferae – **St John's-wort Family**

Hairy St John's-wort	FW
Slender St John's-wort	RL
Trailing St John's-wort	RL
Square-stalked St John's-wort	FW
Imperforate St John's-wort	RL
Perforate St John's-wort	CW

Violaceae – **Violet Family**

Sweet Violet	CW
Hairy Violet	FW
Early Dog-violet	FW
Common Dog-violet	FW
Heath Dog-violet	RL
Marsh Violet	RL
Field Pansy	CW

Cistaceae – **Rock-rose Family**

Common Rock-rose	FL

Curcurbitaceae – **Gourd Family**

White Bryony	CW

Lythraceae – **Loosestrife Family**

Purple-loosestrife	FL
Water-purslane	RL

Onagraceae – **Willowherb Family**

Enchanter's-nightshade	FW
Large-flowered Evening-primrose	UW
Rosebay Willowherb	CW
Great Willowherb	CW
Hoary Willowherb	FW
Broad-leaved Willowherb	FW
Square-stalked Willowherb	FW
Short-fruited Willowherb	RL
Pale Willowherb	RL
Marsh Willowherb	RL
American Willowherb	*CW*

Haloragaceae – **Water-milfoil Family**

Whorled Water-milfoil	RL
Spiked Water-milfoil	UL

Hippuridaceae – **Mare's-tail Family**

Mare's-tail	RL

Cornaceae – **Dogwood Family**

Dogwood	CW

Araliaceae – **Ivy Family**

Ivy	CW

Umbelliferae – **Carrot Family**

Marsh Pennywort	RL
Sanicle	UW
Rough Chervil	CW
Cow Parsley	CW
Bur Chervil	UL
Shepherd's-needle	*RL
Alexanders	*RW*
Great Pignut	UL
Pignut	FW
Greater Burnet-saxifrage	FW
Burnet-saxifrage	CW
Ground-elder	*CW*
Greater Water-parsnip	RL
Lesser Water-parsnip	UW
Moon Carrot	RL

Tubular Water-dropwort	RL
Parsley Water-dropwort	RL
Hemlock Water-dropwort	RL
River Water-dropwort	RL
Fine-leaved Water-dropwort	RL
Fool's Parsley	CW
Fennel	UL
Pepper-saxifrage	UW
Hemlock	FW
Wild Celery	*RL
Fool's Water-cress	CW
Lesser Marshwort	RL
Corn Parsley	RW
Stone Parsley	FW
Caraway	*RL
Wild Angelica	FW
Wild Parsnip	FW
Hogweed	CW
Giant Hogweed	*RW*
Knotted Hedge-parsley	RW
Spreading Hedge-parsley	RL
Upright Hedge-parsley	CW
Wild Carrot	CW

Pyrolaceae – **Wintergreen Family**

Yellow Bird's-nest	RL

Ericaceae – **Heath Family**

Heather	RL
Bilberry	RL

Primulaceae – **Primrose Family**

Primrose	FW
Oxlip	RL
Cowslip	FW
Water-violet	*RL
Yellow Pimpernel	RL
Yellow Loosestrife	UL
Creeping-Jenny	FW
Dotted Loosestrife	*RL*
Bog Pimpernel	*RL
Scarlet Pimpernel	CW
Blue Pimpernel	RL
Brookweed	RL

Oleaceae – **Olive Family**

Ash	CW
Wild Privet	CW

Gentianaceae – **Gentian Family**

Yellow-wort	UL
Common Centaury	UW
Lesser Centaury	RL
Autumn Gentian	UL
Chiltern Gentian	RL

Menyanthaceae – **Bogbean Family**

Bogbean	*RL
Fringed Water-lily	*RL*

Apocynaceae – **Periwinkle Family**

Lesser Periwinkle	*UW*
Greater Periwinkle	*UL*

Rubiaceae – **Bedstraw Family**

Field Madder	UW
Squinancywort	UL
Woodruff	UL
Fen Bedstraw	UL
Common Marsh-bedstraw	UW
Lady's Bedstraw	CW
Hedge-bedstraw	CW
Upright Hedge-bedstraw	RW
Heath Bedstraw	FL
Cleavers	CW
Corn Cleavers	*RL*
Crosswort	RL

Convolvulaceae – **Bindweed Family**

Greater Dodder	RL
Dodder	RL
Hedge Bindweed	CW
Large Bindweed	*FW*
Hairy Bindweed	*RW*
Field Bindweed	CW

Boraginaceae – **Borage Family**

Common Gromwell	UL
Field Gromwell	UL
Viper's-bugloss	RL
Common Comfrey	UW
Russian Comfrey	*FW*
Tuberous Comfrey	*RL*
White Comfrey	*RW*
Bugloss	FL
Green Alkanet	*UL*
Borage	*RL*
Field Forget-me-not	CW
Early Forget-me-not	UL
Changing Forget-me-not	UL
Tufted Forget-me-not	FL
Water Forget-me-not	FL
Hound's-tongue	RW

Verbenaceae – **Verbena Family**

Vervain	RL

Callitrichaceae – **Water-starwort Family**

Common Water-starwort	FL
Blunt-fruited Water-starwort	UL
Various-leaved Water-starwort	UL
Intermediate Water-starwort	RL

Labiatae – **Labiate Family**

Bugle	FW
Ground-pine	RL
Wood Sage	FL
Skullcap	FL
White Horehound	*RW*

Red Hemp-nettle	UL
Large-flowered Hemp-nettle	RL
Common Hemp-nettle	FW
Lesser Hemp-nettle	UW
White Dead-nettle	CW
Red Dead-nettle	CW
Cut-leaved Dead-nettle	UW
Henbit Dead-nettle	UW
Yellow Archangel	FL
Black Horehound	CW
Betony	UW
Hedge Woundwort	CW
Marsh Woundwort	FL
Field Woundwort	RL
Cat-mint	RL
Ground-ivy	CW
Selfheal	CW
Wild Thyme	RL
Large Thyme	UL
Basil Thyme	UL
Common Calamint	RL
Wild Basil	FW
Marjoram	UL
Gipsywort	FW
Corn Mint	FW
Whorled Mint	UW
Water Mint	FW
Spear Mint	*UW*
Wild Clary	RL

Solanaceae – **Nightshade Family**

China Teaplant	*RW*
Deadly Nightshade	RL
Henbane	RL
Black Nightshade	CW
Green Nightshade	*FW*
Bittersweet	CW
Thorn-apple	*UW*

Buddlejaceae – **Buddleia Family**

Butterfly-bush	UL

Scrophulariaceae – **Figwort Family**

Mudwort	RL
Moth Mullein	*RL*
Twiggy Mullein	*RL*
Orange Mullein	*RW*
Great Mullein	UW
Dark Mullein	UL
Common Figwort	FW
Water Figwort	CW
Snapdragon	*RL*
Lesser Snapdragon	RL
Small Toadflax	UW
Purple Toadflax	*UW*
Pale Toadflax	*UL*
Common Toadflax	FW
Ivy-leaved Toadflax	*UW*
Sharp-leaved Fluellen	UW

Round-leaved Fluellen	UW
Foxglove	FL
Thyme-leaved Speedwell	FW
Heath Speedwell	UL
Germander Speedwell	CW
Wood Speedwell	UL
Marsh Speedwell	RL
Brooklime	FW
Blue Water-speedwell	UW
Pink Water-speedwell	UW
Wall Speedwell	CW
Green Field-speedwell	UW
Grey Field-speedwell	UW
Common Field-speedwell	*CW*
Slender Speedwell	*UW*
Ivy-leaved Speedwell	CW
Crested Cow-wheat	RL
Field Cow-wheat	RL
Common Cow-wheat	*RL
Eyebright (2 species)	
Euphrasia nemorosa	UL
Euphrasia pseudokerneri	RL
Red Bartsia	FW
Marsh Lousewort	*RL
Yellow-rattle	UW
Toothwort	RL

Orobanchaceae – **Broomrape Family**

Common Broomrape	UW
Knapweed Broomrape	RL
Greater Broomrape	*RL

Lentibulariaceae – **Butterwort Family**

Bladderwort	RL

Plantaginaceae – **Plantain Family**

Greater Plantain	CW
Buck's-horn Plantain	RL
Hoary Plantain	FW
Ribwort Plantain	CW

Caprifoliaceae – **Honeysuckle Family**

Dwarf Elder	*RL*
Elder	CW
Guelder-rose	FW
Wayfaring-tree	FW
Snowberry	*FW*
Perfoliate Honeysuckle	*RL*
Honeysuckle	FW

Adoxaceae – **Moschatel Family**

Moschatel	UL

Valerianaceae – **Valerian Family**

Common Cornsalad	UW
Keeled-fruited Cornsalad	RL
Narrow-fruited Cornsalad	UL
Broad-fruited Cornsalad	RL
Common Valerian	FL

Marsh Valerian	RL	Hoary Ragwort	CW
Red Valerian	*UL*	Oxford Ragwort	*CW*
		Heath Groundsel	UL
Dipsacaceae – **Teasel Family**		Sticky Groundsel	FW
Teasel	CW	Groundsel	CW
Small Teasel	UL	Carline Thistle	FL
Devil's-bit Scabious	UW	Wooly-headed Burdock	*RL
Field Scabious	FW	Greater Burdock	UL
Small Scabious	FL	Lesser Burdock	CW
		Musk Thistle	UL
Campanulaceae – **Bellflower Family**		Welted Thistle	CW
Canterbury-bells	*RW*	Woolly Thistle	UL
Clustered Bellflower	FL	Spear Thistle	CW
Giant Bellflower	UL	Dwarf Thistle	FW
Nettle-leaved Bellflower	UL	Marsh Thistle	FW
Creeping Bellflower	*RW*	Creeping Thistle	CW
Harebell	FL	Cotton Thistle	*RL*
Venus's-looking-glass	UL	Saw-wort	UL
Sheep's-bit	RL	Greater Knapweed	FW
		Common Knapweed	CW
Compositae – **Daisy Family**		Cornflower	*RW*
Hemp-agrimony	UW	Chicory	*UW*
Goldenrod	RL	Spotted Cat's-ear	RL
Canadian Goldenrod	*UW*	Smooth Cat's-ear	*RL
Daisy	CW	Cat's-ear	FW
Blue Fleabane	UW	Autumn Hawkbit	CW
Canadian Fleabane	*FW*	Rough Hawkbit	FW
Common Cudweed	RL	Lesser Hawkbit	UW
Small Cudweed	UL	Bristly Oxtongue	*CW*
Heath Cudweed	RL	Hawkweed Oxtongue	UW
Marsh Cudweed	FL	Goat's-beard	CW
Elecampane	*RL*	Prickly Sow-thistle	CW
Ploughman's-spikenard	UL	Smooth Sow-thistle	CW
Common Fleabane	FW	Marsh Sow-thistle	RL
Trifid Bur-marigold	UW	Perennial Sow-thistle	CW
Stick-tight Bur-marigold	*RL*	Prickly Lettuce	FW
Nodding Bur-marigold	RW	Great Lettuce	UL
Gallant Soldier	*UL*	Common Blue-sow-thistle	*UW*
Shaggy Soldier	*UL*	Wall Lettuce	UL
Corn Chamomile	RW	Common Dandelion	CW
Stinking Chamomile	UW	Nipplewort	CW
Yellow Chamomile	*UW*	Large-flowered Nipplewort	*RL*
Sneezewort	UW	Rough Hawk's-beard	RW
Yarrow	CW	Smooth Hawk's-beard	CW
Scentless Mayweed	CW	Beaked Hawk's-beard	FW
Scented Mayweed	FW	Mouse-ear Hawkweed	FW
Pineappleweed	*CW*	Fox-and-cubs	*UW*
Corn Marigold	*UW*	Common Hawkweed	UW
Tansy	UW		
Feverfew	*UW*	*Alismataceae* – **Water-plantain Family**	
Oxeye Daisy	CW	Arrowhead	UL
Mugwort	CW	Lesser Water-plantain	RL
Chinese Mugwort	*RL*	Water-plantain	FW
Wormwood	*UL*	Narrow-leaved Water-plantain	UW
Colt's-foot	CW		
Butterbur	UL	*Butomaceae* – **Flowering-rush Family**	
Winter Heliotrope	*RW*	Flowering-rush	UL
Field Fleawort	RL		
Common Ragwort	CW	*Hydrocharitaceae* – **Frogbit Family**	
Marsh Ragwort	UL	Canadian Waterweed	*UW*

Nuttall's Waterweed	*RL*
Curly Waterweed	*RW*

Juncaginaceae – **Arrowgrass Family**
Marsh Arrowgrass	UW

Potamogetonaceae – **Pondweed Family**
Broad-leaved Pondweed	UW
Red Pondweed	*RL
Shining Pondweed	RL
Long-stalked Pondweed	RL
Perfoliate Pondweed	UL
Flat-stalked Pondweed	RL
Small Pondweed	UW
Blunt-leaved Pondweed	RL
Curled Pondweed	UW
Fennel Pondweed	UW
Opposite-leaved Pondweed	RW

Zanichelliaceae – **Horned Pondweed Family**
Horned Pondweed	UW

Liliaceae – **Lily Family**
Fritillary	*RL
Martagon Lily	*RL*
Spiked Star-of-Bethlehem	UL
Star-of-Bethlehem	UW
Bluebell	CW
Few-flowered Leek	*RL*
Ramsons	UL
Field Garlic	RL
Wild Onion	UL
Lily-of-the-valley	RL
Herb-Paris	RW
Butcher's-broom	*RL*

Amaryllidaceae – **Daffodil Family**
Summer Snowflake	*RL*
Snowdrop	*UW*
Wild Daffodil	RW

Dioscoreaceae – **Yam Family**
Black Bryony	CW

Iridaceae – **Iris Family**
Stinking Iris	UW
Yellow Iris	UW

Juncaceae – **Rush Family**
Hard Rush	CW
Soft-rush	FW
Compact Rush	UW
Heath Rush	RL
Round-fruited Rush	UW
Slender Rush	*RL*
Toad Rush	FW
Blunt-flowered Rush	UL
Bulbous Rush	RL
Sharp-flowered Rush	UL

Jointed Rush	FW
Field Wood-rush	FW
Heath Wood-rush	UL
Great Wood-rush	RL
Hairy Wood-rush	UW
Southern Wood-rush	RL

Gramineae – **Grass Family**
Giant Fescue	CW
Meadow Fescue	CW
Tall Fescue	CW
Various-leaved Fescue	RL
Red Fescue	CW
Fine-leaved Sheep's-fescue	RL
Sheep's-fescue	UL
Perennial Rye-grass	CW
Italian Rye-grass	*CW*
Squirreltail Fescue	FW
Rat's-tail Fescue	UW
Fern-grass	UW
Annual Meadow-grass	CW
Rough Meadow-grass	CW
Smooth Meadow-grass	CW
Narrow-leaved Meadow-grass	UW
Flattened Meadow-Grass	UW
Wood Meadow-grass	UW
Reflexed Saltmarsh-grass	*FL*
Cock's-foot	CW
Crested Dog's-tail	CW
Whorl-grass	UL
Quaking-grass	FW
Wood Melick	UW
Reed Sweet-grass	FL
Small Sweet-grass	UL
Floating Sweet-grass	UW
Plicate Sweet-grass	FW
Hybrid Sweet-grass	UW
Great Brome	*RL*
Barren Brome	*CW*
Hungarian Brome	RL
Hairy-brome	CW
Upright Brome	UW
Field Brome	*RL*
Meadow Brome	UW
Smooth Brome	UL
Soft-brome	CW
Slender Soft-brome	*UW*
False Brome	CW
Tor-grass	FW
Bearded Couch	FW
Common Couch	CW
Wall Barley	CW
Meadow Barley	FW
Foxtail Barley	*UW*
Wood Barley	RL
Wild-oat	*CW*
Winter Wild-oat	*UW*
Downy Oat-grass	UW
Meadow Oat-grass	UL

False Oat-grass	CW	Slender Spike-rush	UL
Crested Hair-grass	FL	Greater Tussock-sedge	UL
Yellow Oat-grass	CW	False Fox-sedge	FW
Tufted Hair-grass	CW	Spiked Sedge	FW
Wavy Hair-grass	CL	Small-fruited Prickly-sedge	UL
Early Hair-grass	FL	Grey Sedge	UW
Silver Hair-grass	FL	Brown Sedge	UW
Sweet Vernal-grass	FW	Remote Sedge	FW
Yorkshire-fog	CW	Oval Sedge	UW
Creeping Soft-grass	FL	Star Sedge	RL
Velvet Bent	UL	White Sedge	RL
Common Bent	FW	Hairy Sedge	CW
Black Bent	FW	Lesser Pond-sedge	FL
Creeping Bent	CW	Greater Pond-sedge	UL
Wood Small-reed	FW	Cyperus Sedge	RL
Timothy	CW	Bottle Sedge	RL
Smaller Cat's-tail	CW	Pendulous Sedge	UW
Purple-stem Cat's-tail	RL	Wood-sedge	FW
Meadow Foxtail	CW	Thin-spiked Wood-sedge	RL
Marsh Foxtail	FW	Glaucous Sedge	FW
Orange Foxtail	RL	Carnation Sedge	UL
Black-grass	CW	Green-ribbed Sedge	*RL
Reed Canary-grass	FW	Distant Sedge	UW
Canary-grass	*UW*	Common Yellow-sedge	*RL
Wood Millet	UW	Long-stalked Yellow-sedge	RL
Common Reed	FW	Pale Sedge	UL
Heath-grass	RL	Spring-sedge	UL
Purple Moor-grass	RL	Pill Sedge	UL
Mat-grass	*RL	Common Sedge	UL
		Slender Tufted-sedge	UL
Araceae – **Arum Family**		Flea Sedge	RL
Sweet-flag	*UL*		
Lords-and-Ladies	CW	*Orchidaceae* – **Orchid Family**	
		Marsh Helleborine	*RL
Lemnaceae – **Duckweed Family**		Broad-leaved Helleborine	UW
Ivy-leaved Duckweed	UW	Violet Helliborine	RL
Fat Duckweed	UL	Green-flowered Helleborine	RL
Common Duckweed	FW	White Helleborine	UL
Least Duckweed	*RL*	Bird's-nest Orchid	RW
Greater Duckweed	RL	Common Twayblade	UW
		Autumn Lady's-tresses	RL
Sparganiaceae – **Bur-reed Family**		Musk Orchid	RL
Branched Bur-reed	FW	Lesser Butterfly-orchid	RL
Unbranched Bur-reed	UL	Greater Butterfly-orchid	UL
		Fragrant Orchid	UL
Typhaceae – **Bulrush Family**		Frog Orchid	RL
Lesser Bulrush	UL	Early Marsh-orchid	RL
Bulrush	FW	Southern Marsh-orchid	RL
		Heath Spotted-orchid	RL
Cyperaceae – **Sedge Family**		Common Spotted-orchid	FW
Wood Club-rush	RL	Green-winged Orchid	RL
Sea Club-rush	RL	Burnt Orchid	RL
Common Club-rush	UL	Early-purple Orchid	UW
Bristle Club-rush	UL	Man Orchid	RL
Flat-sedge	RL	Pyramidal Orchid	UW
Common Cottongrass	UW	Fly Orchid	RL
Common Spike-rush	RL	Bee Orchid	UW

Bibliography

Books on Bedfordshire Wildlife

Bedfordshire Bird Atlas B. D. Harding, Bedfordshire Natural History Society, 1979
Bedfordshire Plant Atlas John G. Dony, Borough of Luton Museum and Art Gallery, 1976
Common Lichens of Bedfordshire, The Frances B. M. Davies, Bedfordshire Natural History Society, 1981
Flora of Bedfordshire John G. Dony, Corporation of Luton Museum and Art Gallery, 1953

Books for Further Reading

Bird Habitats in Britain R. J. Fuller, T. and A. D. Poyser, Calton, 1982
Britain's Structure and Scenery L. Dudley Stamp, Collins, London, 1946
Ecology of the English Chalk C. J. Smith, Academic Press, London, 1980
Heathlands Nigel Webb, Collins, London, 1986
Trees and Woodlands in the British Landscape Oliver Rackham, Dent, London, 1976
Wild Flowers of Chalk and Limestone J. E. Lousley, Collins, London, 1950

Gazetteer and Place Name Index

All places mentioned in the text, and tables, are listed with their Ordnance Survey National Grid Reference. Brackets indicate the parish of a locality, or the appropriate town or county. The Grid Reference for larger sites refer to a central position, and, for a few sites it is given in brackets; these sites, effectively, no longer exist.

General Index